# A Wolf in the Snow

SMELL OF BLOOD ON SNOW

SMELL OF FEAR

SMELL OF *DEATH*

WRITTEN BY: BEN CHESSELL
ART BY BRIAN O'CONNELL
LETTERING BY: MATT MILBERGER

FEEL OF MUSCLES POUNDING

HISPO STRENGTH

SMELL OF FEAR

SIGHT OF HERD SPLITTING

SOUND OF GRINDING THUNDER

PREY IS TRAPPED

5

RUNNING

LEAPING

HOWLING

SOUND OF APE SCREAMS

CLOSE FOR THE KILL

KRUMP

SMELL OF OIL AND FILTH ON FUR...

SCREAMS OF DYING PREY

FAMILY

SMELL OF PURE SNOW OVER FALLEN

SOUNDS OF
TRIUMPH

# RED TALONS
## TRIBEBOOK

No Compromise

By Ben Chessell

# Credits

**Author:** Ben Chessell
**Developer:** Bill Bridges
**Editor:** Ed McKeogh
**Vice President in charge of Production:** Rich Thomas
**Art Directors:** Lawrence Snelly & Aileen E. Miles
**Comic book art:** Brian O'Connell
**Interior art:** Ron Spencer
**Front and back cover design:** Matt Milberger
**Typesetting & Layout:** Matt Milberger

# Special Thanks

One last time for my pals in Editing & Development…

**Ken** "Tempestuous" **Cliffe** for helming another dead project — er, I mean a project about the dead.

**Richard** "Mother's physick" **Dansky** for helping us get over our retreat colds with the chicken soup on the backseat.

**Ian** "Initiate of the Porcelain God" **Lemke** for praying outside of church at the retreat.

**Jennifer** "Queen of the Damned" **Hartshorn** for playing Anne Rice's Halloween party with her band, Trio Nocturna.

**Phil** "Nature Boy" **Brucato** for communing with the wild when (almost) everybody else was playing Family Feud.

**Ethan** "On the road" **Skemp** for being a Sam & Max fan.

**Cynthia** "Bug bait" **Summers** for learning that mosquitos are not the biggest bugs at NERO.

735 PARK NORTH BLVD.
SUITE 128
CLARKSTON, GA 30021
USA

WHITE WOLF GAME STUDIO

Profuse apologies to Larry Friedman for leaving his name out of the art credits for Rage Across Appalachia.

# Author's Note

*For wolves*
*Not the book, for which you would have little use,*
*but the effort at understanding.*
*I enjoyed your company.*
— Barry Lopez, dedication for *Of Wolves and Men*

The Red Talons represent the "other." They are everything we don't understand — the wolf, the predator, the wilderness, the dying creature. I wrote this book with a great love for and fascination with wolves. When I began, I thought I knew a great deal about the animals. After more research, I found I was wrong. What most biologists and naturalists know about the wolf is inconclusive, based on little empirical research. Indeed, the research that has been done has served only to reinforce the elusive and enigmatic nature of the wolf, difficult to explain using strictly biological principles. All that can confidently be said is that we need to know more.

Despite this lack of information, the wolf is an icon for many conservation and environmental efforts. It is a great comfort, in a world of destruction and desecration, that people feel the need to conserve something that they do not understand, simply for its own sake.

## Contents

# Introduction: Always

Our blood is the blood of Gaia,
A wounded blood.
We know Her pain. We are the Red Talons.
None can quench our anger.
You dare ask "When will we Rage?"
We have never ceased. We are the Red Talons.
Since the days of the Impergium,
Until the last hours of the Apocalypse,
We are always. We are the Red Talons.
— Scent-of-Red-Snow

We are wild — unquenchably wild. Red Talons are different than all the Garou. We are not a balance between wolf and human. We are creatures — beasts — hunters who are capable of taking the form of another, lesser beast for a time. Even in that form we understand that we are still creatures. We are unafraid to be animals. We are unafraid, as many are, of the will of Gaia, the will of the earth. If we look after Her, then She will provide for us. If we fail in this, She will provide for none.

The Red Talons are dying. We are now so few that our wisdom is almost lost to you, but still you do not understand. You embrace the ways of the Defiler and then turn to us when all is lost — we cannot help you. We can hardly help ourselves. The very laws of Gaia will be our eventual undoing. Yet we fight on. We are the Red Talons.
— Crookpaw

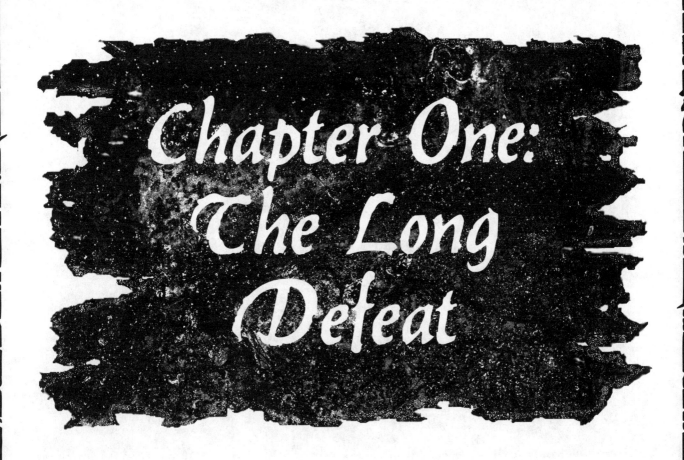

# Chapter One: The Long Defeat

*So, so you think you can tell Heaven from Hell, blue skies from pain.*
*Can you tell a green field from a cold steel rail? A smile from a veil?*
*Do you think you can tell?*
*And did they get you to change your heroes for ghosts? Hot ashes for trees?*
*Hot air for a cool breeze? Cold comfort for change?*
*And did you exchange a walk on part in the war for a lead role in a cage?*
— Pink Floyd, "Wish You Were Here"

It falls to me to talk of history. The Red Talons, my tribe, are not concerned with the past, except to acknowledge the sadness and tragedy that has been wrought there.

You think us creatures of anger, and that we are. But our Rage is different from yours. We are not the carriers of Wyrm-tainted fury; ours is the understanding that we are the hunters of Gaia. Our anger is the response of those who have seen their world torn down.

But more often we feel sadness. Again, unlike you, this is no Wyrm-spawned Harano that saps our strength. It is an understanding of how things are and how they should be… how they might have been. Maybe it is the understanding, never spoken, that the Red Talons are dying, that our time is past. We have no place in your Weaver-ruled world, where the Wyld is wrapped in plastic and every meal bears the tang of the Wyrm. We will not have this world, and it will not have us.

We place little stock in the great deeds and tales of the lore-wise tribes, and even less importance in the lists and dates of human scholarship. It takes a Red Talon who is exceptional, different… metis… to talk of our history at all.

Red Talons live their history through moots where tales are told in howls by long-dead ancestors who enter into the living to give guidance. Those great Talons of old who have had the misfortune to share my metis body with me have taught me much of their earlier times.

I am named Crookpaw and nothing else. A description of infirmity is all that is my name. I have earned no other title of worthiness. Having been denied the experiences that my full-blood lupus brothers and sisters enjoy, I have acquired a fair grasp of human speech, and can thus tell the legacy of my tribe. For though my tribe will not have me, I will have none but the Red Talons.

# The History of the Red Talons

*If we seek solace in the prisons of the distant past*
*Security in human systems we're told will always always last*
*Emotions are the sail and blind faith is the mask*
*Without the breath of real freedom we're getting nowhere fast…*
*History will teach us nothing*
— Sting, "History Will Teach Us Nothing"

We Red Talons remember everything, and we remember nothing. We are concerned with the patterns of Gaia, not dates or the counting of years. We remember only those things that made us what we are. We do not write our history down, but remember it in tales and songs, acknowledging the long line of wolves that pad silently before us. These tales would slowly die if locked in the cage of written words. Deeds that are sung can live forever.

Preserve the paw that makes the mark, so that it might make its mark on others. Weep not that the mark has been washed away by the rain.

# The First Story

*I'm the red wolf, says the dark*
*old father.*
*All right, the red-dawn-wolf am I.*
— D.H. Lawrence, "The Red Wolf"

It has elsewhere been told that the Red Talons sprung from the very womb of Gaia Herself. What tribe would not claim this lineage? The Red Talons, however, are truly born of wolf, as are no other. Wolf was the favored animal of Gaia, ruling over Her paradise and ensuring that Her balance was maintained. There are many versions of this story.

Some say it was the Wyrm who broke this paradise. In his jealousy, he slithered in and corrupted the youngest humans. But this stinks of the humans' own story too much for me.

Some say it was the Weaver who, in her desire to create, stole away some of the creatures of the Wyld. The Weaver secreted them in a cave and showed them her lore of tools, changing forever their relationship to the world. When Wolf, sent by Gaia, came to find them, they were frightened and stung him with their spears and sticks. His death was the first great tragedy, but his rebirth by Gaia was a greater tragedy still, for he was charged with thereafter warding humans.

But I favor a different telling, and for this (and my metis scars) I am seldom asked to address a moot or to instruct the pups. I think that it was Gaia Herself who made the humans, just as She made us. Or rather, the humans, made by Gaia, grew unaided into what they are now.

Once they were monkeys, eating leaves in the trees and fearing the ground lest the wolf might eat them. After coming out of the trees they made tools and weapons, fire and dwellings, protecting their young as we protect our young. The forces of Gaia shaped them, just as they began to shape Gaia. The humans are a creature different from us. Never satisfied with what they have, they always desire better... and more. They have vanity and greed. Whether this stain of the Wyrm was in their hearts from the very beginning, or whether they were tricked or corrupted into the having of it, we will never know and do not care.

While we ruled over the wilderness, they began to carve out a space for themselves. They were clever and skillful; it cannot be denied. Without their tools and walls, however, they are defenseless. They have come to rely on their creations to compensate for their furlessness.

When humans and wolves first walked the earth together, in the same age, there were born Garou. The seeds of the first Garou were sown by Gaia in the bloodlines of humans and wolves so that Her two favored children might cooperate and unite into one creature that could defend Her. It was a tragedy that Gaia chose humans to be part of Her defense when they were instead to become Her greatest enemy. Homid Garou do not understand this tragedy.

The first Garou born was a wolf. Who can say whether he was a Red Talon? In such times "tribe" had no meaning. Tracks-in-Fresh-Snow he called himself, and for a short time he was lord of all of Gaia's creatures. He delighted in his wolf and human forms, and moved among both races. He mated with a human woman, and she gave birth to the first homid. The Red Talons are descended from Tracks-in-Fresh-Snow; he is our father as Gaia is our mother. Many of the other tribes advance a complicated argument, claiming that his homid daughter was the first true Garou, as Tracks-in-Fresh-Snow had no Garou parent. Or they deny his existence.

This denial is meant to take honor from the Red Talons. We bear this affront as we bear all offenses: with defiance and contempt. But our Rage smoulders.

## The First Metis

A great deal can be learned about the Red Talons from the story of the first Red Talon metis. Maybe the story is true... maybe it is myth, but I have made it my story — committed it to memory — and I tell it often.

Red Talons had witnessed the whelping of metis in other tribes, and found them to be anathema, abominations. The great lupus found an explanation easy to come by, however. The other tribes were tainted by their homid stock, and

homid breeding was a strange process. Why then should not the breeding of the homid tribes be equally strange (and equally tainted)? No metis were birthed in Red Talon packs, whose members mated with wolves and kept their line strong in both the Garou and their Kinfolk.

But the Red Talons were young then. Human ideas like love and sex for pleasure were alien to them. These emotions rose up through their hated homid side, but remained ignored and dormant. The early Talons, like those of the modern world, seldom adopted Homid form, thought or speech. Although this was in times before the creation of the Litany, for which we care little (having our own code), mating between Garou was strictly forbidden. Red Talons considered themselves to be in no danger from this affliction, seeing no use in the creation of sterile progeny. But, as has happened so many times to my tribe and to all Garou, this confidence and pride was to precede a fall from grace.

How typically tragic that it was the advent of human love which caused this fall of the Red Talons. Although wolves feel affection for their mates and packmates, it is not the same as the troubled, overcomplicated passions that wrack humans and homids. The love of wolves is a simple love, born of the need for mutual survival and cooperation. The love of humans is a confusing, troubled thing.

In the late spring, when each Red Talon pack was to break up for a time, its members going their separate ways, two young lupus decided to visit a human settlement together. This was in the time before the Impergium, and though Red Talons had always regarded the humans with suspicion, good relations existed between humans and Garou. The human settlements were not too large, and they understood their place in Gaia's delicate balance. Most Red Talons paid humans no heed, thinking them lesser creatures and unworthy of the attention of great Garou. But these two young Talons, Leaps-the-Creek and Tail-Like-a-Branch, were curious about humans, and had determined to learn something of them.

Leaps-the-Creek was a young male of six summers; Tail-Like-a-Branch, a female of similar age. As with most lupus, their First Change occurred for them within two to three summers. The two had been companions for the last few years, for they came from the same wolf pack. (In those early days, Gaia sometimes blessed the Garou with multiple Garou births to a single litter.) The two Garou planned to spend all summer at the human settlement.

There was a man in the settlement called Tarn. Tarn was the grandson of one of the wise men and had not yet found himself a lifemate, much to his family's shame. As he saw the arrival of the two Talons... as he watched them take the Homid form out of politeness to their hosts, and as he saw Tail-Like-a-Branch's nakedness before it was covered by a human blanket, he determined that he would take her as his lifemate and be the father of Garou. This would alleviate the shame he felt. Tarn was not a beautiful man but he was crafty and a fine warrior. He bided his time.

During that summer, the two Garou lived among the humans in the village, eating, hunting and playing with them all the time in their Homid forms, as they had intended. The two stayed close together, as foreigners will among strangers, but slowly the humans came to accept them and value their great skill as hunters and foragers. The humans observed the Garou closely, and learned much from them concerning Gaia and Her laws. The young Garou watched the humans just as closely, and came to understand a great deal of their laws and customs.

It is said that the Garou are gifted to understand humans and beasts, but I say there is nothing in this to marvel at. Humans themselves are also beasts.

Leaps-the-Creek and Tail-Like-a-Branch made many friends and companions in their time among the humans. Leaps-the-Creek watched as his packmate befriended Tarn. Tarn flattered Tail-Like-a-Branch, and brought her many gifts. The humans understood what was happening, but the young Garou could not. Leaps-the-Creek continued to smile at the sight of his lifelong friend's happiness. The two Garou were sad to leave when the snows returned and the appointed time had come.

As the Garou bid their farewells, Tarn approached the two and asked Tail-Like-a-Branch, in the way of his people, if she would be his lifemate. Then, the Garou understood, as they stood upon the cold tundra, anxious to take their Lupus forms after a year of playing Homid. A gust of cold wind cut through their inadequate, unfurred skins. Tail-Like-a-Branch paused for a moment in contemplation. She was ready to mate, and this man seemed as good as any. Tarn produced a spear, and said that he was willing to fight Leaps-the-Creek for the right he requested.

The people stood silent. The Garou had yet to speak. Slowly, as if he did not understand his own words, Leaps-the-Creek said, "Tail-Like-a-Branch is my lifemate." Tail-Like-a-Branch was silent. The silence deepened as the people nodded their heads and turned to leave. Tarn, however, was not so easily defeated.

He ran at Leaps-the-Creek with his spear raised. Leaps-the-Creek was both stunned by his own words and the realization that was coming over him; surprised by the sudden attack, he failed to dodge, and the first spear thrust pierced his side. But Garou are not slain by such wounds; he leapt up from the bloody snow in Crinos form. Tarn fought bravely, but the battle was short and victory assured. The two lupus fled into the snow, leaving the people who had been their friends weeping.

That night, in a hollow lined with pine needles, Tail-Like-a-Branch licked the wounds of her packmate, and the two nuzzled together against the cold. They mated there, for many reasons, and perhaps not the same for each of them. But they mated there and parted company until the pack would rejoin.

Leaps-the-Creek never returned to the pack. He was never seen again by any Garou, and maybe he was the first victim of Harano. But this is a story about another tragic first.

Tail-Like-a-Branch returned to the pack with a swollen belly, and none thought it strange, as it was natural for Garou to mate in the summer when off on their own. The elders mourned the loss of Leaps-the-Creek, but even they did not wonder about the pup growing inside Tail-Like-a-Branch. Finally, the pup was born and a hideous, small, Crinos creature it was — as I have heard it said all metis are.

All pups are born blind and hairless, but this pup (named Sadness by his mother) had no fur to shield him from the snows, and only one of his eyes ever opened. The elders conferred over what should be done about the metis cub, and reached a decision that maintained the pride of the Red Talons above all else. Tail-Like-a-Branch fought to defend her offspring, and was slain in front of all the pack by the oldest of the Ahrouns, Black-Paw. Black-Paw then took the little metis in her mouth and crushed the life out of it with her jaws, not eating it for fear of contamination.

That is the end of the story, except to say that the pack broke apart after that, having witnessed that cruel act, and ran together no more. In killing Sadness, Black-Paw had given birth to grief and doubt. Since that time, many other metis have been treated like Sadness, but other packs have learned from that story, and more care is taken to prevent the creation of metis than is invested in their destruction.

This disgrace I bear myself: with heavy shoulders and my nose set into the wind. But my Rage stirs.

When finally all Red Talons have gone from Gaia it will not be as the Croatan were lost, slain in battle with the Wyrm. Red Talons are too strong to fall in battle; we shall fall because the world moves beyond us. We are not great changers, we Red Talons, though we can change our forms. Even as we cling to our wolf side, we cling to a Gaia that will soon disappear. Our close ties to Gaia make us subject, as are all of Her wild children, to the forces of extinction, against which we Rage. We are constant and unflinching, unwilling to adapt to new ideas or situations; it is not our way. Such was the impact of homid emotions on the Red Talons.

## A Great Offense

One of the saddest defeats of the Red Talons — one which helped build the Rage of the Impergium — was when some of our wolf brothers and sisters became the helpmates and playthings of the humans. The settlements of humans had already begun to expand, and although they still feared the wilderness, their hunting expeditions became more sophisticated. Having seen the efficiency and skill of the wolf packs and the Garou, the humans, who are nothing if not adaptive, began to recruit hounds to help them in their hunting. At first, these hounds were treated as partners in the endeavor, and had no further part in human life. Soon, however, the hounds became dogs (later to become lap dogs) and lost their dignity and freedom. The Wyld went out of them, and the Weaver entered in. The Red Talons watched this process with disgust and Rage.

Not yet ready to intervene and kill the humans involved, those who seethed at the ignobility of the new status of the dog turned their anger upon the dogs themselves. The way in which the humans used these animals — made them work, hunt and labor for human gain — enraged my ancestors and drove them to ever more violent acts. There had been resistance and anger at the harnessing of oxen and other hoofed creatures for human bidding, but these animals were our prey, and, although proud in their own way, did not inflame the fires of our Rage. To enslave our brethren, though, separated from us by only a few mothers and pups, was too great a crime to be borne in silence.

So when dogs — so-called wolf-hounds and others — were made to be a human tool, Red Talon patience and restraint were broken. One-Ear-Black, a mighty Galliard, led a wild run into human settlements. Her intention was to free the hounds, to release them from their servitude. Never did she believe that the dogs would resist, or that they would greet the Talons with snarls and bared teeth. One-Ear-Black was crushed when she realized that dogs had become companions of humans, and that they were more frightened of the Garou than of the Wyrm. Indeed, they could no longer smell the Wyrm in their own kennels.

Howling piteously, she set upon the penned hounds that she had intended to free, beginning an enmity between wolves and dogs that exists to this day. Humans gift their dogs with chains and spikes to keep them safe from us. It is not enough. Dogs no longer know Gaia, and it is another thorn in the paw of the Red Talons. When the Impergium finally came, the dogs stood beside their human masters and suffered with them beneath our fangs.

We reserve special hate for those creatures that are hybrid; some dog and some wolf are in them — an insult. Humans keep them as prisoners, and hope to capture some of the nobility of the wolf for their entertainment. This is anathema to us.

We bear this insult as we bear any other: with Rage and sadness. But our Rage begins to grow.

## The First Extinction

There was a time when we did not notice the humans. Maybe the Theurges were uneasy at the new habits of the creatures, their groupings and buildings, but Garou had foreseen nothing of the permanency they would achieve. Wolves had no such structures, and Garou had no need for them, so we watched with curiosity as humans grew and ploughed and hunted.

When Red Talons hunt, there is consideration made for the hunted and for the hunted of next season. What I mean is, Red Talons do not prey on a herd that is near to collapse. Garou do not kill all the young of any creature, knowing that to do so is foolish, preventing that food from being available the next year. The humans did not understand this, and we did not know that they did not understand until it was too late.

Animals had been lost before. In the earliest years, in Garou infancy, many creatures walked the earth that are now gone, and we hunted them then. But we did not drive them unto death. It was by Gaia's will that they left, a will that we understand well (only too well, for we may soon ourselves be its victims). These creatures are gone because Gaia had changed, and the world for which they were made was now gone. What the humans did was something different, a wound that festers in our conscience to this day.

The humans had come to lose their fur over time and had become pink and vulnerable. There was a great need among them for the hides of other creatures to keep them warm (truly they are paradoxical creatures — strength garbed in weakness). In packs, the humans hunted the beasts with thick hides. We soon taught them not to hunt wolves, though sadly, this is a lesson they have since forgotten. They turned their attentions to larger animals, many times stronger and more dangerous than they. Some hunted bison; others, deer. One group were called the mammoth people, and their lives revolved around the hunting of the great furred mammoths.

In much the same way as wolves might, many humans would cooperate; using clever strategy and their human tools, they would tire and then kill the great mammoths.

At first, we felt that this was good. One mammoth beast would keep many humans warm and fed. Although the humans did not treat their prey with the respect that a hunter should, they did little harm. They used all parts of the fallen prey to make their clothes, weapons and dens, and this was good. We never thought that the humans would be so foolish as to hunt too many beasts.

It was long before we realized the effects of our lack of vigilance. When next Garou traveled the runs of the mammoth, they found few left, and those few were mostly old or sick. There were no calves. Stunned, the Red Talon Philodox, Runs-Wisely, tried to save what few mammoths had survived and to prepare them for the coming spring hunts of the human tribes. Next, Runs-Wisely traveled to the humans to tell them that they must not hunt. Again, the Red Talons were shocked — not by how few humans there were, but by how many. The tundra was dotted with settlements like a diseased skin.

Undaunted, the Red Talons approached the human leaders, and told them they must not hunt mammoth this season. The human gestured to show the Red Talons how many of her people were cold: "This year we have even more people who need to be warm."

Runs-Wisely was a gentle creature; he left to ponder the human's words. He was a clever Garou, but he was unable to solve the puzzle, unable to imagine how far the humans would go in their selfishness and short-sightedness. And so it was that, in the next hunting season, no one was there to defend the last of the mammoths as the humans hunted them down with ambushes and spears.

When Runs-Wisely returned to see how the mammoths had recovered, he found one old, bald, bull mammoth left. All the others were dead. He spoke with the old bull, who told him of the coming of the humans, year after year, and the slaughter of his family. Still, Runs-Wisely could not understand the human behavior.

Together, the Garou and the mammoth traveled to the human settlement to talk again with the leader there. When Runs-Wisely asked the leader what had happened, the leader told him of the great winter cold, and how the people had needed all the furred-skins to survive. Runs-Wisely felt a black anger rise in his stomach as he asked, "But how will you survive the next winter when all the mammoths are dead?"

"We will hunt another beast," the woman replied.

Only then did Runs-Wisely understand.

As the humans speared the last, old, bald bull mammoth, Runs-Wisely forgot wisdom, and slew humans on all sides with teeth and claws and pure anger. Runs-Wisely was slain eventually by many human weapons. Many spears and axes pierced his flanks as the humans harried, tired and ran him down until he could fight no more.

This was the first time that humans had killed a Garou, and was to be the event that ignited the Impergium… which had been a long time coming. Finally, the homid Garou were presented with an undeniable example of human power and depravity. A Garou was dead, and an animal kin extinguished because of human need. The Silver Fangs could no longer ignore our pleas for direct control of the humans. A grand moot was held, and the Impergium was ordered.

Humans have driven many more beasts to their extinction since the Impergium. Our "enlightened" homid cousins see this but do not act. We bear this foolishness as we tolerate all the excesses of the homids: with little regard and lonely action. But our Rage grows.

# The Impergium

*They mostly come at night… mostly.*

— Newt, *Aliens*

Our glory is past. The Impergium is over. We were there, the wolf in every fold, the hunter and the shepherd. We were the lords of the earth. Now, we die, and Gaia groans under the weight of swollen flocks. The Impergium was a time of greatness, a time when the hateful humans understood their place — or rather, we understood it and made them see our understanding. In that time, wolves were proud, and humans were fearful. We even respected them as the hunting wolf respects the moose (though these humans have no hooves and horns of their own — these they build from rocks and trees). We would look them in the eye, those who were to die, and tell them, as wolves tell their prey, that they must die, and that their death was for

the good of Gaia. That is how it should be. But I would never give a human such a boon today.

Imagine the scene: A small human herd with its constructions of ice, wood and stone. Around a fire they sit and stand as the ancient night closes in. They look at the moon, fearful to find that it is full. Quickly they count their numbers, accounting for all their pack.

The warriors shake their heads, knowing that it was a bountiful spring, and that many human pups play around the fire, tied by thongs of hide to a post in the middle of the village; too many. These infants are sent inside, to wait together in the hall. If the wolves are to come, it will be tonight.

The warriors sharpen their spears or repair axes, as they sit around the built-up fire. The mothers of the children join them. All know that resistance is futile; the wolf-men (as they knew us then) are too strong and too fast. They hope that the hunters hunt elsewhere this night, at another settlement.

As the night wears on, they fall asleep, one by one, illuminated by the glowing embers, each one believing that they have kept watch long enough, that they are safe tonight. Two men remain awake, staring at each other in the firelight. They are both old men, and they know. The wolves will come. A child will die tonight.

Never, in all our years as their shepherds, did we treat theirs as now they treat ours. In those times, we were more numerous than we are now, and they were less. Red Talons roamed the ancient tundra, carrying out Gaia's will, preventing the clever humans from becoming too many. We thought then that the humans understood; it was the way, the balance that must be kept. But they, the humans, were of the Wyrm from the very beginning. Some Red Talons knew that then; all know it now. Yet still we killed only some, maintaining their numbers as we would any other beast under our care.

Many counseled for utter eradication of the humans from Gaia. Despite what many have said since, this was never the desire of the Red Talons. I know what my ancient brothers and sisters felt about the humans: they were herd animals and a special problem. Herd animals should not be driven to extinction, even these humans who had done such things to Gaia that might never be repaired.

I grin with pain at the thought of the smallness of the crimes that angered those early Garou, compared to the abominations that we now see, horrors that would cause the old Talons to slay humans in their tracks. But the Talons then felt that the destruction of every human was against Gaia's law, as had been the humans' destruction of the mammoths.

Now, we feel differently about humans. They have waived their right to the protection of Gaia and become a disease. No longer can we pick the diseased creatures from their herd — all the herd is diseased. We leave them quietly

to die, and yet they do not. It is not the Red Talons who have failed; it is all Garou.

Yet we bear this burden as we bear the others: with silence and strength. But our Rage grows.

# Betrayal and the End of the Impergium

It is easy to see why the Red Talons believe that compromise is betrayal. The first betrayal was the first compromise, and so it has been since. It is said, by Children of Gaia and others, that the Impergium was our great mistake (they, of course, deny personal blame). If such is the case, then we Talons welcome the accusations. We would begin anew today had we the numbers. I say, however, that the great mistake was ending the Impergium. Had it been maintained, then to this day Gaia would remain pure, and the humans would be no more or less a part of the balance and pattern of all life.

Why should the humans have no predator, yet breed out of all proportion? Yet the hunt was ended. The tribes were tricked and influenced by the homid Children of Gaia, Stargazers and others — all born of human. By the time the Red Talons were recalled from their tireless duty as shepherds for the human flocks, the decision was made. The Red Talons arrived at a great moot to find homids congratulating each other on the success of their "peace."

These homids had mistaken inaction for peace, as always they do. Peace is not to be found in stillness. It is a noble thing to seek peace, that is sure, but it is found in the eyes of the dying moose that is your meal, or in the silence of a forest glen, or in the myriad smells of snow with the return of winter. The homids knew nothing of peace — they had betrayed all Garou and Gaia.

We bear this insult as we bear any other: with bitterness and regret. But our Rage grows.

# The Culling Continues

We did not fight then; there were too many Garou who opposed us, although many of us wanted to fight. We withdrew and held a moot of our own. Other lupus were present, but the numbers were ours. There we made a decision. Most of the Red Talons refused to accept the Children of Gaia's initiatives, and continued to cull the human flocks. Alone or in small packs, they visited the settlements that other Garou had already visited spreading their message of peace. The Red Talons waited quietly for the other Garou to leave, hiding in the forest. None can find a Red Talon in the wilderness when she does not want to be found. After the homids left, my ancestors descended on the humans, picking young and old, sick and injured as their targets. Those final days of the Impergium were bloody indeed, and many more humans were taken than was needed to cull their flocks.

Much meat was buried beneath the snow, for in those times, human meat was still sweet, free from toxins and Wyrm spittle. I think that the Talons who killed in those final days of the Impergium knew, somewhere deep inside, that this was a last and futile chance to stave off the human assault on Gaia. And they tried… with fang, heart and blood.

What those Garou who clamored for the ending of the Impergium did not understand is that they are responsible for the weakening of the human animal. Humans multiply, and many become fat and lazy, sick and weak. When we were their masters, we killed such infirm among them, as we might kill sick caribou or buffalo, and kept their living numbers strong. Sometimes we would take healthy men or women when the mood took us, but culling usually kept the humans not only manageable but healthy and resilient. These days, one small sickness could wipe them out.

After the Impergium had ended, the humans grew more and more to rely on their tools and constructions to protect them from and reshape the world. Even things in which we find joy — rain, snow, wind — the humans shut out and brush away.

The humans are a herd, like any other. They are a herd that has grown beyond imagining, beyond terror. They have grown this way because we have not been allowed, by our less wise and short-sighted cousins, to prey upon them. It is not that their flesh is special — I have tasted it, and it carries little nourishment. It is better, true, after having been buried for several days in the black earth; the fat comes away from the meat more easily. But human flesh is full of tastes and smells that make most of us sick.

But the herd is no longer culled, and the hunters are held back from their task by short-sighted homids. We bear this hurt as we bear any other: with anger and mourning. But our Rage grows.

# The War of Rage

*Perhaps this final act was meant*
*To clinch a lifetime's argument*
*That nothing comes from violence*
*And nothing ever could*
— Sting, "Fragile"

There has always been some enmity between wolves and bears, between Garou and Gurahl. We never saw eye to eye. The great war between the Garou and the other changers was a sad time. The Silver Fangs were responsible for the war, but even then, we doubted their voice. We were never convinced by the voice of any homid, be he Silver Fang or Glass Walker. We had to protect our caerns.

The war was bloody, and the Gurahl and others struck back at more than just the Silver Fangs. Our Kinfolk were attacked in retaliation for the war, easy victims for the Gurahl and their allies. This we could not tolerate, and sadly, we joined the conflict in defense of wolves under our protection.

Though the Garou claim victory in the war, the Red Talons are not proud of our part in it. We gained much territory and many caerns that had once belonged to the Gurahl, but were not glad. Had the other changers fought only the Silver Fangs, then perhaps we would not have been part of the fight. But they were led by vengeful homids (as the Garou are now). If, perhaps, those born of wolf and those born of bear had been allowed to reach some agreement, then the war might have been short… if at all.

But the war was long. Each side believed it defended its territories. Kinfolk and hunting grounds. Territories had previously overlapped, and new boundaries were drawn in blood. But Red Talons never fought with the Corax, the wereravens. Ravens are our friends, and many of us follow the Raven. He teaches our pups to play, and we allow him to pick the bones of our kills. Red Talons hid many Corax at the time of the war, in secret caerns and other wild places. Some Corax counseled that we join with them and the Gurahl to resist the Silver Fangs. But we could not do this, and the Red Talons sadly drove the Corax from hiding, turning their backs on the slaughter.

Many modern Garou blame the Red Talons and believe that, because we advocated the Impergium and because might is our way, we had a great part in the war. They are wrong, but their ignorance does not surprise us. We hold the Gurahl caerns, safe from homid corruption, pretending they are our own, in case the Gurahl one day return to claim them.

We bear this prejudice as we bear other insults: with silence and hatred. But our Rage grows.

# The Rise of the Weaver

*I know, that the sunset empire shudders and shakes*
*I know, there's a floodgate and a raging river*
*I say, see the silence of the ribbons of iron and steel*
*I say, hear the punch drunk huddle drive hammer and wheel*
*sometimes you're beaten to the call*
*sometimes you're taken to the wall*
*but you don't give in*
— Midnight Oil, "Sometimes"

We have seen Gaia die around us in ways that my ancestors never dreamed. When, for a time, the dead look out through my eyes and see the world as it is now, I feel their anguish course through my crippled body.

After the Impergium and War of Rage, the Red Talons retreated to the wildest parts of the world. We had spilt enough blood and could do no more, since our efforts against the humans were halted.

We then recognized our privileged duty as the protectors of the secret and sacred places still left. We sought to defend the wilderness, not to attack the problem. We understand

our mistake now. We should have tried harder to warn the homids, but they would not have listened to us. They kept their our counsel, and we kept ours.

When again Red Talons emerged to see what it was the humans were doing, they were confronted with the first gusts of the great tornado of destruction that was to come. Cities were springing up. Everywhere the ground and the forests were plundered for the materials to build human homes. The first time we entered such places, we were stung by the absence of Gaia. She has fled these palaces of the Weaver and Wyrm, and will not return.

Now these offenses are everywhere. Every day, forests die and the concrete scab swells. The earth's skin grows hard, and the creatures flee, leaving only the accursed humans and their Weaver master. It is said that the Wyrm went mad. Maybe. But the Weaver has become insane also, and is greedy. Only the Wyld remembers anything about the balance, and one cannot maintain the balance when two have forgotten. The homids say the Weaver is misguided, that it is the slave of the Wyrm. I say that homids are misguided, that many of them are slave to the Weaver. There is no excuse that either the Weaver or the homids offer that can satisfy the Red Talons.

We bear this hypocrisy as we bear all hurts: with insight and purity. But our Rage grows.

# A New Wilderness

It is said among Red Talons that there will be new blood, but there will never be new land. It is said, therefore, that to spill blood to save land is a bargain well struck.

Once, there was a new land.

It is well known that the first Garou in the new wilderness were the three tribes who call themselves the Pure Ones: the Wendigo, the Uktena and the Croatan. It is a terrible misfortune that the Red Talons arrived in the new wilderness at the same time the homid Garou and their filthy Kinfolk did. A Galliard, Sky-Runner, was the first to set paw upon the shores of the new wilderness, and was amazed by what she found there. Huge areas of the land were unspoiled, not like the forests for which she had fought in her old home.

At first, there was cooperation between Sky-Runner and the Garou she met in this Gaian paradise. With the help of a Croatan Theurge, she opened a Moon Bridge and brought several packs of Red Talons to the new land. Sky-Runner and the first Red Talons to come founded many caerns that are still kept sacred today. These few packs walked the length of the new land, marveling at the beauty that Gaia had wrought here and kept secret from them for so long. There was envy in some, that the Pure Ones lived in this special land where no Red Talons had yet walked, but mostly it was wonder that filled their hearts.

Meanwhile, the European Garou and their Kinfolk were establishing settlements of their own. Land was claimed by humans, and there was violence between them and the native peoples. Red Talons paid this little heed, as violence between humans has never been our concern. The Pure Ones felt a need to protect their Kinfolk, as did the European Garou. Humans were responsible for the war, though the Garou involved showed no great reluctance to fight. Also, the lupus of this new land were unready for the anger of the Red Talons. They did not understand our commitment, our smoldering Rage. We had been at war for as long as they had been at peace. This divide persists, even to this day, and separates us from those who might otherwise be our greatest allies.

So it was that war broke out between the Pure Ones and the Garou from Europe. Many believe that the Red Talons fought with the invading Garou on their side. The truth is less simple. Some Red Talons fought with the invaders, while a few fought with the Pure Ones, expressing pent-up Rage against their European cousins. Most of the Red Talons declined to enter the war, dismissing it as homid politics. However, the Red Talons feel little of the remorse that is now felt over that conflict. To us, it was homid slaying homid in pride. The blood that soaked the earth made rich the grasses.

The defense of the new wilderness was a different matter. There were mighty realms of the wild to be found in this new place. Although human Kinfolk of the Pure Ones had lived here for many centuries, they had not had changed the earth as had the humans who lived in our old home.

And there were wolves. Wolves who at first were blind to our kinship with them. Soon, however, the Red Talons established packs and territories and began to make their gentle but firm mark on the new wilderness.

Although the Wyld was strong in this place when first we arrived, the Weaver quickly took hold, and the humans from Europe demonstrated they had learned nothing from their meeting with new peoples. It was the sheer speed and ferocity with which the wilderness was destroyed that forced the Red Talons to abandon the policy of defense and protection that had existed since the end of the Impergium, and to go back to an earlier and purer idea.

The humans had to be stopped or completely wiped out. In this notion, we had some support from the Wendigo, who are perhaps closest to us in the way they think, but the Europeans opposed us again. There was some conflict at the time, but the European Garou had far greater numbers, and we were again rendered impotent. We have always been too few, but few can accomplish much. Especially if those few are Red Talons and their Rage is true.

## Diminishment, Slaughter and Gaia's Laws

The rest of our history, that of recent times, has been sad and punctuated by loss. We remain angry, but our anger is cooled by constant tears. Well named is this history: "The Long Defeat." All around us we see the proof of our inadequacy, evidence of the defeat of the Garou. Humans prosper under the tender care of the Wyrm. Wolves diminish and are slaughtered.

Always we have followed Gaia's laws. Why is it that we are punished for our loyalty and the humans are rewarded for their ignorance and greed? The humans have breached Gaia's laws, causing the extinction of beasts by misguided hunting and mindless massacre. There is a law under Gaia, a law that changes beasts as the years pass, a law by which all creatures change with the changing world. The humans try to understand this law, calling it "natural selection" and "evolution." Such words mean nothing to us. The Glass Walkers claim to understand the law, saying that they prosper because they follow this law. But humanity is the force that changes them.

The Red Talons understand this law, this pressure for change in a changing world. The Red Talons defend this law, allowing creatures to live under Gaia. But we do not change. We are the Red Talons. It is the one law of Gaia we do not obey. And we will suffer for it… one way or another.

## A New Impergium

Do you not see the bitter irony of the day? The Impergium has returned, but it is the humans who practice it upon us. What are our numbers now? The Garou are too few. The Red Talons are even fewer. Daily our homes are burned and our Kinfolk slaughtered. This is the Impergium in truth. We run to the national parks. What is this but cowardice? What is this but captivity?

There is only one way. We must turn this around, tear down the cages and bite the masters. We must admit the horror of our situation and use what strength we have to tear out their throats. We are still strong. No human could stand against us. Even the Red Talons alone could still do what must be done, if it were not for you other Garou standing in our way saying, "Hold, there is another way."

There is no other way.

We must cut out the infection from Gaia, and that infection is humanity. They are uncontrolled and uncontrollable. The only answer is to kill every last human, to make toothless the Wyrm. Then we can heal Gaia. Don't talk to me of peace, don't talk to me of reconciliation, don't talk to me of healing. The Red Talons understand these words. We understand them better than any.

Before we have peace, before we have healing, we must kill. It does no good to seal the poison into the wound; first you must clean the wound. It is no good to believe humans will change. They will not. They have had the freedom to change, and they become more arrogant, more evil every new day. The Impergium must return. Are we to be predators or prey?

# The Red Talons and the Apocalypse

*He told of death as a bone white haze,*
*Taking the lost and the unloved babe*
*Late too late all the wretches run*
*These kings of beasts now counting their days.*
*From mother's love is the son estranged*
*Married his own, his precious gain*
*The earth will shake in two will break*
*And death all around will be our dow'ry*
— Queen, "The Prophet's Song"

The Apocalypse. Spoken of by the great lorespeakers of all the tribes. A time when the earth will boil and the trees will be laced with fire. Waiting for the signs of the Phoenix? I tell you it is happening now. This is the Apocalypse, and we are losing. The Red Talons, the Garou, we are all dying. There will be no great final battle but this. That is not the way of Gaia. The Garou — unless some great effort can be mustered, unless some great realization can overcome them — will simply and slowly disappear. There will be none to witness the end. That is the way of such things.

The tragedy of the Red Talons is that we are being defeated. We are losing the battle to an enemy beneath contempt. The soft, pink, defenseless humans have proven themselves more than a match for red fangs and quick claws. While the humans breed and overrun the earth, we Red Talons die out. It is as though Gaia has forgotten us. It is as though we have no place in her plan. Refusing change, we must cease to be.

But the plan has gone awry, and we have not forgotten Her. Even though the Theurges see our end, the Red Talons will keep fighting. Our Rage is endless. Our Rage sees no reason. Our Rage knows no restraint. Wait not for a sign. The time to Rage is now.

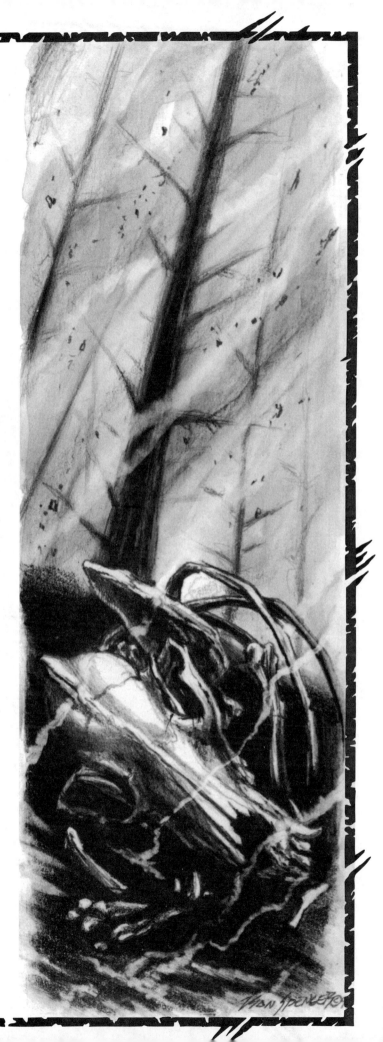

# Chapter Two: Paths in the Snow

*A few still hunt way out beyond philosophy*
*where nothing is sacred till it is your flesh*
— Les Murray, "The Conquest"

I have spoken with many different Garou. The stories that are not mine have been well remembered by me, but are the words of others. I know less of such matters than I would like, but the Red Talon blood in my veins lends me enough insight to present the wisdom of my elders so that you homids might understand. Where I can, I will tell you which great lupus it was that told me the thing that now I tell you.

## The Terror of Two Legs

The Theurge, Stands-Against-the-Stream, a mighty and revered Red Talon, told me the following thing. This is her wisdom and not mine:

"Much is said by homid Garou about the terror of the Change. They whine like pups, and talk of the fear they had when they found they were of wolf. I laugh at them. There is no fear in finding that you have a grace, balance and speed that you never had before. It is the lupus who knows real terror of the Change — I have not been so scared since then. Not of any Wyrm creature or human cruelty. When I found I was of human, I felt terror and shame.

"Humans had killed my wolf mother, and I thought, 'How can I be one?' After the Change came on me and I had killed the hunters in my first Rage, I came back to myself. I lay naked in the snow in my two-legs form for the first time, muscles screaming, covered in blood that coated my skin as if it were fur. The wind cut me like daggers, and the snow burned me with its cold. I tried to stand but could only fall, slip and roll. I could smell nothing and hear only the wind. I wanted to die.

"But no true wolf wants to die. That is the way of the humans; we abhor such weakness. I crawled on my human limbs to a fir branch in the snow and pulled it over me to keep the wind away. So I used my first hated tool, and came to understand the humans better. I lay there, unable to change, not knowing what creature I was, woman or wolf, until my father came and found me. That was true terror. But there was to be more.

"When I first had changed, I had still thought as a wolf. Later, I realized that I must think like an ape. I cannot take my wolf mind into my ape body. Humans have devious and clever minds. I want none of this. When I am on two legs, my mind is more like a human woman than the alpha wolf I am. This is more frightening than you can understand."

Here she backed away, hackles raised and lips drawn back to reveal fangs, frightened by her own words. She would say no more for several hours.

## Dominance and Hierarchy

Red Talons, like our wolf brethren, have strong laws — a strict system of leadership and hierarchy. Although it is always clear to each member of a pack what his or her particular rank is, the alpha does not always determine what the pack will do. An older Talon who, though past her prime, has knowledge of the territory in which the pack is about to travel, may lead the pack for a time. Deference to the alpha is demonstrated by the way a Talon holds her body.

When approaching the alpha, a young Red Talon must stay low, in head, body and tail. The pup might nuzzle the alpha or rest his head on the alpha's back. If the pup is feeling the need for particular submission, he might take the alpha's muzzle in his mouth and gently squeeze it. In turn the alpha will stand higher than the pup and tolerate his affections. It is never necessary for a Red Talon to use clumsy, inexact human speech to communicate such relations. We learn these things as pups and never forget them. There is more in the glance of an alpha, in the way he holds his tail, than can ever be said in human talk.

Among the Red Talons, it is a matter of great import that a leader emerge for each pack. That Garou will be the strongest and wisest Talon, the best able to lead the pack successfully against the Wyrm. Red Talons who mingle in packs made from the members of other tribes must content themselves with the games and laws of other Garou. But when the Red Talons are alone, they have no use for Gamecraft or other such folly.

It is clear most of the time who is best suited to lead the pack. Those with the healthiest coat, the fullest stride, the whitest teeth and the brightest eyes will be alpha. Other

Garou can see these things, these marks of strength and health. These signals cannot lie. Gaia does not lie. When it is clear who is to be alpha there is no fighting. Red Talons are not so foolish as to risk precious Garou blood fighting against an outcome that is preordained.

Sometimes, however, it is not so clear. There might be two or more Garou, each of whom has a healthy coat and sharp fangs, and each of whom would be alpha. Still the Talons do not fight each other, for though we can often be found fighting homids to make them see their ignorance, we do not willingly fight each other. When conflict must occur over who is to be alpha, the two Talons involved assess each other's ability in ways that do not usually kill or injure either Garou. No Red Talon has been known to engage in a klaive duel, at least not with another Red Talon.

Red Talon facedowns consist of a series of rituals that are designed to test the two Garou who are vying for the position of alpha. First they might walk up and down together, watching each other for signs of weakness. This is as far as many contests go. If neither backs down, they might next stand eye to eye or nose to tail, reading each other's scent and face. Only if many such rituals are passed and each Garou still judges himself to be the equal of the other does a fight begin. There is no duplicity in these contests. No Garou can hide his true condition from the practiced eye of a Red Talon alpha and a pack of would-be followers.

# The Pack

*So, in this moon, we climb the hills*
*lift our eyes toward the Wolf Trail*
*and remember that our lives*
*and songs are stronger*
*when we are together.*

— Joseph Bruchac and Jonathan London, "Thirteen Moons on Turtle's Back"

I have heard that humans compare the associations that they make with each other to the packs that wolves create. In this, as in all other things, they are wrong. Wolf packs and the packs of the Red Talons are sacred groups. Together we are more than what we would be were we alone. The pack is strong. When a single pack is made entirely from Red Talons there are connections that no homid could understand. Every inch of my body speaks to those packmates that know me. My scent tells them whether I am happy or afraid, my eyes speak to their eyes. When we howl together, the sound is the anguish of Gaia Herself.

We lie together on warm rocks as the sun sets, and each Garou knows his or her place. This knowledge gives strength and security. The special wisdom of each Talon is useful to the pack; we are not so proud that we cannot learn from one another. The young learn from the old; this is natural, and even the humans have learned this trick. But in the pack it

is different. The knowledge that passes is absolute, not changed or governed by jealousy and prejudice. There are no lies in the pack. If there is disagreement, then the two Garou involved settle their differences, usually without bloodshed.

The pack is dangerous — dangerous to others, dangerous to its prey. The humans have forgotten just how dangerous we are.

We metis are often refused the security of the pack. I feel the absence of such succor too greatly to doubt its importance.

# Camps

*If the answer isn't violence*
*Then neither is your silence*
— Pop Will Eat Itself, "Ich Bin Ein Auslander"

Factions such as camps are human ideas, homid perversions. Wolves are not creatures of politics, and neither are the Red Talons. Nevertheless, these ideas have infiltrated our tribe, and thus we have camps.

Most of us do not admit that these camps exist, saying that their names come from the lies of the homid tribes trying to understand us. Among the Red Talons, the boundaries among the camps are difficult to distinguish, and what one Red Talon believes may actually fall under the auspices of several of the camps. Camp members may not identify themselves as such or even admit that camps exist, but we are an angry group and, inevitably, factions develop. Sometimes these factions are shortlasting, and disappear before they can be truly recognized. It is thus hard to accurately describe the beliefs of a particular group. Those that can be named are the longest enduring of the Red Talon groups, with many members at any one time. The camps are not as important or as organized as they appear to be in the other tribes — but they *do* exist. We hide them for shame, not because we do not know of them.

# The Lodge of the Predator Kings

The Red Talons who are most adamant about the absolute and utter destruction of humans and their society are generally thought to be members of the Lodge of the Predator Kings. They claim to remember an older time when the apes knew their place — in the trees — and wolves roamed supreme over Gaia's mantle, with only other mighty predators to fear and respect. They believe that an alliance with the other animal breed changers — other predators — is the only way to halt the ascendance of the homid Garou and their Kinfolk.

The Lodge members prefer to run as Hispo, claiming that this is the true form of all Red Talons of old. In this way they demonstrate their shame of the wolf of today. Gaia took the dire wolf from her mantle; now, only the Garou walk in its tracks. But it is gone. The wolf remains. This we must remember.

## Torn Ear Speaks:

Gaia needs us, now more than ever before. Animals are strong — stronger than they know — but they must be led. They require fighters to lead them in battle against their tormentors, captors and enemies. We are those leaders. Gaia has untapped armies, waiting for the leadership of lupus, feline and ursine. We are the ancient sentinels, the forgotten generals.

The way to victory is through the mustering of the forces of Gaia Herself and the minions of the Wyld. The humans hand-feed the Wyrm, and still the Garou do not act. It is useless to protect what wilderness is left because humans will not stop. There is no choice left. No room for choice. There is no compromise.

# The Warders of the Land

The Red Talons who are called Warders of the Land make up the bulk of my small tribe. This is the most tenuous and least obvious of the groups because it consists of all those Red Talons who are not obviously members of the Lodge of the Predator Kings or of the Whelp's Compromise.

Some Warders of the Land argue that what wilderness remains is best protected through defense; others argue that the only way to protect the Wyld is to attack the humans outright. The Warders are aware of the balance of Gaia and the natural laws. They try to see things in this light, make decisions and take actions that consider this balance.

## Bloodmoon's Creed:

I have only one answer to the question that all Garou must face: We must kill. Humans are not special; they are not important. They are beasts that have grown too great. They have come too close to the sacred places; they do not see that all wilderness is sacred to us. We are the Warders. We must guard what remains. We are the hunters. We must cull the herd. We must kill.

# Whelp's Compromise

The only group in the tribe that could truly be called a camp is the Whelp's Compromise. Called by the homids the "anti-extinction faction," they are a group of young Talons who have taken on many homid ideas and behaviors. They argue like homids, and do not show respect for their elders. They have no pride, and, when challenged by an alpha or other elder, immediately roll and show their throats. In this way they ensure that they are not hurt by the elders, who cannot betray this most sacred of behaviors. And so they practice their profanity freely. We are unable to silence these few, feeling it is better to keep them within tribal packs rather than to allow them to move among the other Garou, threatening the name and honor of the Red Talons.

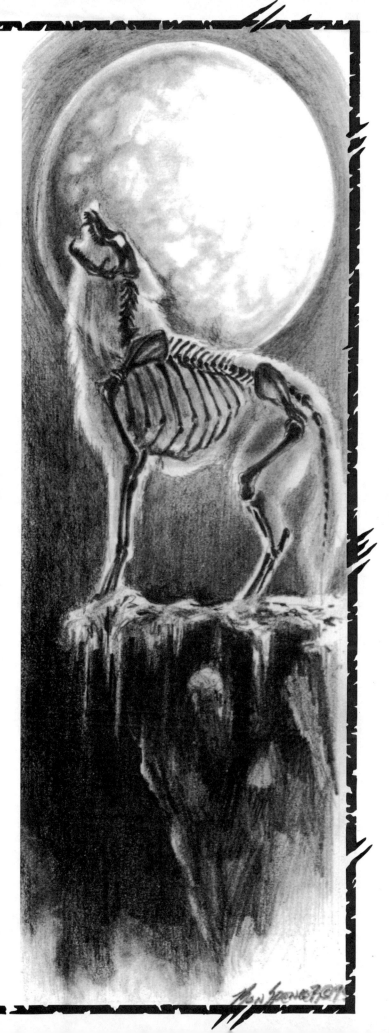

### One-Leaf-Ear is Heard:

To be a small wolf amongst such great ones is ever daunting. We have found a way to make ourselves heard, however. We have stopped fighting our elders, giving in to them while they are present and changing our voices as soon as they leave. We are accused of every evil: that we are like homids, like humans or even agents of the Wyrm. We are not traitors. We believe in the Red Talons, but we would not see ourselves waste our energies in one useless attack against the unassailable might of humanity. Surely such an effort would result in the end of the Red Talons and not the end of the human disease. Furthermore, we would not have the Red Talons reduced to humanity's level. Humans are the only creature that forces its might onto other creatures so insanely, driving them to extinction. We would not do this to them. I would not have my tribe do such things. Then truly the Wyrm would laugh at us.

# Totems

## Griffin

You call him Griffin, and maybe he once was. To you, he is a beast of legend, from the myths of human heroes. To us, he is everything that is noble in the animal, in the hunter. He is the talons and the fangs, the muscle and sinew — those things with which the beast makes his life. Griffin is a hunter and a warrior. We are hunters and warriors. When the humans paint Griffin, they draw a fearsome beast. That he is, and so are we. They would do well to fear us.

We remember Griffin in our moots and when we make our kills. We invoke his name in a sacred howl before we begin a hunt or an act of war, for his spirit guides us best in these activities. Sometimes a Red Talon becomes so infused with the spirit of Griffin that we perform a sacred rite, dedicating him to do the work of the tribe. The Talon then runs alone and slays all creatures of the Wyrm he can find. Eventually he dies. Griffin understands this.

## Old Wolf of the Woods

The story of Old Wolf of the Woods is known well to the Red Talons. One of our greatest totem spirits, this ancient hunter stalks the woods of the Umbra and enacts the sacred lifepath of the wolf. He is the guardian of our spirit, and understands the cycles and rhythms of Gaia like no other. We remember him as the shadow wolf, the ever-wolf, and he is in all of us as he is in our wolf brethren. When the time of the Apocalypse is upon us, Old Wolf of the Woods will come back to Gaia and fight for his children.

Old Wolf of the Woods is a strange spirit. He is both totem and ancestor, creature and spirit. He makes his home in the deepest Umbral forests that is all woods. Born from the womb of Gaia, he has taken on the forms of many Garou in his long life. When he is old and no longer hale enough to take part in the hunts of his realm, he chooses a Red Talon to lay him to rest and assume his mantle. So the cycle goes.

# Breeds

Wolves may be unique in having markedly different human personalities. In human terms, some are more aggressive or shyer or moodier, and pack society allows these individual temperaments to mature.

— Barry Lopez, *Of Wolves and Men*

Almost all of the Red Talons are lupus. There have never been any Red Talon homids, nor do the Red Talons have any human Kinfolk. Very rarely are Red Talon metis born, and even more rarely are they allowed to survive. Even in these desperate times, among a tribe that understands its scarcity only too well, the arrival of a metis cub is met with anger and violence.

## Lupus

Stands-Against-the-Stream has spoken of being lupus:

"We are born of wolf, and we die of wolf. When we sleep, it is as wolf. We can take the two-legs form, with no fur, no balance, no smells, but we do not like to. We are fastest, strongest and safest with four paws planted strongly on the snow. As lupus, we run with our brethren. As lupus, we mate with them, and stave off the day when our line will fail. There are not many of us; there are not many wolves. It has been said that we should mate with human packs and make homids — this would not work, and we would not do it. Better to die lupus than be born homid.

"Lupus is a mighty creature, and gentle too. In us is a balance that comes from our understanding of the earth. We run low to the ground; we are never far from it. We can sense things we cannot describe to you — not smells or sounds, but senses that go beyond the humans', beyond the homids'. We know where our prey will be before it is there. How do we know this? you ask. You can never know with your rational, calculating human brain. We are lupus; we do not think of it. We know."

## Metis

It is not without bitterness that I speak of the treatment of metis by my tribe. Rarely are such creatures as I born, but much rarer is our survival. Most packs would slay metis instantly, eating the dead cub to return the tortured flesh to Gaia and so as to not waste a meal. I ask you, how can one whose parents both are lupus not be lupus? I am no hybrid, no monster of homid and lupus, not even a mule who was made by different tribes, yet I am metis. I am scorned. It is their own shame that makes them drive me away. I was not even allowed the position of the scapegoat, to follow the pack at a distance, to pick the bones of its kills, sharing them with ravens. I will never have a mate, never cubs.

Sometimes I hate my packmates for this, yet their blood is in me and I understand.

# The Auspices

*All that is now*
*All that is gone*
*All that's to come*
*and everything under the sun is in tune*
*but the sun is eclipsed by the moon.*

— Pink Floyd, "*Eclipse*"

The shapes of the moon that govern our whelping are those that make our place in the pack. All packs need all moons; packs that lack a moon are weaker than those that are whole.

Each Garou has a role to play, bestowed by Luna when she blesses him with the mark of the Garou. It is foolish to think that Ragabash is like Ahroun or that Theurge is like Philodox.

## Ragabash (The Invisible Moon)

The New Moon is my auspice. It is the Invisible Moon, for on such nights it is very dark, and we hunt by scent alone. Our prey cannot see us in the dark, and when we move into the wind it cannot smell us. We are invisible.

We Ragabash have a special place among our packs and tribe. The Red Talons, more than any other tribe of Garou, have a strict hierarchy. The alpha is ruler, and is seldom, if ever, a Ragabash. Our role is to be the only Garou allowed to question the alpha. We may ridicule, embarrass and joke about the alpha. When she responds with a challenge, we, never hoping to be alpha ourselves, respond submissively, acknowledging her dominance. In this way we can criticize the leadership of the alpha without threatening her position. This role is vital to the survival of the pack. If there were none to question the alpha, a bad leader could lead the pack to disaster just because he was the strongest.

## Theurge (The Listening Moon)

This is the Listening Moon. It is still too dark for sure sight in the hunt, but we can hear our prey. It is also during this moon that the spirits whisper into the world; if we are quiet and still, we can hear them. Those born on these nights can understand them.

Stands-against-the-Stream is a Crescent Moon:

"The way of the Theurge is the way of Gaia. We bear a great burden. Knowledge is ours, and secrets that can be heard by no other Garou, not even those of our own packs. This is hard. Sometimes we know the future, but we can say nothing of it. The Theurge guards her pack while they are in the Umbra, and at all times from the spying and stalking of baleful spirits. The Theurge tells Gaia what the pack is doing and who they are, that She might be merciful and give the pack good fortune. We are the heart of the Red Talons, the heart of the Garou and the heart of Gaia Herself."

## Philodox (The Traveling Moon)

This is the night of half-light. It is light enough for our prey to see us, but not as well as on other nights to come. It is time to move across the land; the hills and trees are seen in their beauty. Packmates are seen nearby; their eyes meet. It is a time for family.

Torn Ear is a Half Moon:

"You may think that I will talk of balance. The balance of the half moon, the balance of human and wolf? All Red Talons understand balance, the balance of Gaia. I am more wolf than human, and no creature walks the middle line exactly. What is Philodox that no other Talon is? Philodox is tolerance. Not always, but when needed. Philodox can listen to any point of view and make judgments based on what he hears. When I strike, it is after I have considered the matter before me. When my pack strikes, it is after it has listened to my ruling. Philodox is sometimes alpha, sometimes not. When Philodox talks to the pack, all listen. If this is balance, then Philodox is balance."

## Galliard (The Howling Moon)

The light is growing. All can be seen but the shadows. What prey do the shadows hide? It is time to howl, to summon the pack and to scare the prey from hiding. Gaia's beauty makes us cry. It is time to howl.

Scent-of-Red-Snow is a Gibbous Moon:

"The keeper of the howl is a sacred duty. A Galliard must do this so that the howl never ceases. When I do not give voice, the howl resounds inside my belly, growing in strength so that when I open my jaws, the howl bursts forth and all that hear comprehend my Rage and love. The Galliard must know much. It falls to me to teach the pups and to chronicle the deeds of the pack, lest we should fall. We use no writing, for such kills a tale. The only living tale is that told from wolf to wolf. I was born under the dying of the gibbous, and my songs are dire. I sing mainly of death, but such songs need not be so baleful. The death of a prey is a sacred thing, and I must sing of the chase and of the bravery of the stag. All such things are my duty."

## Ahroun (The Seeing Moon)

The light is everywhere. There is no hiding. A time for boldness. The prey can meet our gaze; the hunt is honorable. All see our glory as we hunt; we see ourselves as we hunt. A time of renown. A time for all to see.

Bloodmoon is a Full Moon:

"To be a Red Talon Ahroun is to be the teeth and sinew of the earth. It is to know the taste of blood and the press of battle. It is to be everything or nothing. The strongest Ahroun will be alpha, leading a pack of strong Red Talons against humans, against the Wyrm. The weaker ones will be scapegoat, unable to lead their own packs, picking at the scraps left by their more generous packmates. Or they will be lone wolves, condemned to travel on their own and do what they may for Gaia. The strongest, though, will lead.

"This is a terrible responsibility. Think carefully before you lead Garou or wolves into battle. If they are slain, then you are responsible. Then you will be the lone wolf. The Ahroun of the Red Talons is the strongest warrior on the face of Gaia. We need no klaives; we need no guns. The weapons that Gaia gives us are superior to these. With claw and fang we make the humans remember us, and tell the Wyrm things it cannot forget."

# Spirituality

*Sister moon will you be my guide*
*In your blue blue shadows I would hide*
*All good people asleep tonight*
*I'm all by myself in your silver light…*
*To howl at the moon the whole night through*
*And they really don't care if I do*
*I'd go out of my mind, but for you*
*— Sting, "Sister Moon"*

Ours is an animal spirit. When we howl together at Luna's brightness, all creatures flee the sound. It is the eerie sound of those whose duty it is to kill giving thanks, giving thanks to their Mother, to their pack and to the earth.

Ours is an unrestrained spirit. No chains bind us, no fence can stay us. We are those who tread the crest of the hunt. We are brothers and sisters together. The smell of my packmate's fur is the smell of safety. We are free.

Ours is a killer's spirit. We are bound to our prey in a sacred bond. Luna smiles upon us as we sleep, nose to tail in the snow. We hunt together, and we are one beast.

Red Talon packs hold moots frequently. In the season in which the pack runs together, there may be a moot every night. No fires are ever kindled, no special place is needed. One Red Talon will be ritemaster, and the others lie on the stone or in the snow as she prepares her rite. We circle her, as hunters might a prey; beginning far away, but getting closer, ever closer. As we come closer, an ever decreasing circle of pacing wolves (for we are ever in Lupus form), the ritemaster begins the rite. Red Talons rites always end in a howl — a long mournful howl to bind the pack together, to tell others of our territory, to sing our anguish to Gaia.

# The Wyrm

What to say of the Wyrm? The Wyrm is all evil but all evil is not the Wyrm. The Wyrm kills us, kills ours and kills Gaia. We fight as we can. We will not win, for the Wyrm defeats us. We will not win unless the humans are driven from Gaia, unless their cities are again sown with plants and overrun by wild beasts. The Wyrm is in all humans. Without humans the Wyrm could have no form. Humans are the Wyrm.

# The Weaver

You might find a Red Talon who will accept that there is a place for the Weaver, but you would need to look hard and long. The Weaver has gone far beyond any such place. We do not believe in a world without pattern — nature is full of patterns — but the Weaver's patterns choke and stifle. The Weaver's webs are the scaffold on which the Wyrm hangs the humans and provides the framework of their machine. Without the support of the Weaver, the Wyrm could never have have been so victorious. Therefore, the Weaver is our enemy.

# The Wyld

The Wyld is often misunderstood. Wilderness is not the same as chaos. The Wyld is a force of life, of creation. The Wyld obeys rules that the others of the Triat have forgotten.

Without the Wyld, the Weaver would have no material with which to build, the Wyrm no force to warp. The Wyld is thus stronger than the other forces. The force of the Wyld is undirected, and can be channeled, through the laws of Gaia or by the others of the Triat. Everything that the Wyld creates begins as good and true, but can quickly be corrupted or stolen.

# The Litany

There are Red Talons who do not even know of the Litany. It is only those Red Talons who interact with other Garou, perhaps in multitribal septs, that have need for the ancient rules. Many of the Red Talon's own instinctive principles are similar to those of the Litany, but others are different.

Torn-Ear has mixed with other tribes, and holds strong opinions about the Litany and its meaning for Red Talons:

## Garou Shall Not Mate with Garou

Metis are abomination. We have no need of them. Garou should mate only with wolves, whom they protect.

## Combat the Wyrm Wherever It Dwells, Wherever It Breeds

The Garou at the moot intone this creed and then do nothing. I say that if you would combat the Wyrm wherever it dwells, wherever it breeds, then come with me to its den, to the city, and kill humans. But they do not come. We are the only tribe that respects this law.

## Respect the Territory of Another

This is the way of wolves. It is the same as to tell a wolf to sleep with his nose out of the wind. We respect it, but we need not be told. Our noses tell us where we should and should not go. Others wander more often into our territory than we into theirs.

## Accept an Honorable Surrender

Any that roll on their backs and show their throats should be spared. It is enough to show true submission to one's elders. If the crime against the dominant Garou is so great, cast out the offender. If the offender does not surrender, kill him. If the offender is human, give him no time to surrender.

## Submit to Those of Higher Station

Garou must have leaders. Those leaders are the healthy Garou and the strong, those that know how to hunt and those that know how to fight. Other Garou should realize this and submit themselves to just leadership.

They are tainted, we are pure. The Silver Fangs still rule, and we follow them, though sometimes their course seems mad. They are pure of blood yet weak of mind. We do not understand this. Is it a Wyrm trick? For now, their lupus still embody the law of the wolf. Their homid are like any other homid, and we do not follow homids.

## The First Share of the Kill for the Greatest in Station

The kill is a sacred thing, to be shared by all who make up the pack. There is a proper way to eat a kill that goes beyond the first share. Cubs must be fed, and elders. The greatest should eat first, but all should soon partake, and all should regurgitate for pups. Greed is the province of the homids, and we have none of it.

## Ye Shall Not Eat the Flesh of Humans

Humans are a herd like any other but their meat is forbidden. There are more of them, it is true. This is more, not less, reason to hunt them down. Hunt them, but do not eat them. Once their meat was good, but no longer.

## Respect All Those Beneath Ye – All Are of Gaia

This is a pointless law. Those who are of Gaia are of Gaia, and any Red Talon can recognize them. Others, beneath or above, should be killed. What is respect if it comes only one way? Respect the quarry you hunt, if it is of Gaia. Forget the humans you slay, even as their blood dries on your muzzle.

## The Veil Shall Not Be Lifted

The Veil does not protect Gaia. The Veil does not protect the Red Talons. Our Kinfolk are slaughtered and our homes destroyed. Kill the humans however you can. Yet fleeing and screaming humans sicken me. They are not good hunting. The Veil is protected by the other Garou, by the Silver Fangs who rule us yet. They must not be allowed to know that we break this law. They wrap themselves in the Veil and ease their own pain, their own guilt.

## Do Not Suffer Thy People to Tend Thy Sickness

Other Garou are ignorant. Old Red Talons are kept in good health by their packmates. They have wisdom we need. We are young. We are strong. But they are old, and they are wise. No Red Talon lives a life of solitude; all are warriors. Any that are old have survived many dangers.

## The Leader May Be Challenged at Any Time during Peace

Among the Red Talons, the leader is the strongest. If another is stronger, then she will be leader. This is the way of the Red Talons. We need no challenges; we need no games. If a Talon does not show the leader the respect he should, then the leader will deal with him. If the leader cannot, then another shall lead.

## The Leader May Not Be Challenged during Wartime

All times are wartime. Gaia is dying, and the humans have overrun the earth. There will be no more peace. The strongest will lead.

## Ye Shall Take No Action That Causes a Caern to Be Violated

The caern belongs to the pack. The pack belongs to Gaia. The caern belongs to Gaia. We suffer no others to come to our caerns. No humans, no homids, no other creatures can find the caerns of the Red Talons. There, as in no other place, is Gaia untainted. In this sacred duty we will not fail, unless every last Red Talon be dead.

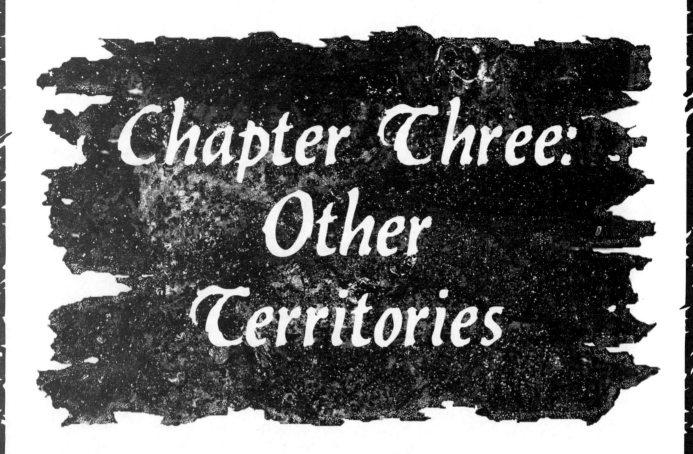

# Chapter Three: Other Territories

*There must be one place left in the world*
*Where the mountains meet the sea*
*There must be one place left in the world*
*Where the water's real and clean…*
*There must be one place left in this world*
*Where we can be*
*— Midnight Oil, "Antarctica"*

Just as wolves avoid contact with human societies, the Red Talons tribe is an insular group. We do not mix with other Garou often or willingly, though some Red Talons do seek to have an influence in wider Garou politics. Nevertheless, Red Talons do come into contact with many of the inhabitants of the world and interact with them.

## Red Talons and The World

*I wish I was a nomad, an Indian or Saint,*
*The edge of death would disappear leaving nothing left to taint*
*— The Indigo Girls, "World Falls"*

I know what I give below because others have told me. One such is Scent-of-Red-Snow, a great Galliard and traveler. She said this to a human Kinfolk:

"I have seen your human world, and I know you do not understand. Whether you are truly of the Wyrm or not means nothing to me. You humans think you are the most important beast on the face of Gaia. You believe you can destroy the homes of other creatures to make more homes for yourselves. You believe yourselves to be so important?

"We have no such delusions. Humans are not important. Red Talons are not important. Garou are not important. Only Gaia is important, and all things on Her are important only to grace Her. No human can understand the silent spirit of the forests. No human can understand the heaving pain of the oceans. No human can understand.

"There is nowhere for us to go. We have no sacred places that are undefiled by the closeness of filth. Our Kinfolk and the other beasts are forced to flee to the high mountains before those too fall to evil. We flee with them when we would rather fight. We are so few, and our pups are fewer.

"Gaia dies a little every day. Some forest, some wetland, some grassland falls to the human's axe and their encroaching concrete deserts every day. How long until the homids can see? How long will the other Garou keep us from human throats? We want to kill. We see no other outlet for the indignance, the Rage that builds inside us, which turns to bitter gall every time we hear the death scream of a tree and we are powerless to help. We hate the humans and hate the homids who keep us from their necks. We hate the Wyrm of sickness, and we hate the Weaver of chains. Homids and even humans of the future will look back and see that we are right. It will be so clear then. But there will be no future. Therefore, we are the Red Talons, and we hate."

# Red Talon Kinfolk: The World of Wolves

*The brains of a wolf do decrease and increase with the moon. The neck of a wolf is short which argueth a treacherous nature. He is exceedingly strong, especially being able to bite asunder not only stones, but Brasse and Iron.*

— Edward Topsell, A *Historie of Foure-Footed Beastes*

Humans do not understand wolves, and this is why they treat them as they do. Should we be surprised that humans do not understand the majestic coursing of the wolf in flight? Should we be surprised that they fear the wolf? I think that the Impergium-old image of the Garou engraved in their race memory has had a bad effect on the wolf. The wolf, however, is not without its defenders.

It is truly the good fortune of the Garou or the good planning of Gaia that we are descended from the wolf. The weaknesses that arise from our human forms are easily compensated for by the strengths of the wolf. The wolf is a truly amazing creature. Even I, who am more than half wolf and who has come to understand some of the deepest mysteries of Gaia, am always learning new things about the wolf.

Once the wolf roamed all the forests of our half of the world. Herds of all beasts were the wolf's to tend, and he prospered. The wolf was the most populous predator of its kind on the face of Gaia.

No longer.

Now the wolf lives only in the forests of Northern America and Canada and in a few other places in Europe and Asia. This loss has not occurred naturally, for the wolf has no natural predator — except, perhaps, during puppyhood. This terrible diminishment of the home of the wolf has been caused by the actions of humans, who cut and burn the forests in which the wolves live and who kill our Kinfolk with traps and guns and poisons.

# Hunting

*A wolf is kept fed by its feet.*

— Russian Proverb

Many animals live alone. They hunt alone and only come together to mate. Wolves are different. Wolves live in packs. A pack has many advantages. Although not every animal in the pack will be able to mate in his or her lifetime, all will help to raise their sister's or father's pups. In this way, Kinfolk pass their blood down through many cubs.

A pack of animals can hunt much larger prey. A lone wolf might be able to kill a moose, but will surely suffer broken ribs or a crushed skull for his efforts. Solitary wolves are more likely to eat rabbits, mice and other small creatures. A pack, however, can succeed well in hunting moose or caribou.

Wolves are clever creatures, and this is obvious when they hunt. First, they approach the herd of prey, singling out the creature that they will eat. Sometimes this is as far as it goes, when the wolves determine that no creature is suitable at that moment. Next, they will meet the gaze of their chosen prey. Once the prey recognizes that he has been chosen, he will run. The wolves follow.

We Red Talons hunt like the wolves. Gaia forgive you if you are our chosen prey. We will chase you, no matter if you have vehicles to escape us. We are tireless. We will chase you, wear you down, cut you with our teeth until you fall, exhausted and alone. Your packmates have long abandoned you. We will look into your eyes, and you will understand — only then — who you are and who we are. We are the Red Talons.

# Red Talons among Kinfolk

We move among our Kinfolk often. It falls to us to maintain their numbers and their strength. Also, if there were no more wolves, there would be no more Red Talons. This is a selfish reason to protect wolves, but we also protect them for themselves. The world would be less without them, less even than it would be without the Red Talons.

When we travel among our Kin to find a strong mate and to sow our seed that more Garou might be born, we live among the packs. If a Red Talon male wishes to mate with a wolf, he must become part of that pack, hunting and running with them, showing that his limbs are strong and his coat glossy. He must show the wolf that he is a good mate, a good sire for her pups. Also, he must best the alpha male for the right to choose his mate (who is often the alpha female). In these contests, no use of Gifts or other Garou abilities is allowed. The contests must be a fair match, wolf against wolf. If the Garou is defeated, as happens more often than you might think, he must leave and search for another mate.

If a Red Talon female seeks to mate with a wolf, then she too must live as a member of the pack for a time. Her mate, who is often the alpha male, must be won over by her and must be convinced that she is a better breeding prospect than the alpha female or any of the other females in his pack. This often results in conflict, which must be resolved as fairly as the male contest.

# The Other Garou

Garou are the chosen of Gaia. Red Talons are those who remain true to Her. The other Garou have lost their way. They are still strong and greater in number than we, but they do not hear the pulse of the seasons, the rhythms of Gaia, as we do. They have become as the humans, separated from that which gives them life.

There are some among their ranks who begin to understand. Some Black Furies, some Wendigo, and all lupus have listened when Red Talons have spoken, and they found that they knew little of Gaia. Most of the others, the great bulk of the homids, are good for little but to protect caerns and fight each other for dominance. What good is a Garou who has forgotten how to hunt? What good is a Garou who cannot sleep on the snow for fear of a chilling death?

The Glass Walkers, in their arrogance, claim that they are advanced. They claim that they have adapted, and will live on after other tribes have died. Let them live on — their world will be one devoid of beauty and truth. Let them negotiate what terms they can with the Wyrm; let them acknowledge their new master. We have no need to adapt. Red Talons are the predators at the top. We are the hunters of Gaia; we are unchanging and eternal. We will die before we change and compromise like the Glass Walkers.

We have no structure for politics as do many other tribes. No Red Talon is answerable to any but the alpha of her pack. No alpha is answerable to any Garou. The Children of Gaia believe this makes us weak. On the contrary, our strength stems from the importance and influence of each individual Red Talon to the fate of the tribe.

# The Other Shapechangers

Just as every creature has its place, every one of the changing creatures has a place on the earth. We regret the War of Rage, and as has been recounted, we did not begin the conflict.

Some of the other changers, Bastet and Gurahl in particular, hide in the wilderness in places where the Red Talons see them. We run far and are elusive. We do not tell of the retreats of these creatures. Garou more foolish and ignorant than we might seek a renewal of ancient hostilities. We are prepared to let them be, and should the Gurahl come to reclaim their former caerns, we will give them up.

# The Wretched of the Wyrm

What to say of the corrupted brood of the great Defiler? They are filth. Worse than the humans, though often part of them, such creatures are nothing to us. Everything they touch is blighted until their bodies are torn apart and their stuff given back to Gaia. Their corpses should not be buried in clean ground. Dig in the concrete and asphalt of the outermost limits of the scabs and bury their foulness there. Gaia and time will reclaim the befouled matter.

## Vampires

We have little business with Leeches. None are our friends. We do not go to the cities where they dwell. I am told that they prey on the humans, who are to them little more than cattle. If they understood the sacred nature of the hunt, the ties that bind the prey to the hunter, then maybe they would be closer to Gaia. But we have little more regard for them than we would for a parasite, a creature with no purpose and no place in the natural order. When all humans are slain, then the Leeches will disappear.

## Mages

It is difficult to tell a mage from a normal human, so we know not how many of these we kill. We are unafraid of their magics. Such tricks can have no effect on the chosen of Gaia. Some Garou have friends among the mages. Not us; we court the alliance of no human. Mages suffer from human greed.

## Wraiths

What do we know of these? What should we care if it is true that a few human souls cling pathetically to life after it has been taken from them? We will create more ghosts as the years pass, sending human spirits to their wretched afterlife with our claws and fangs. Perhaps those that die of fright on seeing a Red Talon's anger become especially pathetic ghosts. A human killed by a Red Talon is gone forever.

## Changelings

These enigmatic creatures are frivolous and pointless. Some do understand the value of the wilderness and seek to protect it. Too often, however, they are tainted, as homids are, by their human blood. They are too much of the Wyld that they forget their duty to Gaia. They might have been friends of Gaia long ago, but now they are cowards. Once, one promised us aid in hunting a Wyrm thing in the scabs, but two moons later he had forgotten his promise and even pretended to know us not. Fool.

# The Deep Wilderness

*I'll be the first to praise the sun,*
*The first to praise the moon,*
*The first to hold the lone coyote,*
*The last to set it free.*
— The Indigo Girls, "Welcome Me"

The wilderness, while dark and strange even to some Garou, is and has always been the home of the Red Talons. It is our bed, our larder and our shrine. Its secrets are in our minds and hearts. We know places where the laws of the Weaver and the pollutions of the Wyrm have not yet reached in any way. Places where the Gauntlet is a small ledge over which we can skip freely, places where the world has been the same since before the humans built their nightmare palaces, places where Gaia Herself would be proud to walk. These are our dwellings. Such places have power and magic. Not the crude magic of the mages, or even the noble magic gifted to us by spirits that we have pleased, but a deep, primal magic, a rhythm of birth and death that pervades all of Gaia, though in the cities it is strangled, choked. Though we cannot hide in these secret glens, their presence gives us hope and fuels our anger. Should ever they fall, then even the Red Talons' courage might fail.

# The Human World

*The paw-print of a two year old Alaskan timber wolf,*
*canis lupus pambasilieus*
*is the same size as the face*
*Of a three month old human child.*
*We humans fear the beast within the wolf because*
*We do not understand the beast within ourselves.*
— Gerald Hausman, *Turtle Island Alphabet*

Humans believe that they are different from other animals. Humans think that only they have culture, and that this sets them apart. What is this culture that they have? Culture comes from Gaia as does every other aspect of their lives. This culture that they claim sets them apart is just their world playing tricks with them. We have such culture; wolves have such culture. What is culture but talk between humans that keeps them from the natural world of which they are deeply afraid?

Once they were apes; once they were furred. They climbed in the trees and ate the leaves. What is so different now, save that they have forgotten? What is so different now, save that their food is not so wholesome? What is different is the Wyrm.

Once they were beasts as any other. They were the children of the Wyld as we are, as wolves are. But they grew tall and spurned the Wyld. They forgot the Wyld as they lost their fur. They came to love the Weaver and its webs and snares. They opened their hearts to the Weaver, and the Wyrm slithered in.

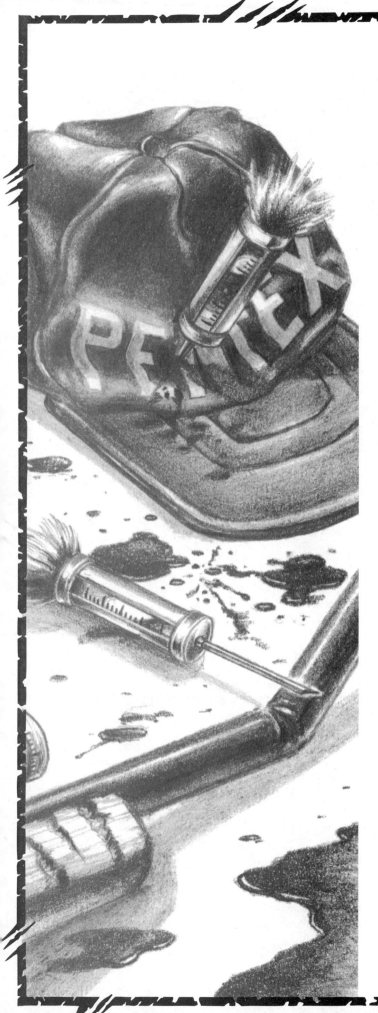

Some humans take their pleasure from extinguishing life with their weapons. One might think that we as wolves could understand the instinct of a hunter. We are not hunters like them. We have nothing but death reserved for these humans. Many wolves will see no other humans in their short lives — should you wonder that we Red Talons rage against such destruction? The smartest and most fortunate among our wolf children mark traps and baits with the smell of their urine, warning other animals and packs of the danger. This we do also, but we have certain strengths missing from even the sturdiest wolf.

There is great pleasure to be gained in making the hunter the hunted. For example, we lie on the snow together. The hunters approach, always downwind, thinking we don't see them. They aim and fire their cowardly weapons from what they think is far away. (It is not as far as a howl travels.) As soon as they have made their shots, we run and are upon them. We run them down and exhaust them, as we might caribou and as they do wolves in their polluting vehicles. We run them down, chasing them until their hearts burst or they beg for mercy. We have none to give.

Some come in the air; they are more difficult to destroy. I once saw a wily Ragabash defend a pack. When the human fired at him he stood, took Homid form before their eyes and fired back with a rusty rifle he had taken from another of their kind. The flying humans crashed in the snow and burned, spewing filthy smoke into the clear air. The wolves of his pack buried the human meat in the snow, leaving its scent so a fox would find it. The meat was not good for wolves to eat.

We are the Red Talons, and we exact revenge.

# The Red Talon Creed

In this time of the ending of days, the Red Talons have established a creed. It comes from the accumulated wisdom of the many Red Talons that have served Gaia truly over our long and sad history. It comes from the conclusions we are forced to draw when we look around us at the world in which we, the last Red Talons, exist.

No creature is so important that it should overshadow all others. The humans must be shown the truth of this.

We are dying, and we must realize the truth of this. We must not Rage against the injustice of this ending but do what we may with our last days.

These are the last days of Gaia. These are the last days of the Red Talons. These must be the last days of the humans.

Do not ask us when we will Rage. Ask instead what good will remain when we have gone and our Rage is but a memory.

# Appendix One: The Powers of the Wolf

## Tribal Weaknesses (Optional)

An optional rule was introduced in the first of the **Werewolf Tribebooks**: tribal weaknesses. These are quirks each member of a particular tribe possesses, usually due to the social or even genetic nature of a tribe. Weaknesses should not always be enforced. There are some situations where a Bone Gnawer may not suffer a higher difficulty on Social rolls. These situations may be rare, but they can occur. For instance, Black Furies suffer from an inborn anger against men, but a Black Fury may not feel anger toward a man with whom she has a trusting relationship.

It is up to the Storyteller to enforce these rules when an appropriate situation occurs in the game. A player may be unwilling to remind a Storyteller that her Uktena's curiosity will get her into trouble.

### Red Talon Weakness

Wyld Affinity: Cannot regain Gnosis in cities

The Red Talons are tied closely to the wilderness, drawing on the ebb and flow of its natural, spiritual life. Because of this, they lack an inherent connection with the Weaver, and may not regain Gnosis within a city. The exception to this is when they are at a caern; they may regain Gnosis as they normally do at these sacred sites. The Storyteller may allow them to regain a few points in the suburbs, if he deems that the 'burbs are rural enough.

## Homid Appearance

Many Garou tribes choose their Kinfolk from a particular broad cultural group or race (e.g, the Shadow Lords with Eastern Europeans, the Wendigo with Native Americans). The Red Talons, being all lupus, obviously do not have such human connections. The only time that any human blood was introduced into the Red Talon line was long, long ago. The Red Talons state that no human was ever part of their breeding, but this seems unlikely.

A Red Talon's Homid form is generally quite primitive-looking. Depending on their Appearance rating, they may look similar to other Garou's Glabro forms. Many have pronounced brows and thick bones. Their skin can be any color, generally determined by the climate in which they grew up as wolves. Those with a high Appearance may have rugged, athletic looks that somehow don't seem ugly, while those with low Appearance may seem neanderthalish.

# Age

Garou most often experience their First Change when they hit puberty. For a homid, that's usually between 12 and 15 years of age. For a lupus, however, it's within two to four years after birth. A wolf matures more quickly than a human, since its life expectancy is maybe 10 years at best. So, lupus enter the world of the Garou with only two to four summers of life experience. This tends to make them more naive than homids, but they still have closer ties to their instincts, and this tends to make up the difference.

After the First Change, all Garou age like humans. This is a tragedy for lupus, as they see many Kinfolk wolf pack generations die natural deaths within this extended lifetime. Sometimes, a Red Talon of only 30 human years (three times the normal wolf life expectancy) may choose the Rite of the Griffin as ritual suicide, unable to live through the pain any longer.

# Gifts

• **Eye of the Hunter (Level One)** — Just as wolves are able to assess a herd of prey animals, this Gift enables a Garou to correctly determine the weakest and strongest member of any group she can see. This Gift is taught by a wolf spirit.

**System:** The Garou rolls Perception + Primal-Urge (difficulty 7). If successful, then the Garou learns which members of a chosen group within sight are the strongest or weakest and which is the leader. If the Garou attacks the group after employing this Gift, she gains one extra attack die against the weakest individual only.

• **Primal Howl (Level Two)** — Wolf howls are frightening to their prey, and an unconscious fear of them still resides within the human psyche, thanks to the Impergium. Although any Garou can howl, a Garou with this Gift can tap into and evoke this deep-rooted fear. In addition, the Garou can make a howl that sounds like it comes from several wolves (or Garou), giving even Wyrm creatures reason to pause. This Gift is taught by an ancestor spirit or a wind spirit.

**System:** The Garou rolls Stamina + Expression (difficulty 7). If successful, anyone (except other Garou or wolves) who wishes to approach the Garou must first make a Willpower roll (difficulty 6) to overcome his instinctive fear. If the Garou approaches him, he must make the roll to stand his ground.

In addition, each additional success after the first makes the howl sound as if it came from one additional Garou (or wolf): A two-success howl sounds as if it came from two wolves or Garou; three successes sounds as if there are three wolves, etc. Each additional "wolf" adds one to the the target's Willpower roll difficulty (maximum 10). If the target of the Gift can see the Garou during the howl, it will be clear to him that there is only one Garou, and the difficulty penalty will not apply.

• **Gaze of the Hunter (Level Three)** — The Garou stares into the eyes of an intended victim, and communicates to them the ancient bond between predator and prey — beginning the sacred hunt. This Gift is taught by the spirit of any predatory mammal — wolf, mountain lion, bear, etc.

**System:** The Garou spends one Gnosis point and rolls Manipulation + Intimidation (difficulty 6 for animals or the human [or other sentient] target's Willpower — whichever is higher). If the Gaze is successful, the target (human or animal) understands the link and will act accordingly: Wild animals will run into the open, allowing the hunter to eventually catch and kill them. Humans and domesticated animals — for whom this is a terrifying experience — may run or cower, terrified. No victim will begin a fight, although if the Red Talon pursues and catches the prey, a battle might result. The Gift does not work on other Garou, but will be effective against most creatures the Garou sets out to hunt.

• **Shield of Gaia (Level Six)** — The Garou can become so attuned to the laws and rhythms of Gaia that the Weaver's laws cease to have any affect on her. This Gift can only be used once by any Garou who learns it; its effects are permanent. The Garou becomes immune to the effects of one form of technology, such as bullets, photography (i.e., cannot be photographed), electricity, chemical toxins, etc. This Gift is taught by an avatar of Griffin.

**System:** The Garou spends a permanent point of Gnosis and chooses the one form of technology to which she will be be immune. It is up to the Storyteller to determine exactly what is and is not included in the protection afforded by this Gift. For example, Garou who chooses immunity to flame-throwers would not be burned by them, but other flames will act normally upon her.

This Gift does apply against Wyrm-tainted technology, although not Wyrm substances. For instance, a Garou who is immune to chemical toxins may not be harmed by the Pentex acid, but the Bane in the acid can still try to possess her.

This Gift is open to a lot of abuse, but the player and the Storyteller should recognize the spirit of the Gift: it is Gaia's protection to Her children from the ravages of the Weaver and the modern world. Just how this is interpreted and how much is permitted depends on the mood and atmosphere of a game. However, no player should be allowed to claim immunity to nuclear weapons.

# Rites

The Red Talons guard secret knowledge about the wilderness and its creatures long forgotten by the other tribes. Much of this knowledge is kept in the form of rites, far too numerous to list here. Each pack knows several rites, generally connected to the natural rhythms and patterns of the area in which they live. They dance the rhythms of the beasts, both extant and extinct, and the changes of the

seasons, lest their ceasing cause the world to change accordingly. Red Talons carry knowledge of these rites with them into multitribal packs, but often perform the rites alone, only including their multitribal brethren if they are convinced of the other Garou's integrity and purity. The rites described below represent some of the more mainstream rites of the Red Talons.

# Rite of Defiance (Caern)

### Level Two

This rite is performed regularly by the Red Talons, and is usually performed at the heart of a caern. It symbolizes the deep connection between the Red Talons and the wilderness they protect and their determination to keep the tide of humanity and the Wyrm from profaning their secret place. The rite is performed every time the Red Talons suffer a setback in this mission. It gives them renewed hope that their task is worthwhile, critical and achievable.

The Garou gather quietly in the caern, spirits low because of their recent defeat. No ritemaster is chosen for the rite; rather, whichever Garou has the most hope in her heart stands and begins slowly and softly to howl. As other Garou find strength in their packmate's bravery they stand and join the howl. Eventually all the Red Talons howl together, the polyphonic sound carrying their defiance all the way to the boundaries of their territory and beyond.

**System:** The self-appointed ritemaster rolls Charisma + Rituals (difficulty 7). If successful, every participant replenishes one point of temporary Willpower. It is possible for a group of particularly downtrodden Talons to lie for days at the caern until one is sure enough to begin this rite.

# Rite of the Griffin (Mystic)

### Level Four

This ceremony is seldom performed by the Red Talons, as it inevitably results in the death of one of their valued members. Sometimes a Talon reaches a point where she cannot tolerate what she sees as the compromise of the Red Talons, and certain death is no longer enough to prevent her from trying to wipe out the humans. The alpha of her pack calls a Rite of the Griffin in which the entire pack participates.

The Garou for whom the rite is being performed stands in a ring formed by her pack members as the ritemaster recounts her greatest deeds and invokes the spirit of the Griffin to inspire the Garou. If the ritemaster is successful, Griffin gives the Red Talon who is to die a final boon. Her Rage and Gnosis are refreshed to their maximum level, and she enters a final and pure frenzy. While in this frenzy, she is immune to any supernatural powers that would force her to diverge from her purpose. She will not leave the frenzy until she dies. The rite ends when the enraged Talon runs off toward her goal and the pack howls a mournful howl after her. The pack then wait for a time and begin the Gathering for the Departed.

**System:** The ritemaster rolls Charisma + Rituals (difficulty 8) to petition Griffin for aid to the despairing packmate. Even if this roll is not successful, the supplicant often travels to a scab and dies in a futile attempt to destroy the heart of the Wyrm.

# Rite of Passage (Renown)

### Level Two

The Red Talon Rite of Passage is conducted in the deepest wilderness. The pup or pups who are to undergo the rite are prepared by a night-long vigil in the heart of a caern. At first light, the young Garou are released, to run swiftly in the bright dawn of Gaia. The pups run until they come to the edge of a human settlement — this is often a long run, as Red Talon caerns are as far away as possible from the filth of humanity. The young Talons must then enter the outskirts and hunt a human. Their prey must be someone who is actively involved in the human's destruction of the wilderness. (Many Red Talons believe that every human fits this description.) They must hunt their chosen prey, often a Pentex employee or the like, and herd him, alive, from the city. The human must be chased or dragged back to the caern without dying, where he will form the end of the pups' Rite of Passage. The Red Talons then slay the human in front of their new pack and present the corpse to the alpha for acceptance. It is expected that the victim chosen will be (at least initially) able to defend himself against the cubs (though not many humans can defend themselves effectively from Garou), and before they are accepted into the pack, the pups are always examined for the scars that demonstrate their initial fight to capture the human.

# Rite of Wilderness Reclaimed (Mystic)

### Level Three

This rite is performed by the Red Talon pack as a whole, and has no ritemaster as such. It is performed in an area that has been defiled by the Wyrm or the Weaver, and is a way for the Red Talons to lessen the blow. Those who are to participate in the rite stand in a circle with their noses touching. They concentrate, and each pack member slowly, over a matter of minutes, slips into a trance state. They then can see the blighted area as it once was, when it was dominated by the natural forces of Gaia. The Garou look at this scene of beauty and rightness for as long as they need, then one by one they break contact, and the vision fades. The Red Talons involved then usually dedicate themselves to returning the area to its natural state. Indeed, in the weeks and months after the performance of this rite, some manifestations of Gaia do begin to return, even if it is just weeds in an abandoned city block or a flower in an open-cut mine.

**System:** All Garou involved in the rite must roll Wits + Occult against a difficulty of the area's Gauntlet. If successful, they gain the vision described above, and the Gauntlet in the area is reduced by one until the next human being (or other nonnatural animal) travels through the area.

# Totems

## Totem of Respect

### Old Wolf of the Woods

**Background Cost:** 6

Old Wolf of the Woods is the heart of the Red Talons. While Griffin is the totem of the Talons' anger, Old Wolf is the guardian of their spirituality. It is said among the Talons that Old Wolf of the Woods is actually not one spirit but a succession of Garou who have each ascended to the sacred duty when their predecessor's health finally fails. Old Wolf of the Woods is a symbol of eternity and wilderness, symbolizing the sacred duty of the Red Talons and their unique strength. Old Wolf of the Woods is not infinite in his strength, however, and when the last wolf vanishes from the face of Gaia, so too will Old Wolf of the Woods.

**Traits:** Packs who follow Old Wolf of the Woods are greatly respected by the Red Talons; each member gains three points of Honor. Also, his Children can share up to five points of Past Life per story. All Gauntlet difficulties are treated as one less for the Children of Old Wolf of the Woods, as his home is the Umbra.

**Ban:** Only lupus may follow Old Wolf of the Woods.

## Totem of Wisdom

### Raven

**Background Cost:** 7

Raven is a gamester and an opportunist. Raven makes no kills himself but is always where death is. Raven plays with wolves, jumping out of the range of their teeth and claws. Through such games, Raven can teach the Garou about the dangers of frenzy, because if one frenzies in an attempt to catch Raven, one is nothing but a fool. Raven is an ancient companion of Wolf and accompanies him on his hunts, hoping to pick the bones of his kills. Raven is a wise spirit, skilled in seeking and finding, not in war. Raven's Children are characterized by their sharp wits and keen eyes.

**Traits:** Raven is nimble and clever. Raven's Children add two dots to their Dodge Ability. He is a wise bird as well as a playful one; his Children each gain one point to their Wits Attributes. All of his Children gain one point of Wisdom.

**Ban:** Raven asks that the Garou who follow him leave the carcasses of their prey for his fellows to eat.

# Fetishes

Red Talons are not great fetish users, preferring to rely on their natural skills and physical abilities to succeed. There are, however, a few items that have been made and used by various Talons.

## Hunter's Bone

### Level 5, Gnosis 7

This fetish is the carcass of a small prey animal, killed by the fetish maker in a single bite. The carcass is then prepared by being dragged around the boundary of a desired territory and buried close to the center. Any Garou who knows the location of the buried fetish can go to that place and attempt to make use of its powers (by activating the fetish). If the Garou is successful, she knows everything that transpires within the bounds of the territory as long as she concentrates (or the scene ends, whichever comes first).

To create a Hunter's Bone, the Garou must engage in a ritual hunt to find the animal and then bind the animal's spirit permanently into its corpse. If a Hunter's Bone is exhumed, it immediately ceases to function and the spirit goes free.

## Pine Cone

### Level 4, Gnosis 6

When the pine cone fetish is held between the jaws of the Garou (difficult in Homid form) she makes no tracks and leaves no scent markings for any pursuers to detect. It is impossible to track the user of a pine cone fetish, even with Gifts that normally aid tracking. If the pine cone is crushed between the jaws, destroying the fetish and releasing the spirit, the Garou becomes invisible to sight and scent for the remainder of the current scene.

To create a pine cone fetish, the Garou must bind a trickster spirit of some kind into a freshly fallen pine cone.

# Talen

## Raven Feather

### Level 1, Gnosis 5

A single raven feather, which must come from a living bird, is braided into the Garou's fur just around the mane. After activating the feather, the Garou gains an unerring sense of the where the closest healthy source of food is, be it game or buried meat. The Garou can use the feather to hunt or to scavenge with equal success. The Garou knows the direction of and the rough distance to the food, but not its nature. Thus, a Red Talon using this fetish to seek game may be disappointed with a carcass buried by a packmate many days ago.

To create a Raven Feather, the Garou must find the feather and bind a spirit associated with hunting into it. This talen can be used multiple times, but when the bird from which the feather came dies, the talen ceases to work.

# Merits and Flaws

## Natural Weapons (3 pt Physical Merit)

Garou with this Merit are greatly in tune with their wolf physique. Their balance and physical acuity in Lupus form is greater than those in Homid form. The Garou can subtract one from the difficulty of any attack roll with a natural weapon (e.g., claw, fangs, punch, kick, grapple) when in Lupus form. However, he adds one to the difficulties of any such attack rolls made while in Homid form.

This Merit costs four points for homid characters.

## Territory (2 pt Background Merit)

The Garou has established a territory for himself (or possibly in conjunction with other Talons or wolves). The territory is defined by scent marks recognized by other creatures (though not humans). The character knows the area intimately and can tell, upon traveling there, whether any others have crossed the boundaries. Inside the territory the Garou can hunt more easily and has an intimate knowledge of all the prey there. Other Garou will not willingly enter the Garou's territory unless they seek to provoke him.

## Breeding Pack (2 pt Background Merit)

The Garou is in control of a breeding pack of wolves. She visits this pack as often as she desires, and mates with whichever of the wolves there she chooses. This pack will rear any pups that spring from these unions, and the parent can return to collect them at the time of the Change (if they happen to be Garou). The breeding pack is not necessarily safe, and the Garou may be called away to defend it at any time. This Merit grants one free point in the Kinfolk Background.

## Ward Pack (4 pt Background Flaw)

This flaw is similar to the Flaw Ward (3 pts), but refers to an entire wolf pack. The Garou is responsible for the wolf pack's safety and good health. The pack is often in need of defense and care, and may have suffered the loss of many members before the Garou was entrusted with its care. Perhaps it is a captive pack or in an area of active wolf hunting.

# Roleplaying a Red Talon

In most roleplaying games the characters we play are in some way extensions of ourselves. We often exaggerate one aspect of our personality or some emotion or desire, but essentially all characters are rooted in us, the players. Even in such games as **Vampire: The Masquerade** and **Werewolf: The Apocalypse** in which the characters aren't actually human, they remain an extension of ourselves. The Kindred and Garou that we portray carry aspects of ourselves as people inside their supernatural skeletons. When the character you play is a lupus Garou, this principle is both broken and doubly true.

A Red Talon lupus has never been a human. This may seem an obvious thing to state, but if you consider the implications of the statement, you can see that it seems inappropriate to invest any human ideas and emotions in a character that has never had such feelings. It would be wrong to look at a lupus as merely a homid with more Gnosis, for example. In the same way a homid Garou identifies with a human who has become a Garou and who views the world from an "enlightened" human perspective, the lupus character has the perspective of an enlightened wolf. A Red Talon lupus expects that his behavior, and the behavior of those around him will be according to the rules that he has learned in his early years. This does not merely equate to an inability to understand mobile phones and read maps. It has much greater implications for communication and cooperation.

Obviously, wolves don't speak, but lupus Garou can and do. A lupus, however, gets more information about a speaker from and gives more to a listener through body language — the way the speaker holds his body, the sweep of his neck and whether his teeth are showing — than he does from the words that are spoken. When portraying a lupus, it's not necessary to crawl on all fours or to make a detailed study of canid social behavior (although there is nothing to prevent you), but you should keep this kind of physical communication in mind. These kinds of cues are present in our own behavior and communication, but a lupus is much more sensitive to them than is a human or homid. It is possible to communicate a lot in the confines of a table and chair. Simple messages can be sent and received by leaning forward and back, angling your head, drawing back your lips in a snarl and so on.

One of the largest and most difficult mental hurdles to overcome in understanding the perspective of the Red Talon lupus is that humans are not important. Our view of the world, however environmentally enlightened we might be, places humans firmly at the top. We cannot help but be anthropocentric. The Red Talons don't recognize this importance, and would gladly kill us all. Taking the animals' point of view, as exemplified by the Red Talons, can be quite liberating. If you try to adopt the viewpoint that would be shared by lupus Garou, you can begin to see what damage we have done to them and their world, and it becomes very easy to understand why the Red Talons want to kill us. Even if you don't intend to play a Red Talon or you play one who advocates total extermination of humans, it is worth having a look from their point of view.

## The World of the Lupus

Another thing that is fundamentally different about the lupus mindset stems from the different way in which she perceives the world. The lupus, in her wolf years, has grown up low to the ground. Her vision is therefore adjusted to see the ground and a close horizon well. Her sense of smell is acute, and she relies upon it most of all her senses for information. A dog can detect the scent of a human fingerprint six weeks after it was laid! This amazing sense of smell has an impact not only on the way a lupus "sees" the world but on the way she interacts with others. With her olfactory senses, she can perceive the past, knowing who has been to a particular place, how long ago and in what state they were when they left. Her hearing is also better than a human's, and she is constantly listening. She is aware of the natural rhythms and currents, and is careful not to be caught upwind of a threat or her prey. These subtle rules that are natural to wild hunters and Red Talons must be painstakingly learned by homid Garou.

# Appendix Two: Cubs

We carry deer-fawns in our mouths
We carry deer-fawns in our mouths
We have our faces blackened
— Wolf-song
— Gary Snyder, "Hunting"

Red Talons, like wolves, vary in personality and temperment. Just because humans cannot recognize the variety of wolf behaviors does not mean variety is not there. Red Talons are traditionally considered by most Garou to be mean, vengeful, human-hating werewolves, at home in the wilderness rather than the city. This image is true, as far as the Red Talons have behaved when in the presence of the other tribes. But when in the deep wild, when away from Garou politics, they show a different face — their true face: that of highly spiritual beings who know and respect their place in nature and Gaia's ways.

True, they will continue to hunt humans with a Rage almost terrifying to other Garou unused to such raw honesty. But they will also keep the Ways, perform the forgotten rites and defend the wilds from all who would harm it.

# Rascal Wolf

**Quote:** *If I do not speak the truth, then why do all the others laugh behind your back?*

**Prelude:** You were never the strongest. Even when you became a Garou, the strongest wolves of your pack could easily drive you away. When you were a young wolf pup, you were the bottom of the heap. You got used to it. You were last to be fed and last to get a bone to bury. During your puppyhood, you learned to be fast and nimble, avoiding even play-fights with your packmates, who were engaged in the serious business of learning to fight and hunt. You were always more interested in something else, although you played with the ravens often. When the old Garou came to claim you, your pack didn't put up much resistance, and you don't miss them much either.

The old Garou was a Ragabash and alpha female of her pack. She taught you the ways of your auspice and protected you from the stronger Red Talons until you learned to fend for yourself. She is too old to be alpha now but still runs with the pack, and is always available to give good advice or savage criticism about how you behave. You learned that your place in the pack was a strange one. While nobody was allowed to question the new alpha, you always seem to be able to get away with it. If ever you go too far, you can always roll on your back in the snow, offering up your throat.

**Concept:** You are both welcome in the pack and laughed at by it. The pack appreciates your presence, but all hope that you will choose another Garou toward whom to direct your keen eye. Thus, you have lots of friends, and although you will never be alpha, your voice is always heard. You often find yourself criticizing other members of the pack — Garou stronger and larger than you. Somehow you seem to get away with this, and those who express their anger too physically are frowned upon. All seem to recognize their need for you in the pack.

**Roleplaying Hints:** Be biting and critical but never confrontational. You are not a warrior and have no interest in defending yourself. If you are threatened, simply run to a safe distance and resume your taunt. Make accurate and (generally) constructive criticisms, not merely random insults, and always keep in mind that you have a responsibility to the pack. That responsibility is to reveal all of the members' shortcomings so that they might be better Garou.

**Equipment:** You have a mouse, which is more a companion than a piece of equipment, which you take with you. The mouse has been convinced that you are not going to eat it, and seems content to hang around.

# RED TALONS

Name: _____
Player: _____
Chronicle: _____

Breed: *Lupus*
Auspice: *Ragabash*
Camp: *Warders of the land*

Pack Name: _____
Pack Totem: _____
Concept: *Rascal wolf*

## Attributes

### Physical
Strength _____ ●●○○○
Dexterity _____ ●●●●○
Stamina _____ ●●○○○

### Social
Charisma _____ ●●●○○
Manipulation _____ ●●○○○
Appearance _____ ●●●○○

### Mental
Perception _____ ●●●○○
Intelligence _____ ●●●○○
Wits _____ ●●●●○

## Abilities

### Talents
Alertness _____ ●●●○○
Athletics _____ ○○○○○
Brawl _____ ●●○○○
Dodge _____ ●●●○○
Empathy _____ ●●●○○
Expression _____ ○○○○○
Intimidation _____ ○○○○○
Primal-Urge _____ ●●○○○
Streetwise _____ ○○○○○
Subterfuge _____ ○○○○○

### Skills
Animal Ken _____ ●●○○○
Drive _____ ○○○○○
Etiquette _____ ○○○○○
Firearms _____ ○○○○○
Melee _____ ○○○○○
Leadership _____ ○○○○○
Performance _____ ●●○○○
Repair _____ ○○○○○
Stealth _____ ●●●○○
Survival _____ ●●○○○

### Knowledge
Computer _____ ○○○○○
Enigmas _____ ●●●○○
Investigation _____ ○○○○○
Law _____ ○○○○○
Linguistics _____ ○○○○○
Medicine _____ ●○○○○
Occult _____ ●○○○○
Politics _____ ○○○○○
Rituals _____ ●○○○○
Science _____ ○○○○○

## Advantages

### Backgrounds
*Allies* _____ ●●●○○
*Mentor* _____ ●●○○○
_____ ○○○○○
_____ ○○○○○
_____ ○○○○○

### Gifts
*Blur of the Milky Eye*
*Leap of the Kangaroo*
*Scent of Running Water*

### Gifts
_____
_____
_____

## Renown

### Glory
● ○ ○ ○ ○ ○ ○ ○ ○ ○
□ □ □ □ □ □ □ □ □ □

### Honor
● ○ ○ ○ ○ ○ ○ ○ ○ ○
□ □ □ □ □ □ □ □ □ □

### Wisdom
● ○ ○ ○ ○ ○ ○ ○ ○ ○
□ □ □ □ □ □ □ □ □ □

### Rank
[_____]

## Rage
● ● ● ○ ○ ○ ○ ○ ○ ○
□ □ □ □ □ □ □ □ □ □

## Gnosis
● ● ● ● ○ ○ ○ ○ ○ ○
□ □ □ □ □ □ □ □ □ □

## Willpower
● ● ● ● ○ ○ ○ ○ ○ ○
□ □ □ □ □ □ □ □ □ □

## Health
Bruised _____ □
Hurt    -1 □
Injured   -1 □
Wounded -2 □
Mauled   -2 □
Crippled   -5 □
Incapacitated □

## Weakness
WYLD AFFINITY:
CANNOT REGAIN
GNOSIS IN CITIES

---

Attributes: 7/5/3  Abilities: 13/9/5  Gifts: 1 Level One from breed, auspice and tribe; Backgrounds: 5;  Freebie Points: 15 (7/5/2/1)

# Mystic Predator

**Quote:** *You think we are the same but you could not be more wrong. I am nothing you can understand and everything you are afraid of.*

**Prelude:** One of a litter of six pups in an Alaskan pack, you were the only one to reach maturity. Born black with a streak of grey, you were well taken care of by your natal pack, though the years were not good ones for them. You were always the outsider, even then. The black wolf among white, the wolf with an unfathomable eye. When the Garou came, you were not surprised. You knew your father was not the alpha of the pack, and the noble grey wolf who arrived to collect you made everything fit into place. Your great connection to Gaia gives you a unique sense of such relationships and natural patterns, and this innate ability enabled you to complete your Rite of Passage with no great difficulty. You traveled with the great Theurge for some time, and he is still a source of guidance for you in time of need. You do not see this as weakness, but keep your elder secret from other Garou to preserve the sanctity of the bond.

**Concept:** You are the "other" — the Theurge, the black, the lupus, the Red Talon — all of these mark you as an outsider, and you are all of them. You embody the reasons why humans can't understand wolves and homids can't understand lupus. You are utterly wild, and no human will ever fathom your mystical depths or resolve the dark questions you pose. The Umbra is open to you, as are the secrets of the natural world. A warrior of a kind, you have appointed yourself guardian of the sacred spirituality of your race, your tribe and Gaia itself. It is your responsibility to handle any violation of that spirit — and there are innumerable breaches. Also, you are the spiritual life of the pack who revere and respect you. You are their sacred link to Gaia, and you lead them in rites and covenants that embody this connection. Finally, you are the predator. You hunt and kill for your own food, understanding like no other the holy link between predator and prey.

**Roleplaying Hints:** You are inscrutable. The observations made by you might be so obscure as to mean nothing to any but yourself. You often stare deeply into other creatures' eyes, trying to discern their inner being and making them uneasy. You speak little, and are not easily swayed to anger. When angry, however, your response is swift and violent.

**Equipment:** You carry little. You know the location of several caches of food in the area but travel without burden.

# Red Talons

Name: _____
Player: _____
Chronicle: _____

Breed: *Lupus*
Auspice: *Theurge*
Camp: *Warders of the land*

Pack Name: _____
Pack Totem: _____
Concept: *Mystic Predator*

## Attributes

### Physical
Strength _____ ●○○○○
Dexterity _____ ●●○○○
Stamina _____ ●●●○○

### Social
Charisma _____ ●●●●○
Manipulation _____ ●●○○○
Appearance _____ ●●○○○

### Mental
Perception _____ ●●●●○
Intelligence _____ ●●●●○
Wits _____ ●●●○○

## Abilities

### Talents
Alertness _____ ●●●○○
Athletics _____ ○○○○○
Brawl _____ ●●●○○
Dodge _____ ●●○○○
Empathy _____ ○○○○○
Expression _____ ○○○○○
Intimidation _____ ●○○○○
Primal-Urge _____ ●●●●○
Streetwise _____ ○○○○○
Subterfuge _____ ●●○○○

### Skills
Animal Ken _____ ●○○○○
Drive _____ ○○○○○
Etiquette _____ ○○○○○
Firearms _____ ○○○○○
Melee _____ ○○○○○
Leadership _____ ○○○○○
Performance _____ ●○○○○
Repair _____ ○○○○○
Stealth _____ ●○○○○
Survival _____ ●●○○○

### Knowledge
Computer _____ ○○○○○
Enigmas _____ ●●●●○
Investigation _____ ○○○○○
Law _____ ○○○○○
Linguistics _____ ○○○○○
Medicine _____ ○○○○○
Occult _____ ●●●○○
Politics _____ ○○○○○
Rituals _____ ●●●○○
Science _____ ○○○○○

## Advantages

### Backgrounds
*Kinfolk* _____ ●○○○○
*Mentor* _____ ●●●○○
*Past Life* _____ ●○○○○
_____ ○○○○○
_____ ○○○○○

### Gifts
*Beast Speech* _____
*Heightened Senses* _____
*Spirit Speech* _____

### Gifts
_____
_____
_____
_____
_____

## Renown

### Glory
○○○○○○○○○○
□□□□□□□□□□

### Honor
○○○○○○○○○○
□□□□□□□□□□

### Wisdom
●●●○○○○○○○
□□□□□□□□□□

### Rank
[ ]

## Rage
●●●○○○○○○○
□□□□□□□□□□

## Gnosis
●●●●●○○○○○
□□□□□□□□□□

## Willpower
●●●●○○○○○○
□□□□□□□□□□

## Health
Bruised ____ □
Hurt -1 □
Injured -1 □
Wounded -2 □
Mauled -2 □
Crippled -5 □
Incapacitated □

## Weakness
WYLD AFFINITY:
CANNOT REGAIN
GNOSIS IN CITIES

Attributes: 7/5/3  Abilities: 13/9/5  Gifts: 1 Level One from breed, auspice and tribe; Backgrounds: 5; Freebie Points: 15 (7/5/2/1)

# Zoo-Born Arbitrator

**Quote:** *You say I know nothing of humans. I have observed them every day of my life, as they believed they observed me, and I know more of them than they ever learned of me.*

**Prelude:** Whelped in an enclosure, you grew up as part of a captive wolf pack. Your home was not as small as a cage, but you never learned to run as other pups did. Your pack was unhappy and uneasy, fed dead meat every day and stared at by humans from behind metal fences. There was no real alpha in the pack, and you did not learn about the social life of wolf packs. You did, however, learn more about humans than most Red Talons. Every day you saw them as they watched you, fed you and wrote on their pages. As you grew you became more and more frustrated with your existence. Some of the wolves befriended your captors and associated with them. Others did nothing but lie in the shade all day, remembering freedom. You first knew you were different when one day you bit a finger from the hand of a young boy who offered you mushy human food, cold and stinging like snow, through the fence. The keepers were very angry with you and locked you up on your own.

That night, you were angry as you saw the half moon shining in the sky. You tore down the fence keeping you from your pack. Then you pulled down all the fences and led your pack off into the night. As you crossed a human track covered with machines, your mother was killed by a metal monster. Sadly, you led the pack off into the mountains. You had little success. Many of the wolves did not know how to hunt or to survive in the much colder mountains. Heartbroken, you led those that could make the journey back to the enclosure. After that, you wandered far on your own, in the wilds and the outskirts of the human cities, until the Red Talons found you.

**Concept:** Born in captivity, you have seen much of the human world and the world of wolves. Although you are new to many of the most basic ideas about wolves, the Red Talons need your valuable knowledge about humans. You are making something of a name for yourself as an arbitrator, negotiating with other tribes who you find it easy to communicate with. The Red Talons are your tribe, and it is superior to all the others. Only Talons could understand the sadness in your heart when you led your packmates back to captivity. You hate captivity more than anything.

**Roleplaying Hints:** Stand still and listen when others talk. You understand the power of listening. When you reply make your words count, and say things only once. If others do not know how to listen, then it is their bad fortune. Always try to find a new point of view. You have seen and felt many things that other Garou never have. Make sure they know this.

**Equipment:** None.

# RED TALONS

**Name:** _____  **Breed:** _Lupus_  **Pack Name:** _____
**Player:** _____  **Auspice:** _Philodox_  **Pack Totem:** _____
**Chronicle:** _____  **Camp:** _Whelp's compromise_  **Concept:** _Zoo-born arbitrator_

## Attributes

### Physical
Strength _____ ●●○○○
Dexterity _____ ●●●○○
Stamina _____ ●●○○○

### Social
Charisma _____ ●●●○○
Manipulation _____ ●●●○○
Appearance _____ ●●●○○

### Mental
Perception _____ ●●○○○
Intelligence _____ ●●●●○
Wits _____ ●●●○○

## Abilities

### Talents
Alertness _____ ●●○○○
Athletics _____ ○○○○○
Brawl _____ ●●○○○
Dodge _____ ●●○○○
Empathy _____ ●●●○○
Expression _____ ●●●○○
Intimidation _____ ●●○○○
Primal-Urge _____ ●●○○○
Streetwise _____ ●●○○○
Subterfuge _____ ○○○○○

### Skills
Animal Ken _____ ●●○○○
Drive _____ ○○○○○
Etiquette _____ ○○○○○
Firearms _____ ○○○○○
Melee _____ ○○○○○
Leadership _____ ●○○○○
Performance _____ ●○○○○
Repair _____ ○○○○○
Stealth _____ ●●●○○
Survival _____ ●●○○○

### Knowledge
Computer _____ ○○○○○
Enigmas _____ ●●○○○
Investigation _____ ○○○○○
Law _____ ○○○○○
Linguistics _____ ○○○○○
Medicine _____ ●○○○○
Occult _____ ○○○○○
Politics _____ ○○○○○
Rituals _____ ●●○○○
Science _____ ○○○○○

## Advantages

### Backgrounds
_Allies_ _____ ●○○○○
_Contacts_ _____ ●○○○○
_Kinfolk_ _____ ●●○○○
_Mentor_ _____ ●○○○○
_____ ○○○○○

### Gifts
_Beast Speech_
_Leap of the Kangaroo_
_Truth of Gaia_
_Resist Pain_

### Gifts
_____
_____
_____
_____
_____

## Renown

### Glory
○○○○○○○○○○
□□□□□□□□□□

### Honor
●●●○○○○○○○
□□□□□□□□□□

### Wisdom
○○○○○○○○○○
□□□□□□□□□□

### Rank
□_____□

## Rage
●●●○○○○○○○
□□□□□□□□□□

## Gnosis
●●●○○○○○○○
□□□□□□□□□□

## Willpower
●●●●○○○○○○
□□□□□□□□□□

## Health
| | | |
|---|---|---|
| Bruised | | □ |
| Hurt | -1 | □ |
| Injured | -1 | □ |
| Wounded | -2 | □ |
| Mauled | -2 | □ |
| Crippled | -5 | □ |
| Incapacitated | | □ |

## Weakness
WYLD AFFINITY:
CANNOT REGAIN
GNOSIS IN CITIES

**Attributes:** 7/5/3  **Abilities:** 13/9/5  **Gifts:** 1 Level One from breed, auspice and tribe;  **Backgrounds:** 5;  **Freebie Points:** 15 (7/5/2/1)

# Metis Scapegoat

**Quote:** *Stare if you must at the hairless wolf. Disgusting am I? My claws cut clean, and my fangs bite deep. I have found strength in bitterness you could never know.*

**Prelude:** Born the offspring of a Red Talon female, you never knew who your father was. Why the pack let you live, you still do not understand. You were never one of them — never even allowed to be. They threw you scraps from their kills when it was clear that you would starve otherwise, but that was the only kindness they gave you. Even your mother was distant, raising you until you were old enough to be chased away, alone. You wandered and managed to hunt on your own for a time. You wandered north and found other Garou, Children of Gaia, Bone Gnawers and others. Many offered to take you in, claiming that they felt no aversion to metis. You were sorely tempted by their kindness but couldn't accept it. The hatred and shame that your Red Talon pack had instilled in you was too great to allow you to accept. Besides, you have a strange kind of pride and believe yourself, despite your hairless body, to be superior to these mongrel tribes.

**Concept:** You are a bitter loner, forming only transitory associations with other Garou. You are full of hate for the Wyrm, the Red Talons, all other Garou and even yourself. Your performances as Galliard are strange. Most often you sing for yourself, for audiences find your songs disturbing. It has been said that you have great insight, but you don't care for such accolades. You have no fur, as Gaia has no forests; you are an omen of things to come, and your songs speak of the Apocalypse. You accept your position as scapegoat in other packs, and don't care any longer what others think of you. If you must nip at the scraps of a kill, then so be it. With your greater understanding (but no greater sympathy) of humans, you are invaluable to a pack of lupus and have served as guide in the past.

**Roleplaying Hints:** You are surly and biting. You can be funny, but your humor is always black. Snarl a great deal, and deliver withering looks to any other characters who make bad jokes. The only folly you tolerate is your own. You are very sensitive to comments about your metis nature, and can be quickly driven to Rage at those who make them.

**Metis Deformity:** Hairless.

**Equipment:** A bag full of various clothes and basic human gear. A book of beautiful, glossy wolf photographs.

# RED TALONS

Name: _____  Breed: *Lupus*  Pack Name: _____
Player: _____  Auspice: *Galliard*  Pack Totem: _____
Chronicle: _____  Camp: _____  Concept: *Metis Scapegoat*

## Attributes

### Physical
Strength ———————— ●●●●○
Dexterity ———————— ●●●○○
Stamina ———————— ●●●●○

### Social
Charisma ———————— ●○○○○
Manipulation ———————— ●●●○○
Appearance ———————— ●○○○○

### Mental
Perception ———————— ●●○○○
Intelligence ———————— ●●●○○
Wits ———————— ●●●○○

## Abilities

### Talents
Alertness ———————— ●●○○○
Athletics ———————— ●●○○○
Brawl ———————— ●●●○○
Dodge ———————— ●○○○○
Empathy ———————— ○○○○○
Expression ———————— ●●●○○
Intimidation ———————— ●●●○○
Primal-Urge ———————— ●●●○○
Streetwise ———————— ○○○○○
Subterfuge ———————— ○○○○○

### Skills
Animal Ken ———————— ●○○○○
Drive ———————— ●○○○○
Etiquette ———————— ○○○○○
Firearms ———————— ○○○○○
Melee ———————— ○○○○○
Leadership ———————— ○○○○○
Performance ———————— ●●●○○
Repair ———————— ○○○○○
Stealth ———————— ○○○○○
Survival ———————— ●○○○○

### Knowledge
Computer ———————— ○○○○○
Enigmas ———————— ●●○○○
Investigation ———————— ○○○○○
Law ———————— ○○○○○
Linguistics ———————— ○○○○○
Medicine ———————— ●●○○○
Occult ———————— ●●○○○
Politics ———————— ○○○○○
Rituals ———————— ●●●○○
Science ———————— ○○○○○

## Advantages

### Backgrounds
*Past Lives* ———————— ●●○○○
*Pure Breed* ———————— ●●○○○
*Resources* ———————— ●○○○○
_____ ○○○○○
_____ ○○○○○

### Gifts
*Beast Speech*
*Scent of Running Water*
*Sense Wyrm*
_____
_____

### Disfigurement
*Hairless*
_____
_____
_____
_____

## Renown

### Glory
●●○○○○○○○○
□□□□□□□□□□

### Honor
○○○○○○○○○○
□□□□□□□□□□

### Wisdom
●○○○○○○○○○
□□□□□□□□□□

### Rank
[ _____ ]

## Rage
●●●●○○○○○○
□□□□□□□□□□

## Gnosis
●●●○○○○○○○
□□□□□□□□□□

## Willpower
●●●●○○○○○○
□□□□□□□□□□

## Health
Bruised ——— □
Hurt  -1 □
Injured  -1 □
Wounded  -2 □
Mauled  -2 □
Crippled  -5 □
Incapacitated  □

## Weakness
WYLD AFFINITY:
CANNOT REGAIN
GNOSIS IN CITIES

Attributes: 7/5/3  Abilities: 13/9/5  Gifts: 1 Level One from breed, auspice and tribe;  Backgrounds: 5;  Freebie Points: 15 (7/5/2/1)

# Lone Wolf

**Quote:** *You see I have no pack. I need none. Do you wish to test my strength against yours? I have learned hard lessons and would be glad to teach them to you.*

**Prelude:** Born in a litter of pups sired by the alpha male of your pack, you would have been destined for glory but for your size. You were a good deal smaller than your littermates, and although you fought bravely with them, you were condemned to the bottom of the pecking order. As you grew you developed surprising strength for your size, but it appeared as if you would never be alpha. Both your brothers vied for the position when your father died. When the Change came upon you, your brothers refused to accept your dominance. In an act which will haunt you for the rest of your days, you killed them both and took over the pack. When the Red Talons came to take you away, you left a devastated pack in the hands of your young mother.

Your brief time at the top ended and you again found yourself at the bottom of the heap. A small Ahroun, you had no choice but to follow the alpha and your elders and do what you could to aid them in their struggle. This subordinate status became too much, and you challenged the alpha for the right to lead the pack. Soundly defeated, you were expelled from the pack. You tolerated the position of scapegoat for a short time but quickly left the pack altogether. Now you roam the wild alone, making humans and Garou fear your territory. You have returned to your natal wolf pack occasionally, and mated with a new dominant female. There will be pups in the spring.

**Concept:** A strong loner type, you take grief from no one. Quick to anger and quick to judge others, you nonetheless understand what it is to be alienated and rejected. Somewhere inside you there is tolerance and kindness, but you never let it surface. You live the life of a wolf without a pack.

**Roleplaying Hints:** You are utterly sure of yourself, despite past defeats. You quickly size up those you meet, dominating them if you judge them weaker, avoiding them if they are stronger. Be forceful and open in your dealings with others; there is no place for subtlety or subterfuge in your vocabulary.

**Equipment:** Other than the scars of your many fights, you carry nothing but your fur.

# RED TALONS

Name: _____  Breed: *Lupus*  Pack Name: _____
Player: _____  Auspice: *Ahroun*  Pack Totem: _____
Chronicle: _____  Camp: *Lodge of the Predator Kings*  Concept: *Lone wolf*

## Attributes

### Physical
Strength _____ ●●●●○○
Dexterity _____ ●●●●○
Stamina _____ ●●●○○

### Social
Charisma _____ ●○○○○
Manipulation _____ ●●○○○
Appearance _____ ●●●○○

### Mental
Perception _____ ●●●●○
Intelligence _____ ●●○○○
Wits _____ ●●○○○

## Abilities

### Talents
Alertness _____ ●●○○○
Athletics _____ ●●●○○
Brawl _____ ●●●○○
Dodge _____ ●○○○○
Empathy _____ ○○○○○
Expression _____ ○○○○○
Intimidation _____ ●●●○○
Primal-Urge _____ ●●●●○
Streetwise _____ ○○○○○
Subterfuge _____ ○○○○○

### Skills
Animal Ken _____ ●●●○○
Drive _____ ○○○○○
Etiquette _____ ○○○○○
Firearms _____ ○○○○○
Melee _____ ○○○○○
Leadership _____ ○○○○○
Performance _____ ○○○○○
Repair _____ ○○○○○
Stealth _____ ●●●○○
Survival _____ ●●●○○

### Knowledge
Computer _____ ○○○○○
Enigmas _____ ●○○○○
Investigation _____ ○○○○○
Law _____ ○○○○○
Linguistics _____ ○○○○○
Medicine _____ ●●○○○
Occult _____ ○○○○○
Politics _____ ○○○○○
Rituals _____ ●●○○○
Science _____ ○○○○○

## Advantages

### Backgrounds
*Kinfolk* _____ ●●○○○
*Past Lives* _____ ●●○○○
*Pure Breed* _____ ●○○○○
_____ ○○○○○
_____ ○○○○○

### Gifts
*Beast Speech*
*Heightened Senses*
*The Falling Touch*
*Razor Claws*

### Gifts
_____
_____
_____
_____

## Renown

### Glory
●●●○○○○○○○
□□□□□□□□□□

### Honor
○○○○○○○○○○
□□□□□□□□□□

### Wisdom
○○○○○○○○○○
□□□□□□□□□□

### Rank
[ ]

## Rage
●●●●○○○○○○
□□□□□□□□□□

## Gnosis
●●●○○○○○○○
□□□□□□□□□□

## Willpower
●●●●●○○○○○
□□□□□□□□□□

## Health
| | | |
|---|---|---|
| Bruised | | □ |
| Hurt | -1 | □ |
| Injured | -1 | □ |
| Wounded | -2 | □ |
| Mauled | -2 | □ |
| Crippled | -5 | □ |
| Incapacitated | | □ |

## Weakness
WYLD AFFINITY:
CANNOT REGAIN
GNOSIS IN CITIES

Attributes: 7/5/3  Abilities: 13/9/5  Gifts: 1 Level One from breed, auspice and tribe; Backgrounds: 5;  Freebie Points: 15 (7/5/2/1)

# Appendix Three: Hunters of Different Prey

*A mountain with a wolf on it stands a little taller.*
— Edward Hoagland, Red Wolves and Black Bears

## Bloodmoon

Bloodmoon is a hater. He hates humans, especially those who were responsible for slaughtering his natal pack just after he had left them to learn the ways of the Red Talons. He hates Garou, who he sees as compromising, weak, foolish creatures who are unprepared to act when action is required. In a twisted way he also hates wolves for the weakness they show in falling before the humans' guns and their inability to prove the superiority he knows they have. Most of all he hates himself for his failure to save his wolf mother and her pack. Bloodmoon failed his Rite of Passage, which involved the protection of his wolf pack, and he has not undergone another. Rather than run with other Red Talons, Bloodmoon surrounds himself with other outcasts — homid, metis or lupus — he doesn't care. He will take any lonely Garou of any breed or auspice, though he prefers Ahrouns like himself.

Bloodmoon leads attacks against human settlements with these ragged packs and with any who will follow him. He strikes indiscriminately, sometimes hitting the heart of the operations of the Wyrm, sometimes in a relatively unimportant area. He is beyond caring.

Bloodmoon has a strange trait. When he assumes Homid form, which is rarely and generally for the short period of time he requires to infiltrate a human area, he appears different from his last Homid form. Sometimes he is black, sometimes caucasian. Another form he assumes resembles a Native American. No one knows whether he has a series of forms through which he cycles, or whether his Homid form is different every time he changes. Bloodmoon has no answer to the mystery. For him, it has always been so, and is merely one more strangeness he incurred at the time of the Change. Some of the Theurges have taken it to be an omen of some kind, but are not specific as to what it might prophesy.

So far, Bloodmoon's ravages have gone unchallenged. This strange trait of his may breed reluctance in those who might otherwise have tried to curb his excesses.

## Scent-of-Red-Snow

A Galliard born under the waning Gibbous moon, Scent-of-Red-Snow has always been a wanderer. Seized at a young age with a lust for journey and discovery, Scent-of-Red-Snow has made her paw prints in many parts of America and beyond. Originally from northern Montana, she appears as a huge, shaggy timber wolf, with a gray-stained muzzle and bright eyes. Scent-of-Red-Snow is a member of no particular camp, and is careful to avoid conflicts between them. She has been known to disarm such conflicts by breaking into an aching, mournful howl that others cannot help but join. One of her great missions is to end factional conflict among the Red Talons, believing that it is a characteristic of humans groups that has tainted her tribe and that it can only weaken Talons against humans and against the Wyrm.

Scent-of-Red-Snow is a doomsayer. Her songs are invariably dark and infused with visions of the Apocalypse and the final death of the Red Talons. She preaches to Red Talons in great moots, begging them to end the madness of Red Talon fighting Red Talon and giving them glimpses of her dark vision. She is a great performer, and her audience is always swayed by her pleas, though this may fade after they have left the moot.

Scent-of-Red-Snow is always prepared to support her claims with action. She has frequently insulted some strong Ahroun only to have him challenge her in front of the moot. She never backs away from such challenges, but the Ahrouns usually do. Hardly ever having to rely on her considerable fighting talents, Scent-of-Red-Snow is well preserved by her reputation and by the fact that deep down all the Red Talons feel her criticisms and know that she is right.

# One-Leaf-Ear

One-Leaf-Ear is the member of the Whelp's Compromise who has obtained the highest profile outside the Red Talon tribe. A small, bristled Ahroun, she has made it her mission to travel among the other tribes and spread the message of Red Talon tolerance. She often asks the protection of the groups in which she is staying when the Red Talons come to fetch her.

One-Leaf-Ear loves the Red Talons, though many of her elders wouldn't believe this. She loves her tribe so greatly that her concern for its future has outweighed her hatred of the humans. She believes that the humans can be controlled and changed, so that wolves and Red Talons might survive. She claims, perhaps correctly, that if the few Red Talons who remain were to attack humanity outright, the backlash from human society would quickly destroy the few populations of wolves that remain in the wild. Even in the unlikely event of Red Talon success, she argues, there would be no wolves remaining to create new Talons, and the tribe that she so loves would disappear forever.

A bright-eyed individual, One-Leaf-Ear is highly charismatic and has swayed several young Red Talons to her cause. She leads such groups in a manner that would horrify the older Talons. There is no alpha in the pack, and decisions are made on a distinctly homid basis. One-Leaf-Ear has been called "monkey lover" and many other names besides, but is undeterred from her mission to change the minds of the Red Talons for their own good and for that of Gaia.

# Crookpaw

Crookpaw is often called more lupus than lupus. Born the offspring of two Red Talons, he has striven all his life to throw off the shackles of his metis heritage. He is a strident hater of humans and advocates their complete extermination. He spends most of his time in his Lupus form, loping ungracefully on his three good legs, his left front paw dangling uselessly. He is a bitter Garou, who has dedicated

his life to learning all there is to learn of the Red Talons and to giving them the voice they refuse to give themselves. Although he is a fierce human hater and homid doubter, he travels among homid-dominated septs, talking of the Red Talons and trying to quell opposition against them.

He has traveled extensively, collecting the lore of the Red Talons, a mission that he performs for none but himself. What he intends to do with the lore he has collated, if anything, remains a mystery. He strives to be the equal of his lupus tribemates, often exceeding them. He lives like a wolf, hunting deer and moose and sleeping on the snow.

There is a strange air about him. Because he is crippled, he will never be the physical equal of any healthy lupus, but wherever he travels, his bitterness, his perseverance and his determination give the Red Talons reason to think. Often a pack is stronger in an indefinable way after a visit from Crookpaw. Maybe he is merely fulfilling the role of the Ragabash, questioning the alphas, reevaluating the laws. Maybe his rare metis blood has found in him some special purpose that will become clear as the Apocalypse approaches.

# Farewell

Wow, has it really been only three years! Werewolf has been around that long, and I've been with it ever since the first edition rulebook was released. But by the time you read this, I will have moved on. I'll be a partner at HDI, a hot new computer gaming company, along with fellow White Wolf alumni Andrew Greenberg, former Vampire: the Masquerade developer.

I'm going to miss working with the Garou everyday, but I still plan to help them stave off the Apocalypse by writing future books. I actually look forward to writing about the Garou rather than helping others write about them. That's going to be Ethan Skemp's problem now. Heh, heh. Poor Ethan will have to put up with the shenanigans of our crazy authors all by himself. The Wyrm works in many ways, Ethan. Beware.

Of course, Gaia works in many ways also, and I'd like to thank all the authors who helped tell the stories of the Garou. You know who they are; just pick up any of the books and read the credits.

May Gaia look over you and the Wyrm tremble at your passing.

— Bill Bridges

P.S. Keep your eyes peeled for Chronicle of the Black Labyrinth in April '96. It's a forbidden book of Wyrm lore, so don't let any Garou catch you looking at it.

# RED TALONS

Name: _____  Breed: _____  Pack Name: _____
Player: _____  Auspice: _____  Pack Totem: _____
Chronicle: _____  Camp: _____  Concept: _____

## Attributes

### Physical
Strength _____ ●OOOO
Dexterity _____ ●OOOO
Stamina _____ ●OOOO

### Social
Charisma _____ ●OOOO
Manipulation _____ ●OOOO
Appearance _____ ●OOOO

### Mental
Perception _____ ●OOOO
Intelligence _____ ●OOOO
Wits _____ ●OOOO

## Abilities

### Talents
Alertness _____ OOOOO
Athletics _____ OOOOO
Brawl _____ OOOOO
Dodge _____ OOOOO
Empathy _____ OOOOO
Expression _____ OOOOO
Intimidation _____ OOOOO
Primal-Urge _____ OOOOO
Streetwise _____ OOOOO
Subterfuge _____ OOOOO

### Skills
Animal Ken _____ OOOOO
Drive _____ OOOOO
Etiquette _____ OOOOO
Firearms _____ OOOOO
Melee _____ OOOOO
Leadership _____ OOOOO
Performance _____ OOOOO
Repair _____ OOOOO
Stealth _____ OOOOO
Survival _____ OOOOO

### Knowledge
Computer _____ OOOOO
Enigmas _____ OOOOO
Investigation _____ OOOOO
Law _____ OOOOO
Linguistics _____ OOOOO
Medicine _____ OOOOO
Occult _____ OOOOO
Politics _____ OOOOO
Rituals _____ OOOOO
Science _____ OOOOO

## Advantages

### Backgrounds
_____ OOOOO
_____ OOOOO
_____ OOOOO
_____ OOOOO
_____ OOOOO

### Gifts
_____
_____
_____
_____
_____

### Gifts
_____
_____
_____
_____
_____

### Renown

#### Glory
O O O O O O O O O O
□ □ □ □ □ □ □ □ □ □

#### Honor
O O O O O O O O O O
□ □ □ □ □ □ □ □ □ □

#### Wisdom
O O O O O O O O O O
□ □ □ □ □ □ □ □ □ □

#### Rank
[          ]

### Rage
O O O O O O O O O O
□ □ □ □ □ □ □ □ □ □

### Gnosis
O O O O O O O O O O
□ □ □ □ □ □ □ □ □ □

### Willpower
O O O O O O O O O O
□ □ □ □ □ □ □ □ □ □

### Health
Bruised _____ □
Hurt       -1 □
Injured    -1 □
Wounded    -2 □
Mauled     -2 □
Crippled   -5 □
Incapacitated □

### Weakness
WYLD AFFINITY:
CANNOT REGAIN
GNOSIS IN CITIES

Attributes: 7/5/3  Abilities: 13/9/5  Gifts: 1 Level One from breed, auspice and tribe; Backgrounds: 5;  Freebie Points: 15 (7/5/2/1)

# Red Talons

| Homid | Glabro | Crinos | Hispo | Lupus |
|-------|--------|--------|-------|-------|
| No Change | Strength (+2)_____ | Strength (+4)_____ | Strength (+3)_____ | Strength (+1)_____ |
| | Stamina (+2)_____ | Dexterity (+1)_____ | Dexterity (+2)_____ | Dexterity (+2)____ |
| | Appearance (-1)____ | Stamina (+3)_____ | Stamina (+3)_____ | Stamina (+2)_____ |
| | Manipulation (-1)__ | Appearance 0 | Manipulation (-3)___ | Manipulation (-3)__ |
| | | Manipulation (-3)__ | | |
| Difficulty: 6 | Difficulty: 7 | Difficulty: 6 | Difficulty: 7 | Difficulty: 6 |

### INCITE DELIRIUM IN HUMANS

## Other Traits

_____ OOOOO
_____ OOOOO
_____ OOOOO
_____ OOOOO
_____ OOOOO
_____ OOOOO
_____ OOOOO
_____ OOOOO
_____ OOOOO
_____ OOOOO
_____ OOOOO
_____ OOOOO
_____ OOOOO
_____ OOOOO
_____ OOOOO
_____ OOOOO
_____ OOOOO
_____ OOOOO
_____ OOOOO

## Fetishes

Item: _____ ☐ Dedicated  Level _____  Gnosis _____
Power_____

Item: _____ ☐ Dedicated  Level _____  Gnosis _____
Power_____

Item: _____ ☐ Dedicated  Level _____  Gnosis _____
Power_____

Item: _____ ☐ Dedicated  Level _____  Gnosis _____
Power_____

## Rites

_____
_____
_____
_____
_____
_____
_____
_____

## Combat

| Maneuver/Weapon | Roll | Difficulty | Damage | Range | Rate | Clip |
|-----------------|------|-----------|--------|-------|------|------|
| | | | | | | |
| | | | | | | |
| | | | | | | |
| | | | | | | |
| | | | | | | |

### Brawling Chart

| Maneuver | Roll | Diff | Damage |
|----------|------|------|--------|
| Bite | Dex + Brawl | 5 | Strength + 1† |
| Body Slam | Dex + Brawl | 7 | Special |
| Claw | Dex + Brawl | 6 | Strength + 2† |
| Grapple | Dex + Brawl | 6 | Strength |
| Kick | Dex + Brawl | 7 | Strength + 1 |
| Punch | Dex + Brawl | 6 | Strength |

† These maneuvers do aggravated damage.

Armor: _____

# RED TALONS

Nature: _____     Demeanor: _____

## Merits & Flaws

| Merit | Type | Cost | Flaw | Type | Bonus |
|-------|------|------|------|------|-------|
| _____ | _____ | _____ | _____ | _____ | _____ |
| _____ | _____ | _____ | _____ | _____ | _____ |
| _____ | _____ | _____ | _____ | _____ | _____ |
| _____ | _____ | _____ | _____ | _____ | _____ |
| _____ | _____ | _____ | _____ | _____ | _____ |

## Expanded Background

### Mentor
_____
_____
_____

### Pure Breed
_____
_____
_____

### Kinfolk
_____
_____
_____

### Past Life
_____
_____
_____

### Pack Totem
_____
_____
_____

## Possessions

Gear (Carried) _____

Equipment (Owned) _____

## Sept

Name _____
Caern Location _____
Level _____ Type _____
Totem _____
Leader _____

## Experience

TOTAL: [          ]

Gained From: _____
_____

TOTAL SPENT: _____
Spent On: _____
_____
_____

# Red Talons

## History

### Prelude

_____
_____
_____
_____
_____
_____
_____
_____
_____
_____
_____
_____
_____
_____
_____
_____
_____

## Description

Age_____
Hair _____
Eyes_____
Wolf Breed_____
Human Race_____
Sex_____

|  | Height | Weight |
|---|---|---|
| Homid | | |
| Glabro | | |
| Crinos | | |
| Hispo | | |
| Lupus | | |

_____
_____
_____
_____
_____
_____
_____

_Battle Scars_____
_____
_____

_Metis Deformity_____

## Visuals

### Pack Chart

### Character Sketch

THE TURKS, THE TZIMISCE, THE RUSSIAN INVADERS...

SO MUCH BLOOD SPILLED, AND THE OLD WOUNDS NEVER HEAL.

# BROKEN TRUST

WRITTEN BY: BRIAN CAMPBELL
ILLUSTRATED BY: ALEX SHEIKMAN
LETTERED BY: MATT MILBERGER
COLORED BY LAWRENCE SNELLY

WHEN WILL THE OLD WOUNDS HEAL?

WHEN WILL THE PAIN STOP?

- 4 -

HE DOESN'T SUSPECT A THING, DOES HE?

NO.

THEN WE WILL BE TOGETHER SOON. BE CAREFUL, MY LOVE.

THE VOIVODE'S TROOPS HAVE BEEN REDUCED BY HALF, MY LIEGE.

EXCELLENT.

EXCELLENT? HOW MANY OF MY PEOPLE HAVE DIED FIGHTING FOR YOU?

IT IS IN THE NAME OF CHIVALRY. THE TURKS AND THE TZIMISCE MUST BE DRIVEN FROM THESE LANDS!

DA. SO YOU HAVE THE SEPTS FOR YOURSELVES...

SUCH IMPUDENCE! WHAT WOULD A BONE GNAWER KNOW OF HONOR?

-7-

# Retribution and Ascendance

## By Brian Campbell

# Credits

**Written by:** Brian Campbell
**Development:** Bill Bridges and Ethan Skemp
**Editing:** Ronni Radner
**Vice President in charge of Production:** Rich Thomas
**Art Directors:** Lawrence Snelly and Aileen E. Miles
**Layout & Typesetting:** Matt Milberger
**Comic Book Art:** Alex Sheikman
**Art:** Andrew Bates, Mike Chaney, James Daly, Matt Milberger, Steve Prescott, Dan Smith
**Back Cover Art:** Joshua Gabriel Timbrook
**Cover Design:** Matt Milberger

# Special Thanks To:

**Aileen** "Evil Christmas Cave" **Miles**, for her honorable mention.

**Larry** "One Hundred Thousand?!?" **Snelly**, for facing the intimidating might of Axis Mundi.

**Matt** "Jedi Master" **Milberger**, for not giving in to hate and the Dark Side when the changes came from the West Coast.

**Katie** "Abu" **McCaskill**, for her production monkey.

**Kathy** "Rincewind" **Ryan**, for having to keep the hintbook in the Parsnip.

**Josh** "Two Shotguns" **Timbrook**, for giving Kyle a quick schoolin' at Durandal.

And, of course,

**Bill** "If Ya Can't Beat 'Em..." **Bridges**, for three years of dealing with miscreant freelancers.

735 PARK NORTH BLVD.
SUITE 128
CLARKSTON, GA 30021
USA

WHITE WOLF
GAME STUDIO

## Author's Dedication

Too many people have dedicated books to their cats, so this one is dedicated to my first two rats. When rodents get opposable thumbs, rats will conquer the world!

### For Scarlet and Patsy.

## Word from White Wolf Game Studio

Well, if you picked up **Red Talons**, you already know the somber news. Bill Bridges, longtime Alpha of the Werewolf line, has left the pack in search of other deeds of glory. Howl of Farewell, Bill — we miss you already.

Now it's my job to follow in those extra large pawprints, guiding the Garou and their allies as well as ferreting out the secrets of the Wyrm. So I'm already abusing my power to commandeer this box and say hello. Bill cooked up a few surprises for you before he left, and needless to say, I've got some of my own to spring. I hope you all have as much fun as I'm going to in the times to come (heh heh).

— Ethan Skemp

## Contents

# Introduction: The Gathering Storm

Sit down, kid. I'm going to tell you some lies.

I call them lies because that's how the other tribes regard them. They're actually truths that the others will not believe. Our family is built upon these truths. We are the keepers of dark secrets, the guardians of beautiful lies that no one else would dare speak. You'll never gain glory by espousing them, but then again, we aren't motivated by praise, honor or glory outside of our tribe — those rewards are for the shallow. We're muckrakers, deceivers and villains, every last one of us. That's our role in the Garou Nation, and it's the only way we can fulfill our destiny.

Even a cynical Ragabash like me knows that. Don't think for a moment that your only enemies are outside this sept. You're a fool if you believe that only creatures of the Wyrm can destroy you. Some of your worst enemies — the self-righteous who would cast you out or execute you — are right here in your own sept. The Garou can be their own worst enemies. I've seen gloryhounds who would sell out their packmates for a chance to be immortalized in sagas, prideful warriors who can only prove their own worth by humiliating their septmates, and weak leaders who would sacrifice scapegoats for the sake of furthering their own power.

The Apocalypse is coming, and "trust" has no place in it. Watch yourself. Skepticism and mistrust are the best defenses you have. When the other tribes gather before the leaders of our sept, they'll endlessly posture in their pompous ceremonies, but their moots are used to hide the deception that they practice themselves. We know all about that deception. If you want to gain respect in our tribe, you're going to have to beat them at their own game. By our rules, that game is called politics.

The Lords have always been masters of politics. Although our role in the Garou Nation has changed, our skill has never diminished. The weakest members of our tribe are diplomats — mediators and counselors, advisors and facilitators who keep order in the sept. That's how we earned our status as Lords and our privilege in the political arena. The strongest of us are leaders. Over the millennia, we've seen what works and what doesn't. The "honor" revered by the other tribes doesn't work, and so we follow a different path.

We follow the will to power. Far too many Garou who have tried to triumph with their pretense at "honor," their concepts of "nobility" and "chivalry." Their weakness has brought about our downfall. The Wyrm will not fight an honorable fight. The situation is desperate, and so we have to overcome the Wyrm by any means necessary. In desperate times, only ingenuity can win over the Wyrm, and only strength can be respected. Only through absolute power can we attain absolute victory.

But who are you to believe me, anyway? I'm a Ragabash. I lie. By twisting truth and lies, I survive. And if you follow my advice, you'll survive, too.

# Chapter One:
# Beautiful Lies

*...this is to be asserted in general of men: that they are ungrateful, fickle, false, cowardly, covetous, and as long as you succeed, are yours entirely; they will offer you their blood, property, life, and children... when the need is far distant; but when it approaches, they will turn against you.*
— Nicolo Machiavelli, *The Prince*

Before you can be accorded status, cub, you must receive instruction. As such, I will retract what I have said about the bitch that whelped you. I will acknowledge that the claw marks you have raked across my face and the temporary loss of vision in my right eye are sufficient redress for my remark. As a Galliard, I caution you that I did not desire a duel. Rather, I would test you in other ways.

If you did not lash out at me in response, I would have had doubts about your eminent rise to the rank of fostern within our tribe. In fact, if you had not retaliated, I may have doubted that you were one of the Lords.

Ah! Sheath your blade. I said "may have." You will note that I choose my words carefully, a quality that you have not yet cultivated. You also lack patience. A Shadow Lord

cub — or a Garou of another tribe — will often demand immediate redress to an insult by resorting to an immediate retaliation with physical violence. You see? I have manipulated you into your outburst of rage. Thus, you have shown me your weakness. Your own prideful rage leads you astray.

Our rage is not an anger that forces us to lash out at the slightest provocation. It is hidden deep within us, like our truest secrets. It burns; it builds; it waits, sometimes for days, sometimes for weeks and sometimes even for generations. A Shadow Lord carries his pain with him always, like a stormcloud that surrounds him. Only justice can ease that pain. Throughout our history, the Lords have burned with the need for revenge, the surcease of our suffering.

Why do you think I have taken you to this lofty mountaintop? You watch the bleak clouds that roil above you — I know your affinity to that gathering storm. I know you carry that feeling in the deepest part of your heart. Your seething anger has made you one of us. Stormclouds gather slowly; so let it be with your anger. Lower your blade. Let the wisdom of your reason stay your hand. The darkness in the skies serves as a warning to all who are beneath it. It is a warning that the tempest is coming.

So has it been with our tribe. The tempest is coming. We have hidden in shadows, and the darkness protects us. When tears fall like rain, when darkness gathers, when the pain and shame becomes unbearable, that is when we are strongest. Our anguish renews us, and thus, we are powerful.

Our pain goes back a long, long way. It began even before we became Lords of Shadows. Sit, child, and as the tempest gathers, I will tell you our story.

# The Earliest Lies

*You know, I read a lot. Especially about things about history. I find that shit fascinating.*

— Cliff, *True Romance*

It is said that any legend, no matter how outrageous, contains an element of truth. Let me tell you a legend, then... a fairy tale, if you will.

Long ago, before the rise of mankind, Gaia was in balance. As it was with our sacred mother, so was it with our Garou Nation. Each knew his role. The warriors exalted in the thrill of the hunt, running together as wolves and men. Those warriors would one day form the Get and the Red Talons. The passionate Garou regaled us in song and story, bringing understanding and healing. Those artisans would later become the Children of Gaia and the Fianna. The mystics followed older gods then, and even among the Uktena and Stargazers today, many of those old ones are still revered. And the noblest of Garou inspired us with their majesty. Our rulers bore the burdens of their duties with equanimity, and their pronouncements demonstrated their sagacity. The Garou who were the most esteemed among us would one day form the Silver Fangs.

I said it was a fairy tale, didn't I?

For the sake of our story, then, I will say that there was a time when our rulers were worthy of great admiration. Moreover, they were worthy of support. Let it not be said that we are without humility, for the Lords have humble origins. Our role in the order of things was to support and advise our leaders. A strong leader is worthy of any sacrifice, and the wisest leaders surrounded themselves with the best advisors and counselors. The sept leaders were our kings, and we, their advisors, were their court of lords.

A good leader will not be above sharing the same tasks as his followers. So it was with our rulers in those early days. When the warriors would hunt, their leader would run with them to see if the hunting was good. When the masters of song and story would recite and perform, their ruler would step from his throne to discuss his praise or criticism, and thus learn the value of the arts. And as the advisors studied and debated, our leaders would occasionally take part in the debates, showing their cunning and ingenuity.

There are some tasks, however, that a ruler cannot practice. A noble man often decries the need to take an unfair advantage over his rivals. He will not spy on the conversations of his detractors or detain those who voice fair criticisms against him. Nonetheless, he may give in to the temptation of using such tactics occasionally and in turn, pass the deed on to someone else. When a loyal man receives such a request, it becomes a true test of loyalty. If your esteemed sept leader asked you to steal from a thief who has stolen from him, you would thus become a thief for the good of the sept. If your honorable leader asked you to kill a man who was plotting to murder your superiors, you would thus become a murderer for the good of your sept.

So it was with our leaders. We were loyal.

In the earliest days, the different social circles within the septs developed their own distinctions, and Garou society evolved into a system of castes. Warriors worked together to plan the defense of our caerns, set traps for game and keep the septs well-fed. Mystics found deeper knowledge as their ceremonies became more elaborate. They kept us in touch with the spirits of our caerns. Artisans created more elaborate arts, and we admired them for their skill. There was also caste of messengers and diplomats, a rank held by our progenitors and those who would later become the Silent Striders. So it was with our leaders. They rose above distinctions of caste and claimed the privileges of rank. Our rulers formed their own privileged elite.

As they rose to the challenges before them, they learned the discourse of leadership. Rulers learn to keep their subjects happy by saying *this* to one man and *that* to another and believing both truths for the sake of harmony. When we, the diplomats, were to speak on their behalf, our Half-Moons quickly learned that any proposition and its opposite could both be true, and we understood instinctively that a sept leader could be an ally of one sept one moon and a dire enemy the next. We did what we had to when we kept a ruler in power, for *this* task was beneath him and ignoble, but *that* task was justified because it had to be done, so we did both. Our reward was the approval of the king, the awarding of status, and our recognition as Lords.

As the caste system grew, we came to understand it, for our Half-Moons had to mediate between all of the castes. The Lords were the keepers of law and the advocates of civility. Just as the artisans valued passion and the mystics praised insight, the Lords revered reason. If a sept leader had difficulty understanding his "subjects," our Half-Moons

were the ones who would speak on his behalf, regardless of whether it would make us appear to be untrustworthy. When the sept leader wanted to find out what his subjects were really saying, our No Moons would stealthily observe. And when a member of the ruling class did not want his champion to declare a duel before a gathering of a sept, it was our Ahroun warriors who would set the ambush.

"Yes, my liege. No, my liege. By your word, he shall die, my liege." Such was our honor. None carried out these tasks as well as the Lords, and the ruling caste gave their blessing. They would not soil their hands with such dishonorable deeds. Our honor was a secret one, just as a loyal man will accept personal disgrace if it benefits the safety of all.

Dare not repeat this, for this truth has become taboo. The truth has become a lie, and now the truth and lie are both correct.

# Breeding Stock

The caste system was the earliest form of civility. The division of auspices was not as clear then. If you needed a Philodox, you spoke to a Lord; if you required a Theurge, you went one of the mystics. Since our tribes descended from these castes, you may begin to understand why the Fianna are renown for their Galliards, the Uktena for their Theurges, and so on. The finer distinctions were not created until our Garou Nation tore itself apart.

The distinctions between us became more pronounced when the rulers took the privilege of maintaining their own Kinfolk. The standard histories, the ones you may hear told by an esteemed Fianna Galliard or a noble Silver Fang, tell us that long before mankind became a threat, the Garou were the "caretakers" of mankind, protecting them from harm. We watched their simple tribes, we learned from their culture and we chose the brightest and the best of them as our breeding stock. The lie is somewhat more cynical than this.

We were more than caretakers, and they were more than slaves. In the earliest days, any Garou could take any man, woman or wolf as his or her mate. Rare were the cases were two would vie for the same lover, but as the ruling class placed themselves farther above their subjects, they demanded the finest slaves. To ensure this, at the behest of the ruling caste, it was decreed that each caste would have its own separate breeding stock.

The most regal rulers valued majestic beauty, and so the "nobility" claimed the privilege of choosing the most beautiful humans and wolves for their mates. After all, they had earned it, hadn't they? Each wise decision (that we counseled) showed their nobility. Each resolution of troubles (that we assisted with) proved them worthy of privilege.

In the privacy of their chambers, their slaves submitted to their desires. "Yes, my master. No, my master. If that is what you wish, my master." When slaves were killed in orgiastic passion or a jealous nobleman killed a slave who loved another, we were still the ones who buried the bodies. We kept the truth from the subjects who worshipped their "noble" rulers, and their "nobility" was preserved. Such was our duty: to preserve the body politic.

The most successful leaders strengthened their caste by using their slavery to justify primogeniture. They had the choice breeding stock, and thus they bred the children most "worthy" of leadership. A beautiful child with a silver coat, a regal child with a noble bearing — clearly such cubs were of the ruling class.

Did you think they survived the opposition of their rivals because of their honor? Certainly not. Honor lies in sacrifice, and we were the ones who sacrificed ourselves for the keeping of the ways. They feigned their honor, and we hid their shame. This is also how the tribes began: with slavery and, as the humans would say, carefully cultivated genetic purity.

Does this trouble you? Pay your misgivings no mind. It's only a fairy tale. Consider it allegory. Tell me I'm lying. Tell me the wonderful preaching you've heard about the noble origins of the Garou.

And I'll tell you how some of us were led astray....

# The Impergium

As we herded our breeding stock, humans began to form their own societies. Their villages became more organized, and the restrictions that we placed upon their wanderings forced them to form communities that were different from ours. The easiest to maintain were communal farms. As mankind settled into its agricultural ways, we were able to control their population. Curiously, the very decision to herd our breeding stock resulted in the beginnings of human civilization.

The Garou, the masters of mankind, carefully controlled humans. They learned to fear us. If they were to stray into the wilderness, they knew we had the right to do with them as we pleased. If they did not, it made little difference — the Garou would still take what they desired and punish those who opposed them. This practice continued for millennia. And the most horrific part was this: It succeeded brilliantly. It was a pure age. The world was in balance, and humanity was subservient to the will of the Garou.

# Old Gods

Although we were once as one, each caste began take to its own customs and its own gods. When we were truly one, we followed all of the totems together, but the ruling caste defied that. Such was their privilege. The rulers isolated themselves more from the commoners by taking their own totem, Falcon. He served only them, and they served only him. They followed his ways, for Falcon was regal and majestic as he surveyed their domain.

As it was, the other castes followed their example. Such was the will of the ruling class. Children of Fenris and Griffin followed the way of War, holding their own ceremonies on battlefields and hunting grounds. Children of Uktena and Unicorn stayed far away from these violent

places to practice their mystic arts. Artists would listen to no muse but Awen, travelers would comfort themselves in their communion with Owl, and the lowliest Garou gnawed the bones left over from the hunt each day and fought to survive with the assistance of Rat.

We were forever beneath those whom we served as we lived in shame and degradation. Our rage began to stir deep in our hearts, but we would not abandon our honor as Garou. Honor is the serving of all above the needs of the one, is it not? They told us we were not worthy of Falcon, and in those early days, those who served followed the way of lesser god. Those of us who served as Lords were as the Crow. Our totem was not strong, but his children watched and listened, gathering scraps and anything bright. That was what obeisance brought us. We watched and waited... and the storm gathered. The Children of Crow, the Lords, cultivated patience.

Yet as the ruling class became more removed from their people, there were Lords who envied them. Within their hearts, they felt ambition. These Lords abandoned their honor in search of power and became more than kings. They were the Tyrants: leaders who sought out weak septs filled with discontent and used them to further their will. These Lords not only approved of the Impergium, they reveled in it. They fought to create dynasties. A darker power drove them to their fate. And we, the Children of Crow, watched in horror as they were corrupted.

# The Carefully Bred Elite

In those early days, most Lords did not wish to rule. There are more valuable talents required to maintain a sept. Rulers are often valued for their charisma, wit, beauty and sagacity, but they cannot do everything. As a sept grows larger, the rulers become more removed from their responsibilities. They delegate their authority. The tasks that were beneath our leaders, the risks that they would not take, became ours. We shamed ourselves for the good of all, for the most loyal Lords would not betray our leaders. If we were to take on the most difficult duties ourselves, we would gain praise among our equals, although ultimately our leaders would take credit for our efforts.

Our rage grew, yet reason stayed our hand.

For those of us who remained quiet, obedience and sacrifice were our cardinal virtues. Each society — the warriors, the artisans, the mystics — has its own secret knowledge and alliances. So it was with us. Crow circled slowly. And those few who sought power disgraced themselves for the sake of attaining it.

Nonetheless, the Tyrants led the way for other ambitious Garou. It had always been possible for those who were not of the carefully bred elite to become a ruler, but it was never easy for them. A warrior or artisan may lead a tribe, but he then becomes a leader first. So it was with the Garou. A leader needs statesmen, diplomats and intermediaries. Without the support of this caste, he can never fully succeed. The ruling caste had our support, and the Lords kept civility. The elite had the most privilege, but we, the honorable Lords, made it possible. As the elite gained privilege, they began to acknowledge this fact less and less.

Diplomacy and eloquence are human traits, but even among wolves, the hierarchy is always preserved. The alpha must appear strong, and so the beta must aid him, watching behind him as he leads. And in the depths of our hearts, our lupine instincts told us the value the beta has. In our discontent, we still retained our instincts. The beta would always have power... even if the alpha changed. In the septs, we maintained our careful civility. "Yes, my liege. No, my liege. How very brilliant of you, my liege. How very good of you to compose such a brilliant plan." We bit back our anger.

## The Rise of Man

The rulers became more elitist in their choices of slaves. In the ceremonies at moots, Garou developed a great contempt for mankind. Breeding with them wasn't enough. Homid Garou hunted them and harried them for amusement. Those of the lupus breed were the most disdainful, and in their frenzied bloodlust, they would often kill and devour humans to sate their more bestial appetites. Whether these victims were "Kin" or not was of little concern. And even worse, the privileged class, especially those who bore the privilege of an esteemed lineage, became even more disdainful of the humans who were not worthy of sating their sexual appetites. They hunted them, captured their loved ones and created more slaves.

Away from these atrocities, men continued to form their own tribes and develop their own civility. Gaia, who provided us with such bounty, considered Man to be one of her creatures as well. As such, there were men that were not ruled by our Nation. They lived apart from our breeding stock, in their own homes and villages. We paid them little mind, for Gaia, in her beneficence, provided us with far more than we required.

The Garou underestimated Man. How to handle the tribes of men became one of the most delicate subjects of discourse. This fragmented us even more. Although the Lords tried to preserve unity, the political boundaries over the issue grew more pronounced. The well-bred elite, the Silver Fangs, once again asked for the support of the Lords to resolve the dispute.

We did.

## In Shadows

A cunning Beta can control his Alpha. A group of elder statesmen can easily frustrate the designs of their leaders. Those who keep secrets can turn against the secretive ones they protect. While the overt structure of the Lords worked to preserve order, we formed a more elaborate hierarchy within our private moots. What could not be said before the other tribes was said when assembled for our own purposes. The summit of a mountain, the privacy of a cave, the hidden island within a swamp — these were all secret places for our true moots, our shadow moots. We had no need of

the other castes, and we feared our leaders. Away from their madness, we would make are our own law. Far from their divisiveness, we would follow our own reason and speak openly of the disaffection that stirred in our hearts.

This was the true beginning of the Shadow Lords.

Our Gaffling crows were our eyes and ears, gathering information. So too were our No Moons, who knew the ways of theft and trickery. We formed our own group of Shadow Mystics, who used the spirits to benefit our conspiracy. The bards and storytellers who secretly worked for us documented the law and would discuss our own interpretations of it. And should the need arise, those with prowess in battle studied their own violent methods of political reform.

We were the kingmakers. We were the masters of politics, the finders of secrets, and the most eloquent of diplomats. And though our strength in the public eye was great, our hidden strengths were even greater.

## The End of the Impergium

Man made war against the Garou. He had no claws, but he had the weapons he used while hunting. He had no Gifts, but his armies grew larger and his tactics more cunning.

You've heard the truth about what happened. Those who were to become the Red Talons organized the lupus Garou as one and swore to wipe out this inferior race. The peacekeepers tried to unify all Garou in the name of peace, no longer exclusively regarding themselves as Children of the Unicorn, but as Children of Gaia. The artisan caste and the warrior caste, the messengers and the Gnawers of Bones, the outraged women who formed the Furies and the isolationists who formed the Stargazers each had their own political opinions.

The Lords prepared to wage covert war against mankind. Thus we would support the body politic. While the Gaians would negotiate peace, we would stealthily eliminate the human leaders. Our Stormcrows would watch the maneuvering of their troops, our tricksters would infiltrate their villages and report to us, and our human Kinfolk would assist us in our campaigns. We knew what really occurred between our two races. If we failed, our leaders would denounce us, but as Lords, as Children of Crow, we would gain honor.

The Silver Fangs still debated the issue. At Silver Fang moots and convocations, sept leaders discussed their policies. As was their habit, they publicly postured and said that they would pursue honorable dealings with mankind, but they covertly supported the efforts of the Lords. Openly, they spoke highly of how eloquently the newly formed tribe of the Children of Gaia formed their treaties of peace, but quietly, they told the leaders of the Red Talons and the Get to defend the septs and retaliate if we were attacked.

Thus they continued their tradition: saying *this* to one group and *that* to another, and believing both and neither. Thus the Silver Fangs failed to take decisive action, and the other factions demanded a decision. The Get and Talons wanted war, and yet they had a compromise. The Children of Gaia wanted peace, and yet they had no way to enforce it. The

Silver Fangs wanted to appear wise, and yet they were made to look weak. And as our part of the compromise, we... were loyal.

The Garou formed their political factions as a way to resolve the issue. The result was the Great Concord, the most important decision in history.

## The Concord

Those who spoke of peace worked quickly. The Gaians sided with the Furies, who in turn sided with a group of mystics who had become so removed from the political furor that they had lost themselves in contemplation. This third tribe, the Stargazers, sided with the Furies and Gaians and took their grievances to the Silver Fangs. In one sept, then, the home of one foolish Silver Fang King, the issue was to be decided in an "honorable" way: by Gamecraft. The future of our world was to be decided by a game. The Silver Fangs were mustering troops for our "defense" and covertly authorizing the shadow war of the Lords, yet one Silver Fang King gave his word to face a Stargazer champion in an "honorable" duel of wits to decide which course to take.

He lost, and in so doing, condemned our world to a slow death.

Our rulers, after centuries of being propped up by the Lords, were weak. As a result, they finally chose the option the always chose: the one that would make them look "honorable." They prided themselves on being noble creatures, and as such, they disregarded our advice and sided with the Children of Gaia, Black Furies and Stargazers. The Garou were to share our world with Man, for he was considered a child of Gaia as well. We were to allow men their villages and their civilization, for if we dealt honorably with men, they in turn would deal honorably with us. In return, the tribes would let us continue to... protect... our breeding stock, and a violent war would be averted.

The Concord was the agreement the Silver Fangs demanded. We had divided into tribes. The Lords were to be the keepers of the ruling caste's law, called the Litany, and within each tribe, the castes became auspices. There was no more need for a warrior caste, for each tribe had Ahroun; there was no more need for a mystic caste, for each tribe had Theurges, and so on.

Along with these distinctions came the earliest form of the Veil. The Silver Fangs, believing in their own lies of "honor" and "respect," decided to let mankind prosper. We would keep our flocks and watch over our herds, but the civilization of the Garou and civilizations of men would exist side by side. We were to learn from them. The Gaians, preaching love and trust, would help them form their earliest civilizations.

Their rivals felt betrayed. The Red Talons were furious. They prowled around our septs and flocks, hoping for war. Since their activities were quite overt, their rivals quickly maneuvered against them. The Get were outraged. They wanted battle and instead had a treaty of peace. Yet they would not openly fight their brethren, because they did not want a civil war against the other tribes.

And the Lords were... loyal. We attacked.

The Silver Fangs were quick to denounce our activities. In fact, they were quick to deny any involvement, accusing us of betraying their wise plan. From moot to moot, the pronouncement was made. The Lords had disobeyed and betrayed the Silver Fangs. They formally denounced our conspiracy against them.

Our rage was boundless.

No longer would we openly support the fools that deigned to rule us. We espoused that a Garou of any tribe could become king, for the Silver Fangs were no longer worthy. We challenged the law, cursed our rulers and openly declared ourselves to be lords of the shadows, that we were forevermore to be Shadow Lords.

## Divided

The Garou set upon a great journey, and each political alliance tore itself from the others. The loyal tribes were to oversee the various cultures of Man, some with the blessings of our rulers, and some with their disdain. The tribes evolved — each tribe followed its own way and found its own culture. The Get traveled to the north and became cold and hard, the Fianna followed the piping of the fae and became wild and free, and so on, each in turn. We, the betrayers, were to choose last. Of course, we evolved as well.

The Lords formed two cultures. There were some that still desired to be one with the Garou Nation, if only to frustrate the designs of foolish leaders. They emigrated to our homelands in southern Europe, where they thrived in lands that reflected their wrath. These Garou spread south to the wine-dark sea of the Mediterranean and north to the cold summits of the Transylvanian Alps. Our Alphas quickly contested for control of the various human tribes.

There were also some among the Lords who wished to form a civilization removed from the rest of the Garou Nation. This camp took to the Far East, where one society of Shadow Lords would isolate their culture from the western world. They were to form the Hakken Garou, a society of Japanese Shadow Lords who would reject the ways of their western brethren. Their story is much like ours, but our story remains in the West.

## The Tempest

In the midst of this, those of us who had followed Crow discovered the bliss that had led the Tyrants astray. Our discontent, our disaffection, and the hatred we had gained through countless generations of pursuing the honor of the Garou fueled our anger. We had been civil, reasonable, restrained and... loyal. Our mystics set forth on their own path to power. Though our Stormcrow Gafflings were useful, the Shadow Mystics wanted to serve a greater force. In studying the elements, they gained an affinity to the anger and turmoil of the storm. In studying the ways of battle, they took upon themselves the aspects of thunder and lightning. In their journeys through the Umbra, they sought out that which Crow served.

There was an older god that dictated where Crow would travel, a darker god. His was the way of discontent. His was the way of anger, the way of vengeance and the will to power. The renegades of our tribe who became Tyrants and served their own glory had known of him, but now their totem called to the rest of us as well. Thus began our glorious ascension under Grandfather Thunder.

See now the tempest that stirs above you. Darkness is your way, the way of shadows. Thus shall you hold discontent as your ally, fear as your friend, doubt as your weapon and the respect that comes from power as your destiny. You burn, and the heavens answer your anger with the sound of thunder.

## The Lie is Complete

We formed our alliance to prevent weak leaders from ever taking power again. Those of us who supported the ruling class showed complicity with their ways and shamed ourselves. The Shadow Lords renewed their study of the ways of politics. The Tyrants of the Impergium were pure, for they had followed both Gaia and a darker god, the Lord of Thunder. Our insight came from discontent, and the anger of generations stirred our emotional tempest. We no longer supported the weak, but instead built up the strong. The ways have changed.

And every last word of my fairy tale is a lie, for it must not be spoken. The open way, the revered story is the way of truth, but we deny it, and thus we follow our beautiful lie. Now you can begin to understand.

Finally... the rain. I thank you for carefully listening to my tale. I would also ask you to leave the way you came. You will find that your blade is no longer with you. While you listened, my ally took the klaive which you in turn acquired from the caern warder of our sept. Such is your punishment for striking me. You must learn to respect your elders.

Ah! Don't get up! The scratches on my face are now healed, and I feel my vision returning in the eye you slashed. I have defeated you, and you are shamed. You would once more raise your claws against me? Would you dare follow me as I leap from this precipice? I am a servant of Crow, and he would carry me to safety. Know now that you have been defeated by Vaclav Stormcrow, Galliard of the Shadow Lords.

## The "Civilized" Western World

*There are 17 different things a guy can do when he lies to give himself away. A guy's got 17 pantomimes — a woman's got 20, a guy's got 17 — but if you know them like you know your own face, they beat lie detectors all to hell.*

— Coccotti, *True Romance*

Okay, kid, so where's the klaive that you were supposed to bring me? Perhaps you should tell me the truth this time. Let's go over your story again. You were supposed to fetch me the klaive of the Fianna caern warder as part of your Rite of Passage. Instead, you tell me that you met with a Shadow Lord Galliard named "Vaclav." He set up a diversion by telling you lies, and a Ragabash stole the klaive from you. Although I am acquainted with all of our allies in this sept and the surrounding country, I've never heard of this name. Vaclav? I don't know of a Shadow Lord named Vaclav.

Are you taken with fever? Perhaps you should lie down. Let me pour you something soothing to drink.

I should tell you what really happened: You never met that Garou, and you did not hear that story. In fact, you never stole that klaive, and its owner has obviously misplaced it. I have not seen it, and you have not seen it. Therefore, we are both innocent.

Absinthe? No? Perhaps later. You shouldn't worry so much. I'm sure you have the makings of an Alpha. If you succeed, you will seek out a caern, begin the slow process of stirring up dissent and seize power. Of course, if you choose the way of Crow, you can begin to serve someone in the tribe who is stronger than you. You will learn these things. You will learn the triumph of becoming an Alpha or the honor of becoming a Crow and serving one.

## A Pure World

Recognizing true leadership is what the Shadow Lords are all about. Before human history began, the Alphas of our tribe, the Lords of the Summit, were unfettered by the human concept of civility. Wherever there was discontent, the Lords seized power and ruled without restraint. They had their rightful place among the creatures of Gaia — at the top! They ruled with absolute glorious tyranny, much to the envy of their fiercest rivals, the ones who would become the Silver Fangs....

You look perplexed. Have you been listening to lies again? The Earth was a glorious place during the Impergium, a world where a Shadow Lord could create a dynasty that would last for centuries. Then the Silver Fangs ruined it all. They had this ludicrous idea called "chivalry." You see, we were all "unchivalrous" because we wouldn't let the lesser creatures, the humans, have their own civilization. They listened to a lot of nonsense about forming a civilization alongside the humans, a coexistence based on "love" and "mutual respect."

Look where it got us. The humans have polluted the Earth, destroyed Gaia, and fed the Wyrm until the coming of the Apocalypse... that's what trust will bring you. That's the story of human history. Humans are far more monstrous than the Garou ever were. You look skeptical. Do you doubt me?

Start sipping that absinthe, kid, and we'll get drunk on history together.

# Contesting Tribes and Contesting Ideas

After the Concord, the Lords established their own homelands and contested with other tribes for portions of Eastern Europe. The Get sided with the most barbaric tribes to the north of us, while the Furies watched over the Grecian lands to the south of us. The Lords were caught between them. In those days, our Alphas fiercely contested with each other for everything they could get. In our homelands, the Thracian and Illyrian tribes were the most successful. They thrived by contesting with other tribes and launching into wars against their neighbors.

While the tribes to north fought, the Lords in the southernmost part of the continent were able to infiltrate the tribes that would establish Ancient Greece. We thrived on politics as always, and so we learned a lot from the humans. There are some who will tell you that Ancient Greece was oh-so-noble because it developed democracy. Nonsense. The most fascinating innovation in Greece was the concept of despotism. The word has been twisted around in recent times. In the beginning, despotism required (or at least implied) the consent of the people living under it. A despot watching over his people was like a master being kind to his slaves. And Garou know all about slaves. Many of us yearned for the days when we were closer with our Kinfolk. While the Furies take credit for the culture of Ancient Greece, but we were there to learn from Athenian despotism at its finest. Mankind had so much to teach us.

Just as there were despots, there were conquerors who advanced human civilization through brilliant politics and military strategy. Greece would never have attained glory if it wasn't for Alexander the Great. Our Kinfolk from Macedonia and surrounding areas — who had learned military tactics under Alexander's father, Philip — rallied behind him. His conquest of the Persian Empire led to the beginning of the Hellenistic Age. More importantly, Alexander served as a paragon of human leadership. Over 1500 years later, Machiavelli was to use Alexander as one of his finest examples of statesmanship.

Alexander's death at the age of 33 was followed by civil war, yet because of him, Greek culture spread throughout Europe and beyond. On his deathbed, he gathered his generals around him. Eager to follow his example, one of his generals wanted to know who his successor would be. "To whom," he asked, "do you leave your empire?" Alexander responded with his last words: "To the strongest." His words proved to be prophetic, and history has echoed them.

In the Hellenistic age, an age of Greek enlightenment, philosophers formed the earliest treatises on politics. If you want to innovate, begin by studying the classics. Aristotle, for instance, began to predict the evolution of human politics. He spoke of three kinds of government: monarchy, aristocracy and polity (a type of democracy).

Each depended on the size of the ruling class. If any of these forms of government became selfish, they would evolve to tyranny, oligarchy or ochlocracy (a type of mob rule). Yet our motives were never selfish. We knew how strong leaders made their countries strong, and so did the humans. What Aristotle disdained, humanity practiced. We honored the Veil and watched Ancient Greece fall.

If only Aristotle had the wisdom his teacher, Plato. He understood us better. Shadow Lord Kinfolk listened to his lectures about the need for philosopher-kings. Men could not govern themselves, and so a few pure leaders had to rise above the dross of humanity and rule through reason. Of course, we learned to be eminently reasonable. We were told by the Silver Fangs to learn from human civilization, and we were avid scholars. We learned that Ancient Greece wouldn't have given way to the Roman Empire if they had been stronger. By 146 B.C., the Romans had conquered the Greeks. The Furies have never forgiven us, but we will not hesitate to give humanity the credit for its own evolution.

# The Glory of Rome

While Ancient Greece was in decline, some Lords of the Summit sided with the tribes that established Ancient Rome. The Glass Walkers are eager to take credit for the Roman Empire. If a Glass Walker Goodfella sticks a gun to your face and tells you his Sicilian ancestors were part of the Roman Empire, it's best to agree with him, but the Glass Walkers didn't follow the political developments of Rome like we did. The vampires like to take a great deal of credit as well, but you don't honestly think the senate always met at night, now, do you? The Shadow Lords continued to study the classics. Nero, Caligula, Trajan — it wasn't hard to learn from the human varieties of tyranny.

While Rome grew, our Alphas were in fierce competition with each other in septs north of the Roman Empire and throughout Eastern Europe. Behind the scenes, we set one sept against another, conquering territory one generation and losing it to a competing Alpha the next. It was glorious. Rather than remaining content to keep our Kinfolk as one people, we bred with many rival tribes. We were evolving as a people, and in the true spirit of the Impergium, the tribes of humanity set themselves against one another to evolve as well. Of course, in accordance with the Concord, we preserved the Veil, but each rise and fall of a rival political power was the subject of endless debate in Shadow Lord moots. We continued to study them.

Then, in the second century A.D., there was a shift in power. The Roman Emperor Trajan showed us his humanity. The Geto-Dacian Empire in our homelands was growing strong, and so Trajan sent his troops north to prove he was stronger. Though his rule was tyrannical, he used his strength to conquer the tribes to the north of the empire. Never before or since this time period have our homelands been more unified. While the Roman Empire was never able to fully subjugate our culture, their strong leadership united our lands... for a while.

Weak leaders who were to follow him undermined the stability of Rome. When the Roman Empire withdrew from our lands in the third century, we could see the beginning of the empire's decline. Strong leaders expanded the empire and grew stronger; weak leaders allowed their territories to break into factions and destroy themselves through rivalry. When Constantine created a second capital in 330, the empire was divided once more, and we were saddened at the decline of a great civilization. As Rome declined, another powerful civilization grew.

# The Dark Ages

At first, the Byzantine Empire held just as much promise as the Roman Empire. We were content to leave them to their own devices. They slowly formed a civilization that glorified a corrupt bureaucracy. The proclamations of their government were held as representative of the will of heaven on Earth, but the rulers of the empire had little control over the corruption that spread. The administration of their empire profited greatly from the taxation and subjugation of their people. The vampires who controlled the Byzantine Empire profited as well. It is said that the Ventrue and Assamites both helped this system prosper. Still, as long as the vampires exploited their people in the Middle East, we were content that they chose to ignore our Kinfolk nearby.

The Garou who remained separate from the great empires of the ages watched other aspects of humanity's evolution. Up-and-coming Lords had a variety of contesting tribes from which to choose. We developed a wide range of Kinfolk — Alani, Goths, Huns, Slovenes, Croats, Serbs, Bulgars — we became "cultured." Our tribe has never been based on the "racial purity" that others espouse. We could see how that was already destroying the isolationist Silver Fangs. Alphas gained favor and lost it as their herds contested. The Bulgars chose to establish their own political state, while the Slavs sided with the emperor in Byzantium. Their Turkish allies were to become a threat later on....

Conquerors — and their lesser known advisors — defined the politics of our homelands in the Dark Ages that followed the Fall of Rome. Shadow Lord Galliards have been known to tell elaborate stories about these leaders. Countries were founded by men who had the initiative to conquer. There was Stephen the First, who conquered the region of Moldavia in the early 11th century. Radu Negru crossed the Transylvanian Alps in the early 14th century and established the sovereign nation of Wallachia. Our people were becoming strong, and at the behest of the Garou Nation, we let them prosper on their own.

# The Rise of the Ottoman Empire

All great things come to an end, and in the mid-15th century, Constantinople fell to the Turks. The Ottoman Empire replaced the Byzantine bureaucracy, but the vampires still kept power. There are young Lords who dutifully recite that the Fall of Constantinople in 1453 brought the end of the Dark Ages. We suspect that the true forces behind this may have involved the vampires, but then again, who are we to say? We had other interests. The many cultures of our homelands were enough to keep us occupied.

Yet the Turks in Constantinople soon contested with our people for our territory. The same armies that spread across most of Europe took our lands from us. Around Wallachia, nation-states fell to the encroaching Ottoman Empire. We were told that the "blood taxes" of human children they took were for their Jannisary troops, but undoubtedly some children were used for other purposes....

The Ottoman Empire was the greatest threat that our homelands faced, much greater than the two centuries of Roman occupation. We understood the Romans, but the Turks had no sympathy for our people. There were Lords working in the midst of the Roman Empire, but the Ottoman Empire was a mystery to us. It would take heroes to respond to their cruelty. The peoples of Wallachia and the neighboring strengths wanted justice, rulers who could drive back the Turks. Again, humanity confirmed what we already knew: Only the strong survived. Not surprisingly, the strongest leader at this time wasn't human at all.

# Vladimir Draculea

His name was Vlad Draculea, but the people knew him as Vlad Tepes — Vlad the Impaler. I'm sure you know this little part of history. Tyrants often do best for themselves when the people of their countries are unhappy. So it was with Vlad. For some, he was a national hero. After all, wasn't he merely trying to bring our great nations together again? Didn't the people of Wallachia want to reunite with their Moldavian and Transylvanian cousins?

Vlad Tepes of Clan Tzimisce was ruthless in his ascendancy. Of that, there is no doubt. Yet among the Lords, there was controversy. Most of the Wallachian Lords supported him, but Lords in neighboring regions were horrified. The actions of Crinos shock troops who were at his disposal resulted in even more horrific rumors of his fearful cruelty. Yet in neighboring septs, other Lords were appalled to see their tribemates resort to such extremes. Siding with an agent of the Wyrm? How could they do such a thing?

The Lords who sided with Vlad Tepes did it because they respected his power. Vlad the Impaler was a prime example of a tyrant. The people were desperate to side with anyone who would liberate them. The Lords who supported him preferred his sense of style to the less elegant methods of the Ventrue and Assamites. He refused to pay their blood taxes, he butchered the emissaries who tried to convince him otherwise and he made his message to them quite clear. If words were not enough, his deeds spoke stronger. Fields of human heads on wooden stakes were just one such method of expression.

The Lords of the surrounding regions were outraged. Wallachia's Sept of the Night Sky was continually responding to accusations from surrounding septs that their alliance with such an obvious agent of the Wyrm was a blasphemy even the Shadow Lords could not endure. The surrounding septs unified against the sept, and the supporters of Vlad Tepes of Clan Tzimisce fell under the claws of their Shadow Lord rivals.

Without the support of the Shadow Lords, what would have been the dynasty of Vladimir Draculea fell before the onslaught of the Ottoman Turks. The Sept of the Night Sky fell to the Wyrm, and our homelands fell further under the subjugation of our oppressors. The Tzimisce assaulted us as well out of revenge, and the epic battles between our two societies were fought openly in our homelands. We lost any semblance of control that we had over our lands and our people.

The Veil was shattered. The Lords and the Tzimisce fought without restraint. The two exemplars of their respective races — the truest of vampires and the truest of werewolves — began centuries of bloody warfare. With the Veil so precariously thin, accounts of our epic battles in the Balkan lands were twisted by the Delirium into the classic legends of our respective races.

## The Madness Continues

Our war against the Tzimisce continued until they faced opposition from a much stronger alliance. The Ventrue found other allies, abandoning their ties with the Assamites to form the Camarilla in the mid-15th century. Soon, the Tzimisce were soon far too busy crusading against them to fight as fiercely against us.

It took over a century for us to rebuild what had been destroyed. Michael the Brave, a Wallachian prince of the 16th century, achieved some margin of success in uniting our homelands. Under his rule, Wallachia, Moldavia and Transylvania were all one country again, but only until the Turks could find other puppets to oversee these areas. We turned against each other in our frustration, and the madness spread.

Our lands were still controlled by others. The faces of the oppressors changed, but the oppression continued. A century later, the agents of the Ottoman Empire in the Balkan States were Grecian princes known as *phanariots*. The feudal lords of the region, the *boyars*, kept local control, but the aristocratic leaders of the region required the support of the *phanariots*. This continued until 1821, when an Anti-Phanariot revolt, led by a Shadow Lord Kinfolk named Tudor Vladimirescu, convinced the Ottoman sultan to appoint native governors. The people were ready to side with anyone to throw off the yoke of oppression, even though the Turks still held control. Humans never learn.

## Russian Influence

The Silver Fangs laughed at our miserable fate. They desired to gain one more chance to humiliate our Lords and our land, and so they contested with the Ottoman Empire for control of our territory. Under the pretense of "rescuing" us, they used our lands as a battleground against the Ottoman Empire. As we were divided and spiritually defeated, they reclaimed the Sept of the Night Sky from the Wyrm in the late 19th century and began to campaign against the Ventrue alliance to the south. By this time, the Ventrue and Assamites had formed the Treaty of Tyre, and the additional backing of the Camarilla had changed the crusade of the Silver Fangs into a futile cause.

Once again, the people were hungry for tyrants to liberate them, and by a cruel twist of fate, this time they had the backing of the Silver Fangs. The Russians could not destroy the Turks, but they were relentless in their efforts against them. Catherine the Second was one of our liberators. Stormcrows circled around the court of Catherine, for despite her backing by the Silver Fangs, she was an "enlightened despot" as cruel as any other. In public moots, the Silver Fangs spoke of the rebirth of chivalry, yet we knew better. The War of 1768, the Russo-Turkish War of the early 18th century, the Crimean War —the Silver Fangs mocked us for over a century by fighting our enemies in our own lands as we were still locked in power struggles against each other.

We sought revenge against them. By the end of the 19th century, the Silver Fangs and their Russian aristocracy had sufficiently entertained themselves by fighting the Ottoman Empire in our homelands. We made reparations to both sides. The Balkan War of the early 20th century repelled the Turks, and as for the Russians, we decided to meddle in their affairs. Revolutionaries, with a little bit of help, brought down the royal family, and in true Machiavellian fashion, exterminated them. The Bolshevik Revolution brought an end to the royal aristocracy and the eminence of the Silver Fangs in Russia. The battle was continued by Brujah vampires and Bone Gnawer werewolves — with a little bit of covert assistance — as they overthrew the aristocracy and brought about a new form of oppression: Communism.

Our Alphas were too caught up in age-old disputes to resist the Communist takeovers of the Balkan nations. Outside of our homelands, our infiltrators were in septs throughout the world, but within our tribe, our Alphas could not find a leader. The political theatre of the Balkan states was as tumultuous as ever, as the people were eager for more powerful leaders. They found them. The Communist powers that came from the failed homelands of the Silver Fangs corrupted our lands as well.

Without unity, we were powerless. Shadow Lord tyrants who seized power as individuals could not stand against their myriad enemies. We had fallen to the same foolish temptations that had defeated the people of our tribal lands. Repeatedly, outside forces kept us divided, and the hostility and rage that were an integral part of our souls kept us apart. The humans knew this practice as "balkanization." Without central authority, without a strong leader, and with interference from outside forces, petty fighting made unity an impossibility. We had to learn stronger methods, and so we once again learned from the humans.

# Modern-Day Evolution

During the 20th century, the science of tyranny continued to evolve. In the failed country of the Silver Fangs, Joseph Stalin perfected dictatorship, a way for a tyrant who has quickly gained power to keep it by repeatedly waging war. The Communist Nations taught us crimes and horrors we would have never conceived in the Impergium. Totalitarianism kept corrupt rulers in power by denying people even the most rudimentary of freedoms. Sexual oppression, religious oppression, cultural control, media propaganda — we were relics of the past, for humans had learned methods that far exceeded our old ways.

History has taught us that only the strong survive, but it has also taught us the value of unity. We are still learning, and one victory in the 20th century has given us hope. We turned to our oldest rivalry to renew our strength. As part of his infamous "shadow campaign," Boris Thunderstrike, Lord of the Summit, conspired and conquered against the Silver Fangs who ruled the Sept of the Night Sky in Wallachia. His call to unity inspired us. Once we were unified, we began to ascend once more. His victory inspired us, and in the face of the Apocalypse, our tribal alliance has brought our age-old glory back to us.

Our homelands are still divided. Humanity is still waging war against itself, just as we did in the wake of our war with the Tzimisce. The butchery of Ceaucescu, the genocidal crusades of the Serbs and Croats, the hatred and bigotry and pettiness of our people has remained after millennia of oppression and subjugation. Our rage comes from a land where humans have been continually divided. We learned from the humans all too well. Now we are desperately fighting for tribal unity. If we cannot heal our homelands, then we will exact our rage on the world as one tribe.

# Shame

*No, I'm just quoting history. It's written. It's a fact.... Now, if that's a fact, tell me: Am I lying?*

— Cliff, *True Romance*

Ten thousand years ago, the noblest and most chivalrous Garou trusted humanity with civilization. The renegade Lords who became tyrants were a threat to them, and so they preferred to uphold the virtues of humanity. The idea that humanity would uphold civility was the greatest lie of all. In our homelands, we've learned all about humanity.

As the Wyrm grew stronger, and as the Apocalypse drew closer, humanity revealed itself as the bestial race it truly was. The divisiveness of our homelands was only one small part of humanity's corruption. No supernatural entity needs to take credit for humanity's horrors — they've evolved the science of tyranny on their own. The 20th century has shown us Batista, Castro and Marcos; Stalin, Mao-Tse Tung and Deng Xiao Ping; Hussein, Hitler and Mussolini. The real beasts of the 20th century have been all too human. No Wyrm spirits possessed them, and no demons controlled them.

There are those who would look back on the Impergium in horror. The monstrous race of the Garou subjugated humanity. The renegade Lords who took up tyranny conquered and plundered. But the Earth was pure, obeying Gaia's will. Human civilization has brought horrors far greater.

Our rivals claim that we wish to subjugate all of creation. Suppose we did decide that and succeeded. Suppose we wanted to bring the Impergium back. Could our methods possibly exceed what the humans have already done to themselves? The human race has shown us its hunger for tyranny, just as the failure of the Silver Fangs has shown us the folly of chivalry. The Lords who speak of the Tyrants of the Impergium know of the glory of a purer age. Our conspiracy brings unity, and the Apocalypse brings the chance for a new age. You, my drunken friend, are an agent of that conspiracy. The world is filled with corruption and deceit. It requires a warrior like you.

And by the way, kid, here's your klaive back. Perhaps you should take it back to its owner before you get caught. You've learned a fair amount about history, but you've got a lot to learn about watching your back. Did you like the absinthe? In about 10 seconds, you're going to pass out. Know that you have been defeated by Tongue-of-Acid, Ragabash of the Shadow Lords.

# Chapter Two: Tribal Politics

And you have to understand this: that a prince, especially a new one, cannot observe all those things for which men are esteemed, being often forced, in order to maintain the state, to act contrary to fidelity, friendship, humanity, and religion. Therefore, it is necessary for him to have a mind ready to turn itself accordingly as the winds and variations force it, yet… not to diverge from the good if he can avoid doing so, but, if compelled, then to know how to go about it.

— Machiavelli, *The Prince*

Hey! Wake up! You should know better than to fall asleep in a rainstorm! Damn, you're pretty messed up, aren't you?

Get up. I know you're in pain, but you have to get on your feet. If you don't get up and fight, this is all life will give you. You're covered in mud and shivering. This is what you are without your tribe: alone and in pain. This is all the world can give you. It wants to bend you to its will. Your world was once a pure world — Gaia's world — but now, it's a world where our race is dying.

It's time for you to fight back.

The strong rule. The weak die. If you walk with me, and learn the ways of your tribe, I'll show you how to fight. I'll show you who your allies really are. Know that you have been aided by Veil-of-Darkness, Theurge of the Shadow Lords.

# Totems

*I'm not running.*
*I'm not scared.*
*Big black monsoon,*
*Take me with you.*
— P.J. Harvey, "Meet Ze Monster"

The very forces of the Earth conspire with us. You require the truth, and the truth you seek can be found in the center of a raging tempest. The way of shadow and the power of the storm are as one.

The storm calls to you. The sacred places of the Earth that we take as our own are holiest when the tempest rages. The winds that howl are cold, cold as our hearts when our prey

pleads for mercy. The driving rain surrounds us, just as false accusations and imprecations are relentlessly driven against us. The skies are bleak, bleak as our future once was when the nobles placed us beneath men and surrendered our world to them. The growing tempest heralds the storm's fury.

As a Shadow Lord, you are at the center of that storm. Just as Gaia is your spiritual mother, the Lord of Thunder is your spiritual father. You are caught between the Earth and the heavens above. In the distance, my child, you will hear the sound of thunder.

Walk with me, child.

## Grandfather Thunder

Grandfather demands respect and exacts fear. These are the two elemental forces of the world. All else is diversion. The Lords of Shadow feel that in their hearts, and each peal of thunder echoes with the purity of that power.

Those who would make their souls one with the fury of the storm have risen above shame. When our destiny was sacrificed for a world of men, when the Great Concord brought the pure age of the Impergium to an end, we called to the heavens for succor. When we were first cast out and betrayed, we howled to the skies to answer our cries for vengeance. Grandfather answered. He answered then, and he answers now.

His is the path of patient vengeance. The storm does not gather quickly. A fool will ignore it, but a wise man will sense it coming and either prepare for the assault or set it to his purpose. The darkening sky is a warning, and the anticipation in the air heralds the inevitable. The foolish man thinks that the storm only brings destruction, but the wise man understands its true purpose. Those who are weak, those who cannot endure it, must hide from the fury of the storm.

His way is the reason hidden beyond pain. In the greatest of tempests, Grandfather's wisdom will come to you. As you find yourself on the field of battle, where all is madness awash in blood, the fury of the tempest will give you guidance. In the raging storm, when all fails and you grasp at the heavens and scream, Grandfather will answer you in the depths of your anguish and despair. The truths you seek lay in the darkness of your heart, and if you can answer your passion with the wisdom to understand it, there, in the purity of pain, you will find truth.

Grandfather does not soar through the skies — he dominates the heavens. Higher than Eagle, higher than Falcon, he is the gray sky that chills the soul, the wind that tears at the heart. Nothing stops the storm, and if you follow Thunder, you must stop at nothing as you ascend. In the gathering storm, and in the aftermath, you hover above your servants. Seeking the greatest heights, wreaking vengeance on those beneath you, the way of Thunder is the will to power.

## Crow

The greatest of us are one with the storm, yet not all of us can reach such ambitious heights. Our servants aspire for what they can attain. Those who would not follow the path of their own ambition must serve those who can. Grandfather has sent his children, his Stormcrows, to watch over these errant ones as they aid him. These loyal Garou are the servants of Crow.

Crow is not regal, nor is he proud. He is a scavenger, an opportunist, a lowly creature who seeks out that which glitters. Value is not a concept he understands. If something catches his eye, he will take it. His superiors will then show him the value of things. He must scavenge and scour the Earth, but he must bring what he finds to the wise ones who guide him.

That is the role of Crow in the order of things, and if his followers understand that, they understand their role in the world. Do not think that they are weak. On the battlefield, Crows circle to torment the very spirits of the dead — that is hardly weakness. Their honor is the sacrifice of the one toward the many. By lowering themselves, our servants of Crow serve the ultimate ascension of their tribe. They are undeniably loyal, and their unquestioning obedience of the Lords gives makes us stronger.

## Raven

Raven is the trickster and keeper of secrets. Raucous and boisterous, self-confident and mocking, he follows his own way. His triumph comes from understanding deception. Yet even he must watch the changing of the wind. In his positive aspect, he is a protector. He knows the ways of deceit and will protect those who scheme against you. In his negative aspect, he is the force of *katabolism*, the bringer of change through destruction. Those who follow Raven taken both of these aspects. Treat them well, and they will aid your triumph.

# Camps

Your spirit is reflected by the dark skies above you, but your allies are found in the camps around you. Although the Lords are the most unified Garou, there is a wide range of philosophies within our tribe. The different camps of the Shadow Lords all serve one ultimate goal — the ascension of our people over any who would oppose us — but their methods for attaining this goal vary widely. Some misled Garou think that the Lords are little more than a group of tyrants who would readily betray each other for the slightest chance of gaining power. This misconception serves our cause well.

All of the camps of the tribe share a common philosophical ground: Power is more respectable than personal honor. In the public eye, personal honor is viewed as a diversion from the goals of the tribe, since "sacrificing the self for the good of all" is the best way to promote our people. Any power gained by an individual serves the whole of the tribe. We cannot repeat the mistakes made in our homelands. We shame ourselves when we turn against each other, but we glorify our tribe when we engage in conspiracy.

There is an old saying among the Japanese Garou: "There are many paths to the summit of a mountain." The different divisions of our tribe, the camps, follow different paths. Not everyone leads to the summit, but each one leads on a different journey. Each camp is watched from the heavens.

# Lords of the Summit

The greatest Lords act as leaders. In desperate times, the Garou Nation cannot be weak, and so any action that will promote strong leaders is justified. Most Shadow Lords belong to this camp. They will proudly proclaim that only the most worthy leaders can lead the war against the Wyrm. Invoking the Litany, Lords with authority will state that since the Apocalypse is at hand, there are no longer any illusions of peace. Their continuous states of "martial law" promote their tyranny. A Lord of the Summit will do anything to achieve power, and once he achieves it, he will not sacrifice it for any reason. These Lords usually hold office until their death.

There are rumors that the most powerful Lords of the Summit are rewarded by Grandfather with a Gift enabling them, if necessary, to mask the taint of the Wyrm. Loyal members of this camp realize that a Shadow Lord leader who has risked his soul for the sake of his people may have "lapses" in judgment, but will ultimately prevail. Sometimes even the taint of the Wyrm may not be enough to stop such a valiant Lord.

## Andrei Night-of-Terrors, A Lord of the Summit, Proclaims:

*The divisiveness of the tribes is pointless! They must be unified as one Garou Nation. We have watched the failures of the other tribes, but now, in the Final Days, the rapid ascension of the Shadow Lords heralds a new age. The Wyrm will be extinguished for all time… and our justice will purify the world!*

# The Bringers of Light

Not all Lords follow the call of ambition. The Bringers of Light follow a different path of conquest. They seek inner strength by continually testing themselves against the taint around them. They know that they must become pure, and as such, they continually place their souls in spiritual danger. Repeatedly, they seek out the temptation of the Wyrm and overcome it.

Following the ancient Shadow Lord credo of "sacrificing the self for the good of all," they undertake hazardous quests to prove their worth. They have been known to seek out prolonged cooperation with Camarilla and Sabbat vampires, lengthy stays in Black Spiral Hives, and extended journeys through corrupt realms, such as Malfeas and the Atrocity Realm.

Many Shadow Lords have fallen to such corruption by following the Bringers of Light, but those who survive such quests are said to be far more resistant to the lure of the Wyrm afterwards. These loyal Garou are often awarded with positions of honor, sometimes even as mediators with Wyrm-tainted enemies. Some Lords have been known to forsake their camp or status to become a Bringer of Light.

It is also rumored that leaders within this camp have a secretive alliance with the Serpents of Light within the Sabbat. The truth of this is highly dubious.

### Rage-of-Darkness,
### A Bringer of Light, Reasons:

*Surely you would not deny that your enemies still have the capacity to reason. Would you deny yourself the chance to betray them? Allow me to employ some… reconnaissance on your behalf. I am a master of my craft. I can obtain for you information about their numbers and possibly their strategy before the night has passed.*

# The Children of Crow

Obedient Lords consider serving strong leaders to be an honorable course of action. Children of Crow follow an ancient tradition: foregoing the call of ambition for the sake of political expediency. They gain power by serving those more powerful than themselves, even if this destroys their public esteem. Yet Crow gives them powers of detection and perception other Garou do not possess. Such servants will never attain positions of authority, but instead sacrifice chance to gain power for the sake of their own tribe. These Garou are also fully cognizant that Crow ultimately serves the will of Grandfather Thunder, yet they trust in Crow's guidance.

It is rumored that there is an alliance between the leaders of this camp and the wereravens. In times of need, it is said, one of the Corax may be called upon to assist a servant of Crow, although there may be a favor requested afterward.

### Carol Graycoat,
### A Child of Crow, Reports:

*I have heard them conspiring outside the bawn of our caern. There are three of them, and one is armed with a silver blade. My Gaffling has tracked them to a meeting place on the outskirts of the city where they received payment from a Glass Walker. One of the Galliards thinks that they are actually plotting against our sept leader, and thus I can use him as a tool to protect you, my lord. Unless, of course, you would like to frame them for something else?*

# The Hakken Garou

These rulers of the Eastern Garou eschew most Western beliefs regarding politics. A strong ruler in this camp must be a strong warrior first and foremost. Much of this camp's philosophy comes from *bushido*, the code of the samurai. Western Lords would place personal power over public honor, but the Hakken place personal honor above power… or even publicly defined honor. Since this code is different from the code of honor of the Western Garou, they are considered *Urrah*. As such, only the Shadow Lords would extend an alliance to them. Grandfather Thunder is also sympathetic to their condition, and thus Hakken possess many of the same Gifts as their Western Shadow Lord brethren.

Hakken Garou harbor a hidden contempt toward Western Garou for their failure to oppose the Wyrm as well as they have. Until the end of the Tokugawa Era in the late 19th century, their country had remained isolated from the corruption of the Western world. When Japan was first westernized (during the Meiji Restoration period), they discovered the true extent of Wyrm taint in the West. Their adherence to traditional bushi honor gives them strength. The Hakken are still skeptical of Western Shadow Lords, but their affinity to Grandfather Thunder and their hatred of both the Silver Fangs and the Concord give them common ground.

It is well-known that the Hakken have a strong alliance with the Kitsune and other *hengeyokai* shapechangers of Japan. It is also rumored that there is a group of fallen Hakken who pursued their own version of the Black Spiral in the 16th century as part of their service to Lord Nobunaga and his undead armies.

### Inui Storm-of-Kyoto,
### A Hakken Garou, Demands:

*Your ways are wrong. I will not be bound by your Litany, submit to your arrogant posturing, or fight in your ludicrous manner. My honor is not the honor of the Western Garou. I will assist you, but my role in assisting you must be defined by my rules.*

# Secret Societies

Not all camps are open in their practices. Each tribe has its own secret organizations, and the Shadow Lords are the most adept at forming secret societies. Lords of all camps are aware of their presence, yet even the most critical of Garou cannot blame all of the actions of these cults on the Shadow Lords.

# The Masks

The Masks revere only one avenue to power: instilling fear. Their devotion to the hideous nature of falsehood is so fanatic that they practice mutilation upon themselves to inspire horror in their victims. Their dark arts seek a form of unholy spiritual perfection: killing foes not through violence, but by pure, undiluted terror. Shadow Lord Galliards know many tales of the Masks, and it is whispered that some of the most nefarious Lords of the Summit have been taught Gifts by the same spirits that obscure the activities of the Masks.

It is rumored that the Masks have also formed alliance with a few of the remaining Nictuku, but as only a few superstitious Nosferatu vampires believe in the presence of such creatures, the charge is extremely doubtful.

### Skin-of-a-Thousand-Cuts,
### Acolyte of the Mask, Whispers:

*Yes… I taste your fear. Your heart is slowing. I can smell your adrenaline. The toxins pollute your musculature, but I prefer my meat that way….*

# The Society of Nidhogg

This mystic society gains power by studying the elemental forces of darkness. By their study of weather magic, they gain a greater communion with Grandfather Thunder.

However, their fanaticism is so extreme that they also claim that sunlight itself is a threat to the forces of Thunder. As such, they gain a gradual revulsion to sunlight and may ultimately seek to plunge the world into eternal darkness.

It is rumored that this Society secretly works with the Lasombra clan of the Sabbat, yet others claimed that they worked against their Shadow Lord brethren in defense of Vlad Tepes of the Tzimisce. As there are many conflicting accounts of what transpired between the Shadow Lords and the armies of the Dracul, this rumor is even more suspicious. The Bringers of Light detest the followers of Nidhogg, and many Lords who value their Balkan homelands are disgusted with these traitors.

## Force-of-Silence, A Follower of Nidhogg, Intones:

*A sacrifice… to Lord Thunder! Your blood is spilled in his name! Let darkness descend and obscure the light of your false honor. By His will, so is it done.*

# The Lazarite Movement

Though most metis bear their shame quietly, some will not deny their own ambition merely because of their lost birthright. The Lazarite Movement began as an obscure attempt to form a new tribe. Just as the Red Talons are composed solely of lupus, the Lazarites sought to bring political unity to the metis Garou. While the movement began with the efforts of a metis Child of Gaia Theurge, ambitious Shadow Lord metis

have since formed splinter groups of the original Lazarites. Their roving bands of the "unclean" have been known to descend on septs and either recruit metis into their religious movement or turn them against their homid and lupus brethren. As the Apocalypse draws near, the Lazarite Movement has suddenly gained a great deal of support from the desperate metis population. Whether the Shadow Lords are behind this is a matter of debate.

## Lost-Son-of-Gaia, A Cultist of the Lazarites, Announces:

*Unclean! Unclean! I will no longer be ashamed to be unclean! Your sins have made us, and I will no longer bear your sins. Gaia will still show her love for me, and your hatred shows nothing but the taint of the Wyrm within you. Yes, you are of the Wyrm, and so I must oppose you!*

# Moots

Do you understand? There are hidden truths and public lies. The moots of the Garou represent their society, but our truths are held in secret, and so our tribal gatherings glorify that secrecy. Before you can revile the truth, I must teach you more of the lies spoken against us. Public lies protect our secret truths.

Some rivals espouse that each Lord desires to attain as much power as quickly as possible. We've had millennia to learn that doesn't work. Seizing power can be done quickly,

but if a Lord hasn't made preparations for what he's going to do afterwards, holding on to power is near impossible. Taking over a sept requires far more than just assassinating a sept leader. Tyrannies that occur overnight don't last.

There's also the false belief that any Lord would readily betray any other Lord. Some of the highest ranking Lords, including the Alphas and the Lords of the Summit, have always had free reign to compete with each other, but that doesn't always hold true throughout the lower ranks. Lords who hold the same level of status may fall into rivalry, but when our tribe is threatened, we have to get organized quickly. We understand betrayal, but unifying ourselves against our rivals is far more important.

We have our own moots for developing our plans. Shadow moots are the means by which we organize ourselves against those who would oppose us. They're always held in secret, as they sometimes involve assistance from co-conspirators. It's not uncommon for a shadow moot to actually consist of several lesser moots, as gathering all the members of a conspiracy in one place can be an extremely reckless maneuver. Just as there are hierarchies within the tribe, a "hierarchy" of shadow moots can be arranged to maintain communication between conspirators. How that hierarchy is built depends upon the relative status of the conspirators. The members of a shadow moot ultimately serve the plans of the tribe, and status keeps them in place.

## Status

Status dictates which moots can be attended by which Shadow Lords. The leader, known as the Grand Master, is sometimes the only participant who knows which allies are involved in which moots. He is sometimes assisted by a Shadow Lord Theurge, or High Priest, who makes sure that the proper rites of each moot are obeyed. The primary goal of these meetings is to pass information from one "cell" of Shadow Lord sympathizers to another. Each meeting may survive a different purpose within the overall shadow moot. As long as the obligatory ceremonies are performed at various meetings, the other requirements of the overall moot have been satisfied.

Not all of the participants have to show up at the same time or even in the same place. The term "shadow moot" also refers to the elaborate social structure of the tribe's conspiracies, both within the tribe and between the Lords and their allies. If a Philodox meets with a group of Alphas and then proceeds to a covert negotiation with a coterie of vampires, technically, his complicity with the vampires is an extension of the shadow moot. It is said that "the enemy of your enemy is your friend," but since nearly every other tribe despises the Shadow Lords, it is possible for enemies of the Garou to briefly work as allies of the Lords.

There are also times when a Shadow Lord will make a sacrifice for the Garou that only other Lords would understand. Shadow moots acknowledge these sacrifices. A Shadow Lord may gain recognition within his tribe that may not be revealed to the Garou Nation. This recognition may even result in temporary Renown, but only if the Rite of Shame is involved. (For more details, see Appendix One.) This shameful rite is also used when a Lord rises in status within the tribe.

Understanding the levels of status within the tribe can help a Shadow Lord understand the elaborate methods of organizing a shadow moot. Who defers to whom at which time depends on who is held in esteem at that gathering and who is not. Away from the eyes of those outside the tribe, this may lead to a series of Facedowns, although it is far more clever to indulge in a Gamecraft to figure out who is more devious than whom. Actual duels are extremely rare, as the tribe values cunning and power far more than physical prowess in combat. Once the shadow moot is over, however, the members are unified in one purpose: triumphing over their rivals by any means necessary.

## Alphas

Extremely promising Lords are considered worthy of becoming Alphas, and as such, they have the privilege of attending any shadow moot. An Alpha would be reckless, nonetheless, if he chose to attend every one. For one thing, a rival of the Alpha would only have to track or shadow her to various meetings to find out with whom she is associated and how the shadow moot is organized. It is more common for a Lord to assign deferential "proxies" to attend gatherings for her. Lords of the Summit are almost always Alphas.

## Betas

Although it would be tempting to consider a Beta to be weaker than an Alpha, that deception often works to their advantage. A Beta may be more powerful than an Alpha if he can influence a more powerful Garou. The Shadow Lords understand that an individual who takes credit for the success of an operation is not necessarily the individual who made it succeed. An advisor who can control the leader he advises can wield a great deal of power.

If a Beta is in a sept where the sept leader is not a Shadow Lord, other Shadow Lords will still secretly treat him as one of the leaders of the sept. A "second-in-command" can perform many activities that a leader cannot, since the leader is usually under greater public scrutiny.

If a leader from another tribe is powerful, a Beta may choose to support him. If the leader has the approval of the Shadow Lords, they may also work to aid him (as long as this ultimately benefits the Lords). If the leader is strong, the tribe will then gain influence without overthrowing him. If the leader is weak, the Beta will turn against him, working without restraint to put an Alpha Shadow Lord or a "puppet" from another tribe in his place. A Beta who successfully deposes a sept leader from another tribe may choose to undergo a Rite of Shame and become an Alpha.

Shadow Lords have a reputation as outstanding mediators and advisors, and even the greatest rulers know how valuable it can be to have a Shadow Lord advisor as an ally. Betas can produce valuable information without revealing their sources (and placing the leader in danger) and can protect their chosen Alphas from conspirators. Nonetheless, the assistance of a Shadow Lord can also have its price. If the leader falls out of favor with the Lords, they will move against him. Of course, the former advisor will then have all the right information at his disposal to assist with this change.

## Crows

Crows hold a level of status below Betas. They perform similar functions, but always serve as lackeys to Shadow Lords of higher status. Their loyalty to the tribe is absolute, as their totem demands such servitude. They care little for status, instead preferring to measure their own worth by the success of the Lord they serve. In facts, Crows regard each other based on who has been more deferential to whose Lord. At a shadow moot, a Crow usually stands two paces behind the Lord he or she serves. If the only individuals present at the shadow moot are Crows, then the "murder of crows" will defer to each other based on "whose Lord is more powerful than whose."

## Ravens

Ravens are typically tricksters and spies. They value their personal independence very highly, and as such, are accorded lower status within the tribe as a whole. A Raven gains respect by succeeding in covert tasks. The most successful Ravens either aspire to become Betas or rise to a position where they control several Ravens at once. This level of status is a very risky one, as a Raven who is discovered knows that he must accept personal responsibility for his actions and may be abandoned by the tribe temporarily if he gets into too much trouble.

These Lords often tend to spend a great deal of time away from their tribe. Periodic shadow moots are required so that the Raven can report to a "higher flying" Raven or Beta. While they are not regarded with as much reverence as the other Lords, they don't usually demand it, either. As some of these Lords associate with individuals who are tainted by the Wyrm, Bringers of Light make for excellent Ravens.

> ## Cubs and Shadow Moots
>
> It is rare for cubs to gain admission to a shadow moot. If they do, they are accompanied by a Garou of higher rank and usually remain fearful and silent. Soon after a cub completes his Rite of Passage in a sept, the Lords of a shadow moot may choose to place him through an initiation culminating in a test of his loyalty or a Rite of Shame.

## Cultists

Secret societies within the Shadow Lords are viewed with great suspicion. They will never be eradicated, and their interpretations of how to best serve the tribe are often somewhat deviant. A Lord who reveals himself to be a member of a cult or secret society without good reason immediately risks losing face within the tribe.

## Vultures

Though this term is not used among anyone but Shadow Lords, it is used to refer to Shadow Lord allies who are not Garou. The secrecy of their involvement with Lordly activities is even more important than the "deep cover" of Ravens. They also stand the risk of being rejected by their own people if they are caught. Gangrel vampires (of both the Camarilla and the Sabbat), Dreamspeakers, Hollow Ones, and Unseelie changelings have been known to gain respect for holding this level of status. A vulture attending a shadow moot must have an "advocate" present to advise him on proper etiquette and speak for him at times. A vulture may make demands, but they are entertained at the whim of the highest ranking Shadow Lord.

## Outcasts

An outcast Garou may still have recourse to gaining audience with a Shadow Lord, and as such, may temporarily be granted marginal status. If he can serve the tribe, he may resume contact. This is extremely risky, as harboring an Outcast is a very serious offense. If an Outcast is brought before a shadow moot, dealing with his issue at hand is usually the only agendum. A Rite of Shame can dedicate him to a task within the shadow moot.

## A Word on Hakken Shadow Lords

There is one "wild card" in the hierarchy of ranks: the Hakken. They claim the privilege of being removed from the intricacies of Western etiquette, and thus are not forced to be deferential to anyone. They will usually respect the leader of a shadow moot, but will never lead one of their own. They will always act on their own sense of honor first, but will rarely betray the Shadow Lord tribe. Toward other Garou, they are civil, yet still treat them as *gaijin*. Hakken are known for being very courteous at such gatherings unless enraged. They do have one other advantage within the structure: They reserve the right to settle a dispute with a Western Shadow Lord by trial of arms. It is also acceptable (if suspicious) for a Hakken Shadow Lord to leave part of a Shadow Moot if his personal honor prevents him from taking part.

---

## Defying Status and Camp

While the system of status within a shadow moot strongly reinforces the political unity of camps, a few exceptional Lords defy the conventions of status. A Bringer of Light, for instance, could make for an extremely fanatical Crow, a very dangerous Beta or a recklessly adventurous Alpha. A Lord of the Summit would feel shame at being anything other than an Alpha (and could never become a Crow), but could still function as a very ambitious Beta or a very high-flying Raven. Any Lord drifting outside the expectations of status had best be damn good at what he does, but if he succeeds, the rewards can be commensurate with the risks.

---

## Ascendance

The term "shadow moot," then, can refer to the actual activities of a secret moot or the members of its conspiracy. The boundaries of where it begins and ends can blur. This ensures the absolute loyalty of the participants. So is it with you. Walk with me a little further, child, and I shall show you.

You have been chosen, and you are now in the midst of your first shadow moot. You have heard elegant stories of the Impergium and deceitful lies about the history of mankind. You have matched wits with a Ragabash, taken communion with a Theurge, and conspired with our allies.

Yes, our allies. See this Garou who stands in the shadows? He is an Ahroun of the Fianna. Attend closely. He has shamed his rival, the warder of this sept. Of course, he would never fight such a powerful warrior before a moot, and so we have left his conspiracy to the shadows. The caern warder wasn't able to fight back because someone took his klaive away... and now someone must finish the deed. Someone must eliminate his rival.

Take your klaive in hand. Observe. The Fianna caern warder has been bound in this clearing. Look! His shieldmate will even act as a witness to a "duel," if you so desire. Shall I untie him for you? Or should I keep him bound? You have power over him. How will you use it? This is the test I set before you. You have a choice to make. Who will you serve —Crow, Raven or Thunder? Is killing the easy solution, or is your choice more insidious? Choose wisely.

Feel the pain in your heart, and answer it. This I give to you as your birthright. Know that you have been chosen by Veil-of-Darkness, Theurge of the Shadow Lords.

## Wisdom

*Can't anybody see*
*We've got a war to fight,*
*Never find our way,*
*Regardless*
*Of what they say.*
*How can it feel this wrong?*
*From this moment, how can it feel this wrong?*
*— Portishead, "Roads"*

My Lord! Come inside. I see from the blood on the sleeve of your cloak that you are truly one of us. Congratulations. My Theurge brother has chosen well, even if your solution was a bit... unusual. Sit before me, and I will complete your instruction. I am Voice-of-Reason, Philodox of the Shadow Lords.

You have begun your journey. Only by logically outmaneuvering rivals can will you ensure your continued ascendance. Fury drives you, but cautious reasoning will save you. While the more headstrong will readily rush into battle with the slightest provocation, a Lord will take the more sensible role: evaluating their efforts. If they will not overtly support you, you must secretly guide them.

# Breeds

*…they had for a teacher one who was half beast and half man, and so is it necessary for a prince to know how to make use of both natures, and that one without the other is not durable.*

— Machiavelli, *The Prince*

Blood follows blood. Among the Garou, werewolves of the same breed develop an understanding that can defy barriers of culture and tribe. Use this to your advantage. Maintaining unity of the Garou by developing unity among the Lords is a practice that has served us well. You may very well work with Lords of all three breeds; you must then understand how to use this to your advantage.

Many septs are reluctant to have more than one or two Lords in attendance. Once we gain sizable membership in a sept, our unity of purpose allows us to slowly seize power. If you only have one or two Lords to aid you, remember that alliance to one's breed can make one powerful as well. By coordinating the efforts of the various breeds, you build upon this principle.

## Lupus

Lupus Lords have difficulty gaining rank in our tribe. Their ability to fully exploit human language gives them a decided disadvantage in manipulating many of their comrades, but as loyal members of the tribe, they still do their part. Their instincts make them highly valuable in hunting down, track-

ing, and shadowing our prey. Lupus lords overtly shy away from our tribe, yet covertly, the alliances that they form with other lupus Garou work to our advantage. They also remind us that the Garou must understand both wolves and men, a fact that has been forgotten in the Garou Nation.

## Metis

Do not overlook what others might reject. Our lessors have praised the malformed in times of need as an easy way of gaining political support, but this tactic has been inexpertly used. The metis now harbor the same resentment towards lupus and homid Garou that has been openly shown toward them. Discontent is always our ally. Taking control of a sept takes time, and thus you must cultivate the sympathy of the disaffected in a timely manner. You may hear of the efforts of the Lazarite Movement to build upon this. Disavow your knowledge of it, and leave it to the shadows. Metis Shadow Lords employ the same tactics as the lupus: declaiming the homids while covertly serving the tribe. Divided, we deceive. United, we conquer.

## Homid

The highest positions in our tribe are usually held by homid Garou. The loyalty of our lupus and metis brethren make this possible. The homids' facility with human language, understanding of human ways, and exploitation of human resources strengthen our tribe. Though we would never breach the Veil, working among humans has taught us many of their most efficient tactics of subversion. Humans have a talent for destroying their own kind, especially in the arts of blackmail, betrayal and political obfuscation. Fortunately, we can use these human tactics for a greater good.

# The Litany

*You must know that there are two ways of contesting, the one by the law, the other by force; the first is proper to men, the second to beasts; but because the first is frequently not sufficient, it is necessary to have recourse to the second.*

— Machiavelli, ibid.

You have the aid of your shadow moot; without it, you are nothing. You are aided by allies — lupus, metis and homids — and without them, you are nothing. Alone, you will feel naught but emptiness and discontent, but allied with your tribe, you will find your place in the world. We can give you the tools to further your own will to power. The greatest of these tools is the Litany.

In the midst of our disagreements and disruptions, the traditions of the Litany have held the Garou Nation together. Our less patient brethren have little patience for complicated legalities, but because our culture values tradition, we still uphold a code of law that was first adapted millennia ago. As part of the agreement of the Grand Concord, we were to solidify our laws into a form that was acceptable to the ruling class at the time. We will never relinquish our advantage in the arts of legality.

The traditions reflect the purer world of the Impergium, where rule by absolute tyranny and the subjugation of mankind kept the Garou Nation strong. Codifying these laws was a necessary compromise when we had to submit to the Concord. On the one hand, the Silver Fangs spoke of a "new age" where an accordance would be formed between wolves and men; on the other, we were to not dispense with our old traditions... merely the ones that did not suit the elite. The Silver Fangs (and their allies, who demanded the Veil) knew that mediators would be required to adjudicate the situational aspects of the law. From the beginning, the law has always been our strength.

# Garou Shall Not Mate With Garou

Finding more warriors in the campaign against the Wyrm is difficult, yet Gaia and Grandfather have provided us with a balance between the tribes and maintained purity within those tribes. There are those who would disturb that balance, claiming that they do so because warriors are too rare. The greatest burden of shame is placed on the offspring — the innocent victims. The law is upheld in persecuting the metis, but for the most part, it has been weakened by those who spawn them.

# Combat the Wyrm Wherever It Dwells and Whenever It Breeds

The Shadow Lords have upheld this dictum in a more precise matter than the other tribes. "Combating" an enemy does not require a physical assault. Gathering information is essential to organizing our campaigns. We have the wisdom to integrate the information we gather to make informed decisions. We wage war by uncovering secrets so that we may act based on reason.

# Respect the Territory of Another

Mutual respect for the territories of Garou is no longer a reality. The rapid expansion of human territories has made marking territory unfeasible, and the etiquette of howls poses a threat to the Veil. Clearly, then, the same liberal interpretation should extend to other necessities. In our shadow wars against the Wyrm, and our efforts to protect the septs in which we live, we have often had to claim immunity from this tradition. Diplomatic immunity is a privilege many of our mediators demand in order to perform their tasks. Those who have studied the intricacies and history of the law know of precedents where our campaigns have saved our Nation. Simpletons untrained in the law claim we have breached this dictum.

# Accept an Honorable Surrender

If only the other tribes had the restraint and foresight of the Shadow Lords. Our covert methods of warfare, our gift at mediation, and our extensive skill at diplomacy with other races has been developed to reduce such bloodshed. Rivals such as the Silver Fangs and the Get would sooner place their own personal honor above their race, preferring to fight to the death in duels or kill our warriors in needless battles. They are the true threat. They have undermined this portion of the Litany and established a precedent by which we are slaves to rage instead of masters of reason. Never use an army of claws to subdue your foe when a knife at the throat will suffice; do not use a knife at the throat to best your foe when simple words will suffice.

# Submission to Those of Higher Station

By keeping strong leaders is positions of power, we uphold the duty history demands of us. This portion of the Litany has been exploited often by those who would place their own personal estimations of worth above traditional measures of renown. We must therefore break this down into situational meaning. To a Shadow Lord, a weak leader must be questioned, but a strong leader, such as a Lord who upholds the intricacies of the Litany, must demand obeisance.

# The First Share of the Kill to the Greatest in Station

Misinterpreting this dictum has led many would-be tyrants astray. Too often, one group of disaffected individuals has seized power believing that their ascendance would solve all their problems. They believed victory would immediately guarantee that conditions would improve, and then, after uncovering new problems, discovered their condition had worsened. Absolute power is a privilege that requires years, or sometimes even generations, to earn. When seizing power and privilege, strike swiftly so that your offenses may be forgotten quickly, but fairly reward those who have supported you, so that you may continue to earn their support.

Weak rulers do not earn this privilege. Regardless of a leader's rewards, his weakness will invite dissension. In fact, a weak ruler is therefore not the "greatest" in a sept or pack, and those who are more fit to lead are then *obligated* by this law to seize the first share instead.

# Ye Shall Not Eat the Flesh of Humans

The Litany and legality are measures to uphold civility. Without the Litany, only the examples of great men inspire us to be more than beasts. Without the light of reason, we are no more than monsters. Moreover, devouring humans is a threat to the Veil and invites investigation.

# The Veil Shall Not Be Lifted

This portion of the Litany is inviolate. When the Veil was created, it was a threat to our rightful place in the world; now that its failure has brought us to the Apocalypse, we must keep it for the sake of our own survival. Our allies must be ever-vigilant, quickly reporting any instance of transgression against this law. The desperate situation of the world and our race justifies a widespread shadow campaign to root out those who would endanger all we have done so that we may preserve our own safety.

# Do Not Suffer Thy People to Tend Thy Sickness

How are we to respond to this knowing that the Silver Fangs are diseased? How much more proof do we need of their widespread mental illness? Why do we suffer to tolerate their presence?

# The Leader May Be Challenged at Any Time During Peace

As one would expect, a strong leader will define what the word "peace" means. If he needs to revoke this definition to protect a strong government, he will not hesitate. Declaring war demands unity. In fact, this portion of the Litany, when taken in the context of the present day, demands that a strong leader must continually be at war.

If a leader is strong, he will be relentless in his efforts to battle the Wyrm without and indefatigable in his efforts to secure his sept within. If he fails in this task and fails to overcome, it is the duty of the loyal Garou who follow him to bring his leadership into question. A strong leader will use whatever physical or intellectual means necessary to counter this. But if the members of a sept find that a leader is weak, they must put him to the test and depose him if they find that he is not to the mark.

# The Leader May Not Be Challenged at Any Time During War

You may ask, then, what a Lord is to do when a sept is triumphant against its enemies and the leader is strong, notwithstanding his membership to a rival tribe. Strength is to be respected above all else. If you find a sept leader who can rule through absolute power, you would do well to ally with him. You gain his sympathy, and even if you are not the Alpha of that tribe, you gain control. The tyranny and absolute power of the Impergium made our race pure. Supporting a leader who can return to those traditional values makes the Garou Nation stronger.

# Ye Shall Take No Action That Causes a Caern to Be Violated

This dictum is inviolate. Those who threaten the security of a caern must face the strictest penalties of our law, and for the safety of all, the Shadow Lords will do whatever is necessary to preserve our safety.

# Private Discontent

We use the law against others; they would then use the law against us. A Philodox has pledged to keep the Sacred Ways, and so, when any who are not of our tribe stray from the law, the Half-Moons must enforce it. At the same time, expecting us to hold to the same law others breach is hypocrisy. Privately, we mock their law, we revile their Concord, and we await the time of retribution. Once we have attained absolute victory, we will remake the law in our own image and ascend to the purity we once had. We will be just, irrefutable and absolute. Until then, this destiny lies before you as a path for you to follow as you journey into the world.

# Chapter Three: Renown and Shame

*Here we may reign secure, and, in my choice,*
*To reign is worth ambition, though in Hell:*
*Better to reign in Hell than serve in heaven.*
*— John Milton, Paradise Lost*

Salutations. I see that you are ready to travel. As an Ahroun of the Shadow Lords, I must now arm you with your weaponry.

Here is your blade, my Lord. You have earned it. At the next moot, we will speak of your defeat of the caern warder, and you will have won your place as a fostern of the tribe. Even more importantly, you will have earned your position in the shadow moot.

A Lord's campaign against weakness unfolds gradually, and designs used to overtake a sept have been known to take generations to realize. Your morale may falter, but the stories of our triumphs can sustain you. The greatest of these have been in our Balkan homelands. The recent triumph of Boris Thunderstrike over his sept leader, Heart-of-Fury, is an example of this, and his victory speech is taken by many young Lords today as an inspiration. Listen and learn.

# Perfection and Dissent

*A Eulogy at the Passing of Heart-of-Fury,*
*Upon the Occasion of His Forced Abdication,*
*Spoken within the Shadow Moot of Boris Thunderstrike*
*of the Sept of the Night Sky, Wallachia,*
*and duly recorded by his Most Humble and Obedient Servant,*
*Ynosh Snatch-Talon, Scribe and Scholar*

Children of the Night Sky! Our victory is complete. As we gather here on this pinnacle, those beneath us acknowledge our ascendance. The body of our former sept leader awaits interment, and soon his followers will surrender the Sept of the Night Sky to his rivals. We will seize the night, and what was once ours will be ours once more. We have acted as One, seizing power for the honor and glory of our tribe, our race and our world. That, my children, is our destiny. Our sacred duty is to wage war against this Wyrm as no others can, and from this, our latest conquest, we will also move onward in our shadow war and purify the septs of our homeland. Thus, before we part under cloak of darkness to take to the field of battle, let us understand what it is to be a warrior in this shadow war.

As the Apocalypse draws near, nothing less than perfection will suffice. The Final Days threaten to destroy everything we hold dear. This is not a time for weakness. Our lessers hold the concept of "self" above all else, but we are as One. The Lords are selfless in devotion to their tribe. The survival of our race requires us to act without restraint and to act in unison.

In our hearts, we harbor eternal discontent. Our pain drives us to doubt and reject. This is part of the order of all things. The creatures of Gaia may curse the storm, but they know its coming is part of the ways of the Earth. We know that Gaia is eternally discontent with her creation — the lesser creatures die and the strong survive. That is the way of all things. Testing the weak is an essential part of nature. Harsh adversity makes for strong survivors. You will be tested, and in turn, will test the world.

As it is with wolves and men, so it is with ideas. We criticize the ways of others, and they either evolve or die. Skepticism and doubt are essential elements of this evolution. Without continually questioning what others hold dear, our race will never evolve to face the challenges before us.

The same may be said of the the body politic. The Garou trust their leaders to surmount impossible tasks. If we are to face the insurmountable and survive, we must do so with leaders who can overcome any opposition. The weak hesitate, but the strong conquer. If our leaders are weak, we will harry them, questioning their authority. Without such opposition, we take on faith that they are strong, and thus risk our own destruction. We will be stronger than them and overcome, as we have proven tonight.

Go forward with this strength. Increase your power by testing yourself against opposition. Each Garou, by rising to meet the challenges before him, seeks to improve himself so that he may better serve his race. You, my Lords, must question what is held as essential as you journey again into the septs of the Garou. Our morality, our ethics, our legalities — each in turn must be put to the test. While others may hold this as sacrilege, we hold it as sacred. You must profane that which is held dear, for if it cannot withstand such opposition, you must reject its worth.

You must take this upon yourself as well. Look to the taint within yourself and question its worth. Revel in your true nature, and then seek to overcome. Rage is seen as a taint of anger, yet the Garou hold it as essential. Thus each of us — Lord and lesser — holds a taint within ourselves. The idea that we ourselves are tainted by the Wyrm by our own rage is seen as blasphemous, but we must question what others have taken on faith. The world has given us pain and rage, but those who are consumed by it have begun their descent into the way of the Wyrm. Let us be stronger than them.

The taint within yourself has consumed the world around you. The world seeks to bend you to its will; instead, you must master the world around you. By overcoming the taint of the Wyrm around us, and facing its opposition, we are tested to the verge of destruction. We strengthen our souls by coming into contact with evil and overcoming it. Those who are weak would hesitate at this task, but those who are strong will set themselves to this with great vigor.

We are also driven by our ambition. It is a raging torrent within us, yet to deny ambition is to deny ourselves. The ascendance of each of us brings the ascendance of our tribe. We must rage at the weak who would confine us and deny our rise to power. Know that your ambition is essential. This will to power tests one's self, just as you would set your might against your rivals. Defying the status of rank is called disloyalty, but your scorn and disobedience should be cultivated carefully. By following the path of turmoil, within and without, and conquering it, we become more powerful. Thus, through wisdom, our taint makes us stronger.

Do not deny the tempest within yourself. When you leave this sept to do battle in our shadow war, use the strength you have gathered here to move ever onward.

The storm calls to you. Answer it, and ascend to your glory.

*Answered by Howls of Triumph and the desecration of the body of Heart-of-Fury, Ahroun of the Silver Fangs. Know that on that night, Boris Thunderstrike took the Sept of the Night Sky and, in reconsecrating his Caern of Will, advanced the cause of our campaign. In the name of purity, thus has it been recorded.*

# The World Before You

*That which does not destroy me makes me stronger.*
— Neitzsche, *Thus Spake Zarathustra*

Here is your cloak, my Lord. May it protect you from the cold winds of fortune as you travel through the lands of the Garou. The cloak does more than protect — it conceals. Know that wherever you travel, your truest secrets and your truest lies are carried with you. Your honor and wisdom are not shamelessly carried for all to see. They are hidden within the depths of your heart, just as you carry yourself under the folds of this, your cloak. If you are to travel, keep this in mind.

## North America

In America, the Lords are wise enough to have thoroughly infiltrated all sides of their nation's political conflicts. There are those who side with the extreme right, glorifying their victories over their adversaries, but there are also Garou who side with the extreme left, acting as incendiary troublemakers and stirring dissent. Regardless of which side is in power, American Lords admire the way their nation has fought for pre-eminence in the world and advanced its beliefs on other nations.

The strongest supernatural force in Mexico and Latin America is the alliance of Sabbat vampires that feeds off suffering and misery in the Third World. The Bringers of Light find this part of the world to be an outstanding battleground for testing their souls. Humans suffer on this battleground, but Garou are purified amidst the carnage.

## South America

The War in the Amazon is the most important battleground in this part of the world. The death toll is high, which means that opportunities for advancing quickly in political status are there. Surviving in the Amazon is difficult, but for Garou who know how to convince others to fight, it makes for an intriguing intellectual challenge.

The phrase "South American Dictatorship" has become a cliché, but many still exist today. In Central and South America, banana republics rise and fall, but an observant Garou can learn a great deal from humans who succeed and fail in such enterprises.

## Europe

Our primary concern in Europe is the protection of our homelands. The Balkan Nations are forever caught in their political conflicts, and so we still debate which factions will triumph over the others. Multinational forces still intervene in the resolution of these conflicts; until they understand the origins behind them, they will never be able to bring an end to the fighting. Other nations have forced their laws upon our homelands for too long. The resolution must come from within or it will never succeed.

## Africa

Third World nations within Africa are waiting for more industrious and powerful nations to subjugate them. While there are Lords who closely watch the powers that threaten the nations of Africa, there are just as many Lords wanting to support the peoples who are to be oppressed. Wherever there is dissent, there is a call for tyrants. When you travel, you will have ample opportunities to answer this call.

## Asia

In Asia, we are usually the guests of the Hakken Garou. These Shadow Lord brethren are civil to us, yet always eager to instruct us. If you are to travel in this part of the world, there is one society of rivals of which you must be especially cautious: the Asian Glass Walkers. Particularly in Hong Kong, the power and organization of the Glass Walkers is strong, and rivalry between their Asian societies and the Hakken Garou is fierce. Watch your step.

## A Word of Caution

Wherever you travel, listen first and act carefully afterward only if you have support. The balance of power in any given area is seldom the way it appears at first glance. Finding dissent and understanding the reasons behind turmoil takes time. There is no limit to the amount of opportunity for an ambitious young Lord, but unless you take your time in seizing power, you can be controlled by the true powers behind any conflict just as easily as you would control the overt powers. Once you understand that caveat, you will see the opportunity for conquest wherever you go.

## The Rivals Who Will Oppose You

*Your hatred has made you strong....*
— Anakin Skywalker, a.k.a. Lord Vader

Here is your pride, my Lord: You belong to the most despised of all tribes. Any who seek power must overcome that, but first, you may take that as a mark of distinction.

Throughout the world, our infamy has spread. The rivals of the Twelve Tribes publicly scorn us and hold us in contempt. You cannot blame me, then, for privately holding them in contempt as well. I know my views upon this subject are not popular ones. I would respond that these views are mine. Your rivals are not your equals. They are your tools. When you go out into the world, you will evolve strategies for using them well.

# Black Furies

Any man who tries to reason with a Black Fury is immediately at a disadvantage. They fabricate and exaggerate any perceived insult to justify their sexist views. This clouds their vision. It is indeed fortunate that the Lords are more egalitarian. Our female Lords can be just as deadly as any Black Fury, yet their cautious ways make them far more dangerous. Also remember that many men of other tribes harbor resentment against the Furies for their sexist views. Do not neglect the opportunity to harness this when it suits you. Again, discontent is always our ally.

# Bone Gnawers

The Twelve Tribes often degrade and insult the abilities of the Bone Gnawers. In fact, overtly siding with a member of this tribe is sometimes seen as a foolish gesture. Do not forget that their lowly station often leaves them underestimated. The Bone Gnawers are outstanding at gathering secrets, and in any city, they will usually do a more thorough job of gathering information than any other tribe (except the Lords, of course). Yet their shame, poverty and decrepitude perpetually places them in need of aid. The members of this tribe are often desperate for warmth, food and companionship. If you can covertly aid them, they may in turn covertly assist you with valuable information. Who would dare say that we are not charitable? I have seen the results of this kindness. It is not uncommon for one desperate Bone Gnawer to sell out his friends, pack and tribe for a warm meal and a place to sleep.

# Children of Gaia

I am astounded that this pitiful tribe has not yet met with extinction. They have preached peace, as they did during the Concord, and it has failed, as it did during the Concord, and yet they openly celebrate, reveling in wanton sexual depravity instead of acknowledging their failure. The Final Days have rendered them woefully inadequate in dealing with reality. Their ways of "peace" and "civilization" have weakened humanity and served the Wyrm. This is not a time for peace.

# Fianna

What charming little Irishmen these Fianna are. I have borne their jeers and insults in silence. For years, their drunken imprecations and stilted witticisms have tormented me. They revel in their emotions, and thus deny reason. A Fianna is useful when you need a bottle emptied or a melody composed, but their drunken ways, their sentimental romances and their quaint customs are not enough for them to be of more than marginal use.

# Get of Fenris

Simplistic fools, but excellent shock troops. If you wish to motivate a Get, exploit his pride and offer him a chance to fight something. They are more than eager to die for false glory. In fact, nothing humiliates a Get more than acknowledging that there is something in the world he cannot fight. If you can exploit this, they will be more than happy to die for you.

# Glass Walkers

The members of this tribe are referred to as *Urrah*, or "tainted ones." Their affinity to the Weaver and communion with the city earn them disdain. Therefore, they are in need of allies. We are more than delighted to assist these outcasts if it serves us. Since their tribe has access to resources the others do not, having the assistance of a Glass Walker will give you an advantage over the elitist Garou of the other tribes, who denounce them. And, of course, if one betrays you, you can always expose him later for what he is: a freakish abomination of Gaia who abandons the Wyld to follow the dangerous path of the Weaver.

# Red Talons

Wonderful allies — simple-minded and pure. Their unrelenting hatred of humanity makes them excellent collaborators. They are not just tools, they are carefully crafted weapons. Feign sympathy for their views when assisting them; denounce their narrow-mindedness if you need to oppose them. Many Red Talons harbor mistrust for any Garou who is not a lupus. This also increases their need for "friends." Don't think for a moment that their reliance on non-human communication implies that they are fully inferior. They are only partially inferior. It merely makes their interpretation of the world inadequate. They need others to do their complex thinking for them.

# Silent Striders

Watch them. One who remains in your pack or sept for a prolonged period of time can slowly be brought under your influence, but the gadflies who wander from caern to caern are pernicious. They will spread rumors, harming you for the most minor of transgressions. They will solicit allies and organize your rivals against you. When you encounter a Strider, ask yourself three things: "Where has she come from?", "Where is she going?" and "How long will she stay?" Then begin to take precautions.

# Silver Fangs

Stop me if I begin to ramble.

Their tribe is dead. It staggers, it poses, it occasionally babbles, but their days of glory are gone. They deserve the Harano that takes them and the mental illness that has ravaged their minds. Some may sympathize with them, regarding them as noble or tragic, but their days of leadership are gone. The world will be ours. Millennia of failure and the death of the world around us show us that their ending of the Impergium was a mistake, following them was a mistake, and ever trusting them again would be a grave mistake. As they stand, they will wear their crowns and hold their sad ceremonies. When they lie interred, I will desecrate their graves.

I will not belabor the point.

# Stargazers

These Garou are so removed from reality that they pose little threat to your political ambitions. Their wisdom is useful, but they do not understand the call of passion. Understanding their motivation can be somewhat difficult, as they are as cryptic as the mysteries that fascinate them. They rarely seek power, however, and so their rivalry is somewhat minor.

# Uktena

How often have the Uktena been held in contempt? They obviously wouldn't hide their secrets so carefully if they didn't have good reasons for doing so. Yet our most industrious efforts to uncover these secrets so often fail. Pity. They are almost mistrusted as much as we are. Stirring dissent against them is then quite easy.

# Wendigo

Again, those with simplistic motivations are easier to manipulate. They have made their priorities clear. Sympathize with them when you wish to exploit them, and denounce them for their lack of foresight if they get in your way. Fanaticism always makes one appear weak. If only they were not so taken with their own grief over their own failure.

# The Monsters Around You

The Twelve Tribes are weak, but at least they are on your side against the Wyrm... so to speak. Their mutual hatred for each other is leverage you can exploit. Should you require further leverage, one need only set them against other races. It is convenient that hubristic Garou instinctively mistrust those who are not Garou. When you negotiate with other races, you will no doubt sympathize with them, but if you must revile them, it is easy to portray them as monstrous.

# Other Shapechangers

How should the Bête, the other shapechangers, regard the Garou? Refer to history. The Garou Nation worked to eradicate the other shapechangers in the War of Rage. We are sympathetic to those who have long-standing grudges.

Be cautious when dealing with them, however. Bastet are devious and extremely territorial. They would sooner fight over land than reason with us. Corax are thieves, although some of the Ravens in our tribe have learned to make bargains with them. Gurahl are unpredictable, and tend to ignore short-term considerations. Ratkin can be useful, but would just as soon sell you out to Nosferatu vampires or Unseelie as betray you to Bone Gnawer rivals.

There is another perspective on this issue, however. The Shadow Lords who left the Garou Nation after the end of the Impergium never declared war on the Bête. The Hakken Shadow Lords instead learned to deal favorably with the *hengeyokai*, the shapechangers of their land. Although you may never see one of the Kitsune werefoxes, it is known that they are allied with the Hakken. The Hakken Garou do not always get on favorably with their Western cousins, but some who would negotiate with other shapeshifters would just as soon have a Hakken mediate.

# Vampires

We have been indoctrinated into "fighting the Wyrm," but launching into all-out war against the Kindred with the slightest provocation is a suicidal maneuver at best. No Half-Moon is as capable of communing with darkness as well as a Shadow Lord Philodox, and so, in many septs, a Lord will often covertly maintain relations with the Camarilla.

Although this has prevented much bloodshed over the last few centuries, it is, curiously enough, generally regarded as treasonous. If you develop contacts, then, and you are caught, do not regard your punishment to be in regards to your efforts. Rather, your punishment is deserved because you were foolish enough to be caught. Your honor as a Garou will be destroyed, but your honor among the Shadow Lords will be highly esteemed in return for your sacrifice on behalf of the tribe.

The Sabbat of the 20th century are generally less devious than the Camarilla, at least from our experience. Their politics are less Byzantine, and the unity of their packs is admirable, even if every last one of them is utterly and completely tainted by the Wyrm. They respect strength and prowess, and as such, the Lords must negotiate with them from a position of strength. The weaker tribes are completely unsuited to this task. Of course, should they threaten our homelands again, and if any of should notice them assembling War Parties in Wallachia or Moldavia, we must exterminate these bastards and show them the true meaning of the word "genocide."

# Mages

If you should ally with a mage, you are to be congratulated. Mages are able to strike at their adversaries in ways that cannot be easily detected. If you are opposed by a mage, she can be quite dangerous, as she can then strike at you without revealing her involvement. Remember this: They are mortal. Mages one can see face-to-face tend to shred quite easily under one's claws. Even their greatest warriors tend to be quite weak in direct combat. Therefore, if you encounter difficulty with one of their orders, employing to meet them face to face will greatly benefit your attempts to overcome them. Heavy blood loss and rent flesh do tend to interfere with subtle spellcasting.

# Wraiths

If only we understood them. Interacting with the physical world is difficult for the Restless Dead, but as spies they would be extremely useful. Who is to say they do not already do this for the Silent Striders? Were it not for our well-defined senses and sharp claws, we could easily be infiltrated by the ranks of the dead. Communicating with them is indeed difficult, and the elaborate nature of their politics makes developing relations with them nearly impossible. Such a pity. The end result is merely further proof of your need to distrust their allies, the Silent Striders.

# Changelings

The Fianna are quite delighted to have relations with the fey... in more ways than one. Like the members of that amusing tribe, faeries will often delight with their outrageous and amusing antics. Most of them pose little threat. The followers of the Seelie Court are especially weak, as they have a thorough dependence on such weaknesses as "chivalry." As we have seen with the impotent Silver Fangs, chivalry is an easy weakness to exploit.

We have been increasingly diligent in developing relations with the Unseelie fey, who usually respond favorably to our overtures. Nonetheless, their reckless natures preclude ever developing a long-term alliance with them.

# The Path of Villainy

I know you, my Lord. We are of the same family. You are driven to desperation by the anger in your soul. That pain must be either healed or purified, both within and without. Within, you must master yourself; without, you must master the world. Until that taint has been driven from the world, your pain will be with you always. Use it as you will.

You are one with your spiritual mother, and so you must feel her suffering. You are as one with your spiritual father, and so you must survive through conquest. You have been chosen, and your destiny lies before you. Know that you are one of the Shadow Lords.

# Appendix One: Hidden Strengths

*Yond Cassius has a mean and hungry look;*
*He thinks too much: such men are dangerous.*
— William Shakespeare, *Julius Caesar*

Evolution is a part of nature, and as such, Gaia has gifted the Lords with talents to allow them to play their role in the way of all things. The Lords are formidable because they gain strength from the dark powers that they serve. The hidden strengths that they employ are even more dangerous when they remain unseen.

## Tribal Weaknesses (Optional)

An optional rule was introduced in the first **Werewolf** tribebook: tribal weaknesses. These are quirks that each member of a particular tribe possesses, usually due to the social or even genetic nature of the tribe. Weaknesses should not always be enforced. There are some situations in which a Bone Gnawer may not suffer a higher difficulty on Social rolls. These situations may be rare, but they can occur. For instance, Black Furies suffer from an inborn anger against men, but a Black Fury may not feel anger toward a man she trusts.

It is up to the Storyteller to enforce these rules when an appropriate situation arises in the game. After all, a player may be unwilling to remind the Storyteller that her Uktena's curiosity may get her into trouble.

## Shadow Lord Weakness

**Failure's Dagger: -1 Renown for failure**

Most Shadow Lords prize winning above all else, and they scorn losers. Whenever a Shadow Lord fails to carry out a task that would normally gain him Glory, Honor or Wisdom, he will lose one point of temporary Renown in that category. (If he would have gained Renown in more than one category, subtract only from the category that would have rewarded the most.) This is in addition to any Renown normally lost.

This does not affect the normal Renown process in any other way; if the Shadow Lord succeeds in the action, he then gains the normal amount of Renown.

# New Abilities (Talents)

## Interrogation

You are able to extract information by fair means or foul. Using a mixture of threats, trickery and persistent questioning, you ultimately learn the truth.

- • Novice: Galliard cub
- •• Practiced: Ahroun thug
- ••• Competent: Philodox legal expert
- •••• Expert: Theurge Judge of Doom
- ••••• Master: Ragabash executioner

# Backgrounds

## Cultist Allies

Although Shadow Lords cannot begin with the Ally Background, cultists can depend on their associates to ally with them. The drawback is that you must keep this alliance a secret. Belonging to a Shadow Lord cult is a disgrace that even fellow Shadow Lords will not tolerate. A cult will still be devoted to a cultist without this background, but a Lord with Cultist Allies will find them to be even more useful than normal.

This is in most respects identical to the Allies Background. The only notable difference is the cult's fanaticism.

# Gifts

• **Cold Voice of Reason (Level Two)** — A cunning Shadow Lord can talk his way out of just about anything. If a Lord is attacked by another Garou, the Shadow Lord may invent a clever remark that will detain his attacker for at least one round. This gift is taught by a Crow-spirit.

**System:** The Garou spends a Gnosis point and rolls Manipulation + Subterfuge (difficulty 8). The attacker is detained one round for each success as long as he, in turn, is not attacked. If the target is assaulted, the effect of the oratory wears off, and the victim may resume his attack. A botch with this Gift will cause the attacker to go into Frenzy.

• **Raven's Wings (Level Three)** — The Garou with this Gift may send a portion of her spirit out of her body in the form of a raven. The raven can see and hear, but it cannot affect the physical world. It is invulnerable to attacks, however. This Gift is taught by a Raven-spirit.

**System:** The Garou spends one Gnosis and rolls Wits + Occult (difficulty 6). The raven may be sent five miles away for every success on the roll. If it goes past this range, the Gift is canceled. While this Gift is in use, the Garou must concentrate to use the raven's senses and may take no other actions in the same turn in which he is communing with the raven.

• **Seeds of Doubt (Level Four)** — By careful deliberation, the Shadow Lord may convince a listener of one false idea.

**System:** The Shadow Lord spends one point of Gnosis and makes an opposed Charisma + Subterfuge (difficulty 8) roll against the listener's Wits + Subterfuge (difficulty 8). If the Shadow Lord succeeds, the listener will believe the lie, as long as it is not actively harmful to him (i.e., "You can walk on air" or "Fire is easily digestible.") If the listener succeeds, he will realize that he is being tricked. If the caster botches, the listener will frenzy.

## Lords of the Summit Gifts

• **Interrogator (Level Three)** — This Gift was originally discovered by a cult of Shadow Lords known as the Judges of Doom. A Garou may use this Gift to terrify his victim into a confession. This Gift is taught by a Fear-spirit.

**System:** The interrogator rolls Manipulation + Subterfuge or Interrogation; the defendant resists with an opposed Willpower roll. If the Garou succeeds, the defendant will be paralyzed with fear for one round and confess the greatest crime that he has committed during the last cycle of the moon. This is long enough for a one sentence confession, but may only be used once per moon cycle. Judges of Doom may learn this as a Level One Gift.

• **Mask Taint (Level Five)** — A Garou with this Gift may completely hide his Wyrm-taint from all senses, including Gifts that detect such taint. This Gift is taught by a Puppeteer Bane.

**System:** The Garou spends one Gnosis point and rolls Appearance + Subterfuge (difficulty 8). The effect lasts for one scene. Every time this Gift is used, the Garou must roll one die. If the number is equal to or less than her Corruption Trait, she adds one to her Corruption, gaining more Wyrm taint. This Gift cannot be used by Garou with Corruption 10.

## Children of Crow Gifts

• **Perceptive Servant (Level One)** — Children of Crow are consummate eavesdroppers, and combined with the perceptiveness one gains by serving Crow, this Gift can be extremely useful. It is taught by a Crow-spirit.

**System:** By spending one point of Gnosis, a Child of Crow can reduce the difficulty of overhearing a conversation or witnessing a secretive activity by 2.

• **Dark Aerie (Level Three)** — This is the same as the Uktena Gift, Spirit of the Bird (**Werewolf**, page 135), save that the roll is against Dexterity + Stealth (difficulty 7). The servant of Crow is enveloped by shadows as he escapes.

## Bringers of Light Gift

• **Purify Scent (Level One)** — If another supernatural creature attempts to determine the breed, tribe or auspice of a Bringer of Light, the target may use this Gift to retain her secrets. A Night-spirit teaches this Gift.

**System:** The Shadow Lord spends one point of Gnosis and rolls Perception + Primal-Urge. The difficulty of discovering the information is increased by 1 for each success (up to a maximum modifier of +3).

• **Pure Identity (Level Two)** — A Bringer of Light can alter his appearance to suggest he belongs to another race. If he remains in homid form, he can appear as pallid as a vampire or as glamorous as an Unseelie changeling. If he desires to keep his "scent" as a Garou, he can affect cosmetic changes and appear as a Black Spiral. This Gift is taught by a Chameleon-spirit.

**System:** The Lord spends three Gnosis, but need make no roll. The duration is one day. Close examination requires a Subterfuge roll to maintain the deception.

• **Purity of Blood (Level Five)** — The disciple has become so resistant to the Wyrm that she may overcome the Blood Bond of vampires. This Gift is taught by an avatar of Grandfather Thunder himself.

**System:** The Shadow Lord must expend two points of Gnosis, spend 10 minutes in meditation and make a successful Intelligence + Meditation roll. Until the Garou uses Purity of Blood, he will be aware that he is Bound, but may nonetheless spend a Willpower point to break his conditioning and use the Gift. Also note that this allows an infiltrator of the Sabbat to shatter the effect of the Vaudelaire.

# Rites

## Rite of Shame (Renown)

Level Two

There are tasks a Lord performs for his tribe and his race that could never be acknowledged at a public moot. The Rite of Shame is a way for Shadow Lords to secretly gain temporary Renown at a shadow moot without revealing their activities to the rest of the Garou.

The spirits summoned during this variant of the Rite of Accomplishment are the same as the spirits summoned in a public moot. They will acknowledge successful tasks performed for the Garou Nation, but only other Lords will know of the actual events. The spirits are the great equalizer in this; they understand the darker truths behind the Garou. In this same sense, the Storyteller must ensure that this additional Renown has been earned. Pleasing the Grand Master of a shadow moot is not enough to earn Renown; the Lords must answer to "higher authorities" as well.

These temporary points cannot be used to gain permanent Renown until the Lord advances in Rank or gains a political position within the sept. In other words, once the Lord has succeeded in furthering his ambition, he may be able to justify his activities. Before his ascendance, only other members of his shadow moot will know of and respect this renown, but once he gains power, he will receive further accolades.

**System:** Depending on the Shadow Lord's deeds, the Storyteller may grant him temporary Renown for tasks that would not be deemed "honorable" by other Garou. If the end arguably justifies the means, the Storyteller may award the Lord a fitting amount of temporary Glory, Honor or Wisdom. Let common sense be your guide — no Gaian spirit will acknowledge Renown for deeds worthy of the Black Spiral Dancers.

## Communion with the Storm (Mystic)

Level Two

Grandfather gives guidance to those who stray from the path of wisdom. In the midst of the raging storm, a Garou can come to terms with the dark ambition and hatred that dwells within his soul by focusing his suffering as a weapon against his enemies.

This rite can only be performed in the midst of a heavy rainstorm or thunderstorm. As an incidental effect, the storm will become stronger in the area in which the ritualist is performing. The ritualist must perform the ceremony alone if it is a personal rite, but a group can perform it if they are united in one task. If successful, the ritualists may face the heavens and speak of that which troubles them. Grandfather will respond with the sound of thunder, and the purity of their task will be felt within their hearts.

**System:** For the duration of the rite, any roll involving Enigmas has a difficulty of three lower than normal (as long as it is not less than a difficulty of 4). The ritualists may bring their grievances to Grandfather. If the solution to the problem requires violence, each ritualist will gain one point of Rage. If the solution to the problem requires wisdom, each ritualist will end the ceremony with one point of Gnosis.

## Calling the Storm (Punishment)

Level Three

This rite is a declaration of war against a ruler who has been tainted by the Wyrm or who has committed a major transgression against the Litany. The accusation of transgression must be pronounced at a moot by one who is not a Shadow Lord. The crime does not have to be substantiated, but it must be true. The rite begins with a gathering

of stormclouds. The amount of time required for this to occur depends on the weather at the time. If rain is incipient, the effects may only require one scene to manifest; if skies are clear, the effects may take a full day. (The Gift is not a "rain dance." It may not be used with impunity in the Sahara Desert or Death Valley. Storyteller's judgment — or Grandfather's judgment — is required.)

**System:** Once the tempest begins, each individual who has conspired against the ruler over the course of the last two days gains two points of Rage; each Shadow Lord also gains one point of Gnosis. The animal instincts of the Garou grow stronger: Any roll involving Primal-Urge (including Tracking) is performed at a difficulty two lower than normal. This will only occur, however, if the charge is true. If the charge is not true, lightning will strike, and each participant in the ceremony will take three levels of aggravated damage.

# Totems

# Totem of War

## Crow

**Background Cost:** 2

Followers of Crow, like most scavengers, trust the strong to do their killing for them. To survive, they follow opportunity, and they excel at finding it. Once they find powerful allies, however, they will patiently and loyally support them. Servants of Crow are typically humble, but if they are betrayed, they never forget the offense. A Crow who has been betrayed will seek out more powerful allies to carry out retribution or go about his or her own revenge with remarkable subtlety.

**Traits:** Crow teaches his followers Alertness 2, Subterfuge 2 and Etiquette 1.

**Ban:** Crow asks that his children remain loyal to those whom they serve. Some children extend this to tribal loyalty, while others will interpret this as fanatic affection or loyalty to an individual.

# Totem of Wisdom

## Raven

**Background Cost:** 5

The children of Raven survive through trickery and deceit. They typically survive by their wits and love "living on the edge." They seek out danger and risk, but they also know themselves well enough to resist corruption when they see it. His children surround themselves with chaos and change, yet they also know how to protect themselves from it. Raven is especially fond of lupus Garou. He is also known for always being hungry, just as his children continually seek ways to satisfy their desires.

**Traits:** Raven teaches his followers Survival 3, Subterfuge 1 and Enigmas 1. Each pack member gains a bonus of one temporary Wisdom point. Children of Raven are also favored by the Corax wereravens.

**Ban:** Raven asks that his children never carry wealth, trusting instead in him to provide for them.

# Fetishes

## Cloak of Darkness

Level 2, Gnosis 2

Cloaks are fashionable among Shadow Lords, and for good reason. In addition to their ability to help hide weapons and to protect against the elements, they can be helpful in stealthy operations. The Cloak of Darkness is one type of cloak that magnifies these effects. Wearing the cloak increases a Dice Pool involving Stealth by 3, and, as an incidental effect, decreases the difficulty for hiding an fetish or talen that is primarily used as a weapon (and can normally be hidden under a cloak) by 2. They are created by binding Night-spirits.

## Blood Chalice

Level 2, Gnosis 4

Merely owning this unholy item is a transgression against the Litany, yet Grandfather holds the Blood Chalice as sacred. Only the most twisted of Lords would dare use it, and the mere possession of a Blood Chalice may be punishable by banishment or execution.

Shadow Lords have no qualms about manipulating humans against their Garou rivals or creatures of the Wyrm, yet there are also humans who are used by the Wyrm to harm the children of Thunder. Lords of the Summit, who value justice above all, may decide to "dedicate" such a creature to Grandfather.

The human is brought to a shadow moot so that he may see what he has opposed. The only purpose of the meeting is to dedicate the human. The Lords then shift into Crinos as a Half-Moon declares the human's crime against the Garou. The human may fight to defend himself, but if he is subdued, his blood is drained into the Blood Chalice. In a distorted interpretation of the law, the Garou have "spared the flesh of the human" by only draining his blood and have kept the Litany intact.

His blood is then drained into a chalice, which is consecrated to Thunder. A Shadow Theurge holds the chalice to the heavens and then consumes the human blood. The soul of the transgressor is obliviated, and the heart of the victim shatters as a peal of thunder echoes throughout the land below. The victim is then interred under a layer of urine and feces. In the process, honor is satisfied: The Theurge gains three points of Honor, the Philodox gains a point of Wisdom and each assistant receives one point of Glory. Only other Shadow Lords will recognize this shameful Renown, but if any of these Lords gain the favor of a Shadow Lord sept leader, he will honor this renown for the purposes of acknowledging permanent Renown.

If a consecrated Blood Chalice is used in another type of ceremony, it will automatically supply one point of Gnosis to the ritualist. Note that the conditions of the ceremony of dedicating a soul to Thunder may be carried out against any human. A ghoul, acolyte, psychic or mage will also suffice. Such is the consequence of acting against the Children of Thunder.

## Assassin's Klaive

Level 5, Gnosis 5

Legendary Shadow Lord Theurges have been known to dedicate klaives for the purpose of destroying rivals of the Lords. These weapons are more like slender daggers than large knives and are designed to be hidden under clothing. By burning a point of Gnosis, the possessor can also surround himself with absolute silence for one scene, mask his scent for one hour or eradicate his footprints while he walks for one day.

## Talens

### Whisper Feather

Gnosis 5

This black feather is used to gather a small wind, which the feather then rides. The user can control where the feather travels. As it drifts, the user can perceive where it travels. He closes his eyes (as the player rolls Perception + Occult) and, for the duration of one scene, can see, hear and smell anything within 10 feet of the talen. The effect lasts for one scene, and the wind cannot carry the feather at faster than a walking pace.

# Merits and Flaws

## Political Mentor (2 pt. Garou Ties Merit)

Although Shadow Lords cannot take the Mentor Background, some politically talented Lords are mentored in the arts of their craft. A political mentor can give general advice, but will not intervene in your personal affairs. He will not take responsibility for your actions, but can be a valuable aid in figuring out the political intricacies of a sept. Storytellers who wish to build the political dimension of their campaign will find it easier if one of the characters has this advantage.

## Diplomatic Immunity (3 pt. Garou Ties Merit)

The Garou Nation holds you in esteem as a mediator. You may travel where you please in the furtherance of your duties. No one may search you, and you are welcome at any moot. Of course, should you abuse these privileges, word will spread. The Shadow Lords have worked hard to build up the few Garou entitled to this privilege, and if an elder of your tribe has found out that you have abused this right, you will be cast out from the tribe. (In other words, whatever you do, don't get caught.)

## Original Sin (1 pt. Garou Ties Flaw)

You are the child or student of an infamous Garou. Galliards have spread legendary stories about him from caern to caern, and the same infamy is extended to you. Within the Shadow Lords, this may work to your benefit, as few would dare betray you, but outside of your tribe, your reputation precedes you. It is assumed that you will resume where your parent or mentor left off. Wear your scorn with pride. This cannot be taken with the Political Mentor Background.

# Appendix Two: Conspirators

"Mad, bad, and dangerous to know."
— Lady Catherine Lamb, speaking of Lord Byron;
*Journal*, March 1812

No Lord can gain power without assistance. Sometimes that aid comes from allies in other tribes, but the best assistance comes from other Shadow Lords. Spies and mystics, warriors and leaders — a wide range of talents are required in any conspiracy. The diverse talents of the Shadow Lords are continually refined as they work to frustrate and overcome their rivals.

# Egotistical Spy

**Quote:** *Guess what a little Stormcrow told me? He told me you're going to die for your crimes, you egotistical son-of-a-bitch….*

**Prelude:** You've always been curious about what other people were really doing. As a small child, you delighted in finding places to hide where you could eavesdrop on other people's conversations. Then when Mommy and Daddy started fighting, you got really good at hiding and listening. Holding a glass against a wall when your mother was alone with her "friend," carefully picking up a telephone when your father was talking to his "friend" — you had an arsenal of little tricks to use. And when they sat down with you and lied to you about what was really going on, you learned that the only way to find out the truth was to uncover it yourself.

When you ran away with your new family, after the Change, you were eager to learn more about finding out the truth. From the time you were nine years old, the spirits were eager to help you perfect the art of silently spying on others. When you were 14 and you caught one of the elders kneeling before her Black Spiral lover, you really weren't surprised. Now you're 16, and as long as you carefully watch the people around you, you can make sure they never deceive you with their lies again.

**Concept:** You've grown up not trusting anyone, and you've lost all respect you've had for people with power. The only way they can be kept under control is if they're watched closely. Now *you* have power as well — the power to destroy the reputation of people who would betray your trust. What you decide to do with this information is entirely up to you. Still, when you want revenge against someone who's lied to you, the best people to help you are your Shadow Lord allies.

**Roleplaying Hints:** If you keep smirking, people are going to realize that you know things they don't. That's the way it should be. They'll respect your talents even more. Don't take anyone's status at face value. A little disrespect now and then is a good way to warn them not to betray what little respect you have left for authority. You're good, and you know it, so the only person you should *really* respect is yourself.

**Equipment:** Leather jacket (to make yourself look tougher than you really are), Swiss army knife (perfect for sabotage), tape recorder, expensive tennis shoes and butterfly knives.

# SHADOW LORDS

Name: _____ Breed: Homid _____ Pack Name: _____
Player: _____ Auspice: Ragabash _____ Pack Totem: _____
Chronicle: _____ Camp: _____ Concept: Egotistical Spy

## Attributes

### Physical
Strength_____●●○○○
Dexterity_____●●●○○
Stamina_____●●●○○

### Social
Charisma_____●●○○○
Manipulation____●●○○○
Appearance_____●●○○○

### Mental
Perception_____●●●○○
Intelligence_____●●●●○
Wits_____●●●●○

## Abilities

### Talents
Alertness_____●●●●○
Athletics_____●●○○○
Brawl_____●○○○○
Dodge_____●●○○○
Empathy_____○○○○○
Expression_____○○○○○
Intimidation_____●○○○○
Primal-Urge_____○○○○○
Streetwise_____●●○○○
Subterfuge_____●●○○○

### Skills
Animal Ken_____○○○○○
Drive_____●○○○○
Etiquette_____○○○○○
Firearms_____●○○○○
Leadership_____○○○○○
Melee_____●○○○○
Performance____○○○○○
Repair_____○○○○○
Stealth_____●●●●○
Survival_____●●●○○

### Knowledges
Computer_____●●○○○
Enigmas_____○○○○○
Investigation___●●●○○
Law_____○○○○○
Linguistics_____○○○○○
Medicine_____○○○○○
Occult_____○○○○○
Politics_____○○○○○
Rituals_____○○○○○
Science_____○○○○○

## Advantages

### Backgrounds
Resources_____●●○○○
Totem_____●●●○○
_____○○○○○
_____○○○○○
_____○○○○○

### Gifts
Aura of Confidence
Blur of The Milky Eye
Fatal Flaw
Persuasion

### Gifts
_____
_____
_____
_____
_____

## Renown

### Glory
●○○○○○○○○○
□□□□□□□□□□

### Honor
○○○○○○○○○○
□□□□□□□□□□

### Wisdom
●●○○○○○○○○
□□□□□□□□□□

### Rank
[        ]

## Rage
●●○○○○○○○○
□□□□□□□□□□

## Gnosis
●●○○○○○○○○
□□□□□□□□□□

## Willpower
●●●●○○○○○○
□□□□□□□□□□

## Health
| | | |
|---|---|---|
| Bruised | | □ |
| Hurt | -1 | □ |
| Injured | -1 | □ |
| Wounded | -2 | □ |
| Mauled | -2 | □ |
| Crippled | -5 | □ |
| Incapacitated | | □ |

## Weakness
FAILURE'S DAGGER:
-1 RENOWN FOR
FAILURE

Attributes: 7/5/3  Abilities: 13/9/5  Gifts: 1 Level One from breed, auspice and tribe; Backgrounds: 5;  Freebie Points: 15 (7/5/2/1)

# Cryptic Shaman

**Quote:** *Heh! Looks like rain. See those birds circling over there? That means it's gonna be a good 'un. Someone's gonna die.*

**Prelude:** You've always been a loner, a misfit who never quite fit in. Since the time you were a metis cub, you've been shunned by others. Your twisted leg only brought stares, and the safest thing to do was spend time alone. In the dead of night, you felt comfortable with the darkness around you. It hid your deformity. Sitting in solitude, as you descended into your morose meditation, you realized the Gift you had. You had an affinity with the night. The spirits of Raven treated you with respect, and you found communing with them to be quite easy.

Borne aloft by spirits of Raven, your journeys through the Umbra eventually led you to people of a similar disposition. They also loved the night, and your talent with the darker spirits made you one of them. They called themselves the Society of Nidhogg, and they sought revenge against those who dared to follow the ways of light and beauty. When you hobble in front of your sept, you're a disgrace, but as part of the cult, you've found glory.

**Concept:** Any pack will no doubt deign to accept you as a member. After all, you're a very capable Theurge. The simple tasks of your art come quite easily to you. You don't need to reveal how you obtain your information since it's easy to pass off your methods as your own "mystic ways." Occasionally, though, a member of the Society will contact you for aid, and your loyalty to them precludes any alliance you have to your pack. If you do well by them, they'll do well by you. Your complete lack of concern for your appearance makes you look like hell... but then again, you know all about hell, don't you?

**Roleplaying Hints:** Act humble around those who don't know your secret affiliations. It throws them off guard. For some reason, those who aren't metis consider your breed to be hopeless as well as deformed. Raven laughs at your deception and admires your talent. When you're with your pack, feign complicity with what they do. They'll expect you to be cryptic when you aid them. Later, when you're among allies, you can follow your darker instincts, and when, at the end of time, darkness falls upon the world, you will have the respect you deserve.

**Metis Deformity:** Twisted leg. Your difficulty in walking reduces any Dice Pool involving movement by two dice.

**Equipment:** Walking stick (usable as a club), black trench coat (to cover the extent of your deformity), black candles, white chalk and your "last resort": a .45 caliber pistol.

# SHADOW LORDS™

**Name:** _____
**Player:** _____
**Chronicle:** _____

**Breed:** Metis
**Auspice:** Theurge
**Camp:** Society of Nidhogg

**Pack Name:** _____
**Pack Totem:** _____
**Concept:** Cryptic Shaman

## Attributes

### Physical
Strength_____ ●●○○○
Dexterity_____ ●●○○○
Stamina_____ ●●○○○

### Social
Charisma_____ ●●●○○
Manipulation_____ ●●●●○
Appearance_____ ●●○○○

### Mental
Perception_____ ●●●○○
Intelligence_____ ●●●●○
Wits_____ ●●●○○

## Abilities

### Talents
Alertness_____ ●●●○○
Athletics_____ ○○○○○
Brawl_____ ○○○○○
Dodge_____ ●●●○○
Empathy_____ ○○○○○
Expression_____ ○○○○○
Intimidation_____ ●●○○○
Primal-Urge_____ ●●○○○
Streetwise_____ ○○○○○
Subterfuge_____ ●●●○○

### Skills
Animal Ken_____ ○○○○○
Drive_____ ○○○○○
Etiquette_____ ○○○○○
Firearms_____ ●●●○○
Leadership_____ ○○○○○
Melee_____ ○○○○○
Performance_____ ●○○○○
Repair_____ ○○○○○
Stealth_____ ●●○○○
Survival_____ ○○○○○

### Knowledges
Computer_____ ○○○○○
Enigmas_____ ●●●○○
Investigation_____ ○○○○○
Law_____ ○○○○○
Linguistics_____ ○○○○○
Medicine_____ ○○○○○
Occult_____ ●●●●○
Politics_____ ○○○○○
Rituals_____ ●●●○○
Science_____ ○○○○○

## Advantages

### Backgrounds
Rites _____ ●●●○○
Totem _____ ●●○○○
_____ ○○○○○
_____ ○○○○○
_____ ○○○○○

### Gifts
Create Element _____
Fatal Flaw _____
Spirit Speech _____
_____
_____
_____

### Gifts
_____
_____
_____
_____
_____
_____

## Renown

**Glory**
○○○○○○○○○○
□□□□□□□□□□

**Honor**
○○○○○○○○○○
□□□□□□□□□□

**Wisdom**
●●●○○○○○○○
□□□□□□□□□□

### Rank
[ ___ ]

## Rage
●●○○○○○○○○
□□□□□□□□□□

## Gnosis
●●●●●○○○○○
□□□□□□□□□□

## Willpower
●●●●●○○○○○
□□□□□□□□□□

## Health
| | | |
|---|---|---|
| Bruised | | □ |
| Hurt | -1 | □ |
| Injured | -1 | □ |
| Wounded | -2 | □ |
| Mauled | -2 | □ |
| Crippled | -5 | □ |
| Incapacitated | | □ |

## Weakness
FAILURE'S DAGGER:
-1 RENOWN FOR
FAILURE

**Attributes:** 7/5/3  **Abilities:** 13/9/5  **Gifts:** 1 Level One from breed, auspice and tribe; **Backgrounds:** 5; **Freebie Points:** 15 (7/5/2/1)

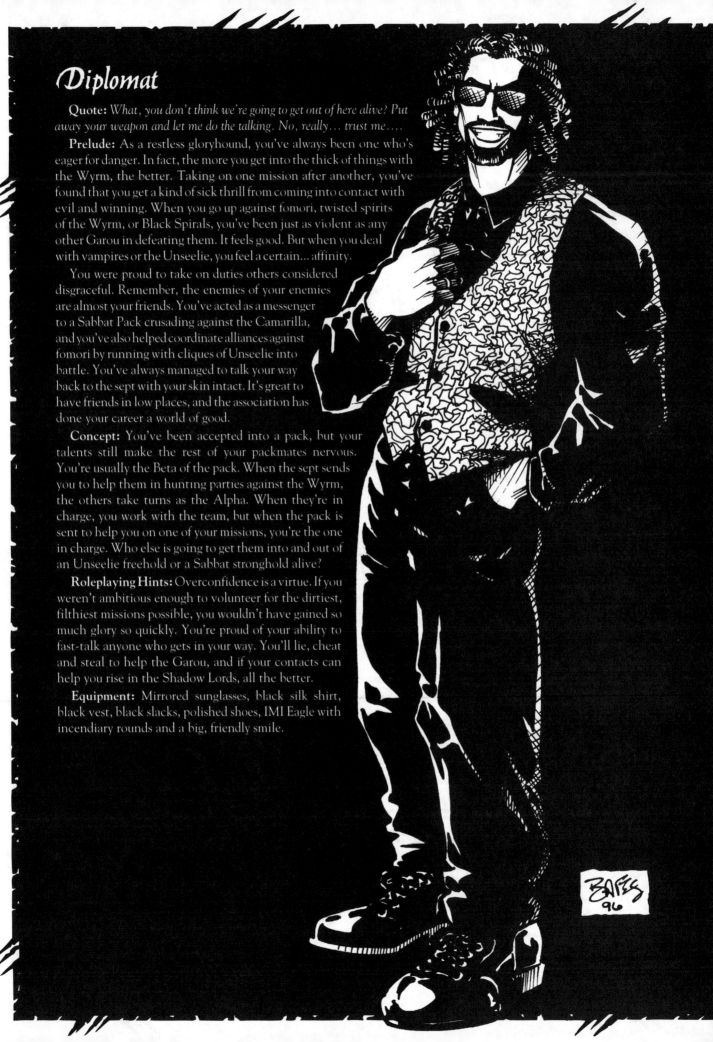

# Diplomat

**Quote:** *What, you don't think we're going to get out of here alive? Put away your weapon and let me do the talking. No, really... trust me....*

**Prelude:** As a restless gloryhound, you've always been one who's eager for danger. In fact, the more you get into the thick of things with the Wyrm, the better. Taking on one mission after another, you've found that you get a kind of sick thrill from coming into contact with evil and winning. When you go up against fomori, twisted spirits of the Wyrm, or Black Spirals, you've been just as violent as any other Garou in defeating them. It feels good. But when you deal with vampires or the Unseelie, you feel a certain... affinity.

You were proud to take on duties others considered disgraceful. Remember, the enemies of your enemies are almost your friends. You've acted as a messenger to a Sabbat Pack crusading against the Camarilla, and you've also helped coordinate alliances against fomori by running with cliques of Unseelie into battle. You've always managed to talk your way back to the sept with your skin intact. It's great to have friends in low places, and the association has done your career a world of good.

**Concept:** You've been accepted into a pack, but your talents still make the rest of your packmates nervous. You're usually the Beta of the pack. When the sept sends you to help them in hunting parties against the Wyrm, the others take turns as the Alpha. When they're in charge, you work with the team, but when the pack is sent to help you on one of your missions, you're the one in charge. Who else is going to get them into and out of an Unseelie freehold or a Sabbat stronghold alive?

**Roleplaying Hints:** Overconfidence is a virtue. If you weren't ambitious enough to volunteer for the dirtiest, filthiest missions possible, you wouldn't have gained so much glory so quickly. You're proud of your ability to fast-talk anyone who gets in your way. You'll lie, cheat and steal to help the Garou, and if your contacts can help you rise in the Shadow Lords, all the better.

**Equipment:** Mirrored sunglasses, black silk shirt, black vest, black slacks, polished shoes, IMI Eagle with incendiary rounds and a big, friendly smile.

# SHADOW LORDS

**Name:**      **Breed:** Homid      **Pack Name:**
**Player:**      **Auspice:** Philodox      **Pack Totem:**
**Chronicle:**      **Camp:** The Bringers of Light      **Concept:** Diplomat

## Attributes

### Physical
Strength ●●○○○
Dexterity ●●○○○
Stamina ●●○○○

### Social
Charisma ●●●○○
Manipulation ●●●●○
Appearance ●●●○○

### Mental
Perception ●●○○○
Intelligence ●●●○○
Wits ●●●●○

## Abilities

### Talents
Alertness ●○○○○
Athletics ○○○○○
Brawl ○○○○○
Dodge ●●○○○
Empathy ○○○○○
Expression ●●○○○
Intimidation ○○○○○
Primal-Urge ○○○○○
Streetwise ○○○○○
Subterfuge ●●○○○

### Skills
Animal Ken ○○○○○
Drive ○○○○○
Etiquette ●●●○○
Firearms ●●●○○
Leadership ●●○○○
Melee ○○○○○
Performance ●●○○○
Repair ○○○○○
Stealth ●●○○○
Survival ●○○○○

### Knowledges
Computer ○○○○○
Enigmas ○○○○○
Investigation ●●●○○
Law ●●●○○
Linguistics ○○○○○
Medicine ○○○○○
Occult ○○○○○
Politics ●●●○○
Rituals ○○○○○
Science ○○○○○

## Advantages

### Backgrounds
Contacts ●●●○○
Resources ●●●●○
_____ ○○○○○
_____ ○○○○○
_____ ○○○○○

### Gifts
Aura of Confidence
Persuasion
Truth of Gaia
_____
_____

### Gifts
_____
_____
_____
_____
_____

## Renown

### Glory
○○○○○○○○○○
□□□□□□□□□□

### Honor
●○●○○○○○○○
□□□□□□□□□□

### Wisdom
○○○○○○○○○○
□□□□□□□□□□

### Rank
[            ]

## Rage
●●●●●○○○○○
□□□□□□□□□□

## Gnosis
●●○○○○○○○○
□□□□□□□□□□

## Willpower
●●●●●○○○○○
□□□□□□□□□□

## Health
| | | |
|---|---|---|
| Bruised | | □ |
| Hurt | -1 | □ |
| Injured | -1 | □ |
| Wounded | -2 | □ |
| Mauled | -2 | □ |
| Crippled | -5 | □ |
| Incapacitated | | □ |

## Weakness
FAILURE'S DAGGER:
-1 RENOWN FOR
FAILURE

**Attributes:** 7/5/3   **Abilities:** 13/9/5   **Gifts:** 1 Level One from breed, auspice and tribe;   **Backgrounds:** 5;   **Freebie Points:** 15 (7/5/2/1)

# Romantic Poet

**Quote:** *How beautiful. How tragic. Perhaps I'd believe you more if you got on your knees…*

**Prelude:** You've always known you were beautiful. People have always been eager to tell you how attractive you are, and the ones who are envious of your beauty say that you've been spoiled by it. You're the epitome of grace and style. The poems you artfully compose are reflections of your own beauty. While you're modest about your poetry, you revel in your true talents.

Of course, it would be a shame if you didn't put that talent to good use. As a Shadow Lord, you know how to take advantage of the weaknesses of others, and loneliness is the worst weakness of all. How many people have shamed themselves for the sake of one torrid love affair? Whether the object of your praise or defamation is Garou, Kin or human, a few kind words and "meaningful" glances is all it takes to win someone over to your side… or condemn them to their own shame.

**Concept:** Let the others worry about what happens in war. You have different weapons. In your own sept, you are acutely aware of the real balance of power. Let them play politics — you have a keen insight to others that you gain from stories of their romantic dealings. You're not weak or cowardly — in fact, you can hold your own on the battlefield — but your real talents count on the only battleground that matters. The politics of disgrace require far more talent than the strategies of warfare.

**Roleplaying Hints:** Flatter members of the opposite sex to keep them off guard. You can feign any emotion to manipulate their weaknesses: remorse, shame, envy, adoration. Your masterworks draw from a vast palette, and every color is a shade of gray. You quickly evaluate what others desire and you can easily pretend to have what they want. Alone with one lover, you can be demure and innocent, yet with another, you can be forceful and demanding. And, of course, like any good Shadow Lord, you understand the intricacies of dominance and submission. You have power — use it.

**Equipment:** Leather and silk, a book of verse, a single rose and a pair of handcuffs.

# SHADOW LORDS

| | | |
|---|---|---|
| **Name:** | **Breed:** Homid | **Pack Name:** |
| **Player:** | **Auspice:** Galliard | **Pack Totem:** |
| **Chronicle:** | **Camp:** | **Concept:** Romantic Poet |

## Attributes

### Physical
Strength _____ ●○○○○
Dexterity _____ ●●○○○
Stamina _____ ●●●○○

### Social
Charisma _____ ●●●○○
Manipulation _____ ●●●●○
Appearance _____ ●●●●●○

### Mental
Perception _____ ●●○○○
Intelligence _____ ●●●○○
Wits _____ ●●●○○

## Abilities

### Talents
Alertness _____ ○○○○○
Athletics _____ ●●●○○
Brawl _____ ○○○○○
Dodge _____ ●○○○○
Empathy _____ ●●○○○
Expression _____ ●●●○○
Intimidation _____ ●○○○○
Primal-Urge _____ ○○○○○
Streetwise _____ ○○○○○
Subterfuge _____ ●●●●●

### Skills
Animal Ken _____ ●●○○○
Drive _____ ○○○○○
Etiquette _____ ●●●○○
Firearms _____ ○○○○○
Leadership _____ ○○○○○
Melee _____ ○○○○○
Performance _____ ●●●●○
Repair _____ ○○○○○
Stealth _____ ●●○○○
Survival _____ ○○○○○

### Knowledges
Computer _____ ○○○○○
Enigmas _____ ○○○○○
Investigation _____ ○○○○○
Law _____ ○○○○○
Linguistics _____ ●●●○○
Medicine _____ ●●○○○
Occult _____ ○○○○○
Politics _____ ○○○○○
Rituals _____ ○○○○○
Science _____ ○○○○○

## Advantages

### Backgrounds
Resources _____ ●●●○○
Pure Breed _____ ●●○○○
_____ ○○○○○
_____ ○○○○○
_____ ○○○○○

### Gifts
Aura of Confidence
Persuasion
Mindspeak
_____
_____
_____

### Gifts
_____
_____
_____
_____
_____
_____

## Renown

### Glory
●●○○○○○○○○
☐☐☐☐☐☐☐☐☐☐

### Honor
○○○○○○○○○○
☐☐☐☐☐☐☐☐☐☐

### Wisdom
●○○○○○○○○○
☐☐☐☐☐☐☐☐☐☐

### Rank
☐

## Rage
●●●●○○○○○○
☐☐☐☐☐☐☐☐☐☐

## Gnosis
●○○○○○○○○○
☐☐☐☐☐☐☐☐☐☐

## Willpower
●●●●●○○○○○
☐☐☐☐☐☐☐☐☐☐

## Health

| | | |
|---|---|---|
| Bruised | | ☐ |
| Hurt | -1 | ☐ |
| Injured | -1 | ☐ |
| Wounded | -2 | ☐ |
| Mauled | -2 | ☐ |
| Crippled | -5 | ☐ |
| Incapacitated | | ☐ |

## Weakness
FAILURE'S DAGGER:
-1 RENOWN FOR
FAILURE

**Attributes:** 7/5/3 **Abilities:** 13/9/5 **Gifts:** 1 Level One from breed, auspice and tribe; **Backgrounds:** 5; **Freebie Points:** 15 (7/5/2/1)

# Wandering Swordsman

**Quote:** *The Wyrm doesn't understand barriers of race or culture. It's everywhere, and I'll travel anywhere to fight it.*

**Prelude:** You have distant memories of your childhood in Kyoto. Your sensei was a warrior of the Hakken Garou, and he taught you the basics of his craft. You were destined to follow him and take his place, but he was disgraced by his rivals and cast out from the Eastern Concordiat. When you were still a cub, he took you with him to the West and taught you to be a master of the sword, and now that he's gone, you've vowed to follow in his footsteps and learn what he could not teach you.

**Concept:** You do not fully understand your spiritual home, and even worse, you may never be able to go back. Your true spirit is a mystery to you, and the deep sadness of Harano has begun to fall upon you. Your honor is now something you must find on your own. Your sensei held the Western Garou in contempt, but you would rather come to understand them as individuals than despise their culture. Because you feel an affinity to Grandfather Thunder, you often side with the Shadow Lords, but you also feel a slight shame about this. Your shame can only be assuaged by victories against the Wyrm.

**Roleplaying Hints:** You may be tempted to bear your pain stoically, but try to understand those around you. Find out about yourself but be understanding to others. You are a very private person, but you are still seeking to find one or two others of a similar disposition in whom you can confide. Although you are not comfortable with the Western Garou, you fight alongside them in battle. While you are removed from the intricacies of the Shadow Lord hierarchy, you feel the same anger they feel towards the rest of the Garou Nation. You may eventually ally with a pack, but in the end, your honor is your own.

**Equipment:** A black coat, blue jeans and a white T-shirt; a pair of Japanese *tabe* for your feet; a small pack with one or two books of Japanese verse; and a *katana* to embody the strength of your spirit.

# SHADOW LORDS

| | | |
|---|---|---|
| **Name:** | **Breed:** Homid | **Pack Name:** |
| **Player:** | **Auspice:** Ahroun | **Pack Totem:** |
| **Chronicle:** | **Camp:** | **Concept:** Wandering Swordsman |

## Attributes

### Physical
Strength●●○○○
Dexterity●●●●○
Stamina●●●○○

### Social
Charisma●●○○○
Manipulation●●○○○
Appearance●●○○○

### Mental
Perception●●○○○
Intelligence●●○○○
Wits●●●●○

## Abilities

### Talents
Alertness●●●○○
Athletics●●○○○
Brawl●●●○○
Dodge●●●○○
Empathy○○○○○
Expression○○○○○
Intimidation○○○○○
Primal-Urge●●○○○
Streetwise○○○○○
Subterfuge○○○○○

### Skills
Animal Ken○○○○○
Drive○○○○○
Etiquette●○○○○
Firearms○○○○○
Leadership○○○○○
Melee●●●●○
Performance○○○○○
Repair○○○○○
Stealth●●○○○
Survival●○○○○

### Knowledges
Computer○○○○○
Enigmas●●●○○
Investigation●○○○○
Law○○○○○
Linguistics●●○○○
Medicine●●○○○
Occult●○○○○
Politics○○○○○
Rituals○○○○○
Science○○○○○

## Advantages

### Backgrounds
FeTish●●●○○
Pure Breed●●●○○
_____○○○○○
_____○○○○○
_____○○○○○

### Gifts
Clap of Thunder
Smell of Man
The Falling Touch
_____
_____

### Gifts
_____
_____
_____
_____
_____

## Renown

### Glory
●●○○○○○○○○
□□□□□□□□□□

### Honor
●○○○○○○○○○
□□□□□□□□□□

### Wisdom
○○○○○○○○○○
□□□□□□□□□□

### Rank
[ ]

## Rage
●●●●○○○○○○
□□□□□□□□□□

## Gnosis
●●●○○○○○○○
□□□□□□□□□□

## Willpower
●●●●●●●○○○
□□□□□□□□□□

## Health
| | | |
|---|---|---|
| Bruised | | □ |
| Hurt | -1 | □ |
| Injured | -1 | □ |
| Wounded | -2 | □ |
| Mauled | -2 | □ |
| Crippled | -5 | □ |
| Incapacitated | | □ |

### Weakness
FAILURE'S DAGGER:
-1 RENOWN FOR
FAILURE

**Attributes:** 7/5/3  **Abilities:** 13/9/5  **Gifts:** 1 Level One from breed, auspice and tribe; **Backgrounds:** 5;  **Freebie Points:** 15 (7/5/2/1)

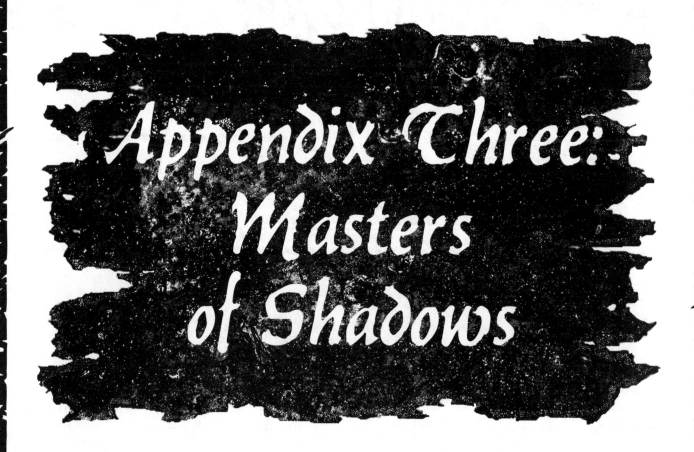

# Appendix Three: Masters of Shadows

## Septumus Dio

As a centurion serving under Emperor Trajan, Septumus Dio learned the arts of war and the way of conquest. His army moved into the northern territories of the Geto-Dacian Empire in A.D. 122 and subjugated the remnants of the Illyrian tribes in northern Macedonia. After these lands were conquered, he stayed behind with the local praetor to establish a Roman settlement.

The local proconsul was sent to this far territory because of his open criticisms of Emperor Trajan. While Septumus was a loyal soldier of the empire, he nonetheless admired his praetor's rebellious streak. Yet at the same time, as he continued to spend time with the local people of the tribe, he gained an admiration for their ways. Soon, he had begun a furtive affair with a young woman belonging to one of the local tribes. He was unaware that she was Kinfolk, yet she was not as innocent. A Kin-Fetch spirit had brought him to her, and she knew of his heritage as a Lord, even if he didn't.

Septumus grew increasingly disaffected with the proconsul's treatment of the local tribesmen. On the dawn before a raid was to take place against a religious ceremony in the hills outside of town, he underwent his first Change. Taken with the fury of battle, he stormed into the tent where his proconsul was drawing battle plans and savagely killed him. He never suspected that the caern they had raided was a Shadow Lord temple, and the troops he led never realized the true circumstance behind his taking power.

Yet Septumus' ascendance was successful, and he ruled over a Roman settlement caught between the demands of the Empire to the south and the needs of the Shadow Lord Kinfolk he watched over. His son then became proconsul after him, and as the son of a Garou and a Kinfolk, bred true with his father's gift. The Sept of Balance in Albania today is the result.

## Alexandru ThunderRage

In the shadow of the Transylvanian Alps, Alexandru ThunderRage led a campaign to force the rulers of the neighboring septs under his will. While the Ottoman Turks and Russian armies contested over his homelands, Alexandru expanded his sphere of influence. By treachery, assassination and subterfuge, he united five septs under his tyrannical rule. By repeatedly turning his would-be successors against each other, he maintained his power. He took the title of king, largely in mockery of the Silver Fang's traditional use of the honorific.

As his power grew, his problems increased. The consolidation of so much power in one place attracted the attention of a Tzimisce voivode in a neighboring district. Mikhail Dombrescu was a statesman among his people, and the power he had gathered in the north was centered in the territories of Transylvania. He proposed an alliance to solidify power, yet beneath his offer was the veiled threat of war.

Alexandru knew that forcing an alliance with the servants of the Wyrm on the septs under him would tear his lands apart. While he bargained for peace, he prepared for war. In the hills of Carpathia, he met privately with a group of emissaries from Mikhail's camp. As they negotiated, two of his Betas surrounded their meeting place with three packs of warriors and slaughtered almost all of Mikhail's negotiators. One survived to carry the ashes to the court of the voivode.

As his battles against Mikhail's armies raged, so did the hatred of King ThunderRage. Alexandru became known for his violent frenzies in the midst of battle. He began to see conspiracies against him everywhere, and Lords who were openly critical of his tyranny were known to mysteriously disappear. At the culmination of his victory at the Battle of Czyrny, he tore the throat from one of his Betas, the former sept leader of the Sept of the Brooding Sky. Garou whispered that Alexandru had been tainted by the Wyrm. Though none could prove it, the rumors remained.

As he continued his campaigns against the Wyrm, he found himself taken by the same madness and corruption that he himself fought. At the behest of his High Priest, he journeyed into the Umbra to seek wisdom. Alexandru's spiritual journey revealed to him the true source of his suffering. It was never the result of the conflict around him. As a Shadow Lord, he was well-acquainted with thriving in the midst of the tempest. The true torment came from within himself. The visions he experienced taught him that until he cleansed the taint of the Wyrm within himself, he would never purify the lands he ruled.

Alexandru returned a changed man. He forsook his rage for the pursuit of wisdom. By allowing his sept leaders to fight their own battles against Mikhail's armies, Alexandru gained their respect. While his reputation for cruelty ensured that none would dare betray him, his rewarding of the sept leaders who served him increased his power. He abdicated his position as King, and the five septs under him renewed their campaigns against the Tzimisces, the Turks and the Silver Fangs.

Alexandru ThunderRage journeyed alone into the Umbra one more time and never returned. He is said to have established another kingdom within the Legendary Realm. The epic poem of his journey through the Umbra and the wisdom he found there has since been passed from each generation of Shadow Lord Galliards to the next.

## Rasputin

Rasputin was a semiliterate peasant who rose to political pre-eminence in the court of Czar Nicholas II through a curious mixture of religious fanaticism and sexual stamina. His alleged ability to "cure" the hemophilia of Nicholas' heir apparent gave him power over Czarina Alexandra Feodorovna, who helped him become a courtier to the royal family. In turn, his influence over the czarina affected the political decisions of the czar.

As Rasputin hovered around the royal court, his allies carefully maneuvered themselves into political positions within the Russian government. Just as Rasputin served others, his political pawns were useful to Setites, Malkavians and others in the years that followed. When Rasputin's rivals finally unmasked part of this conspiracy, they began to plot his assassination. Shadow Lords claim that Rasputin would not

have been able to infiltrate the court of Czar Nicholas without the assistance of Gaia and Thunder, while some vampires posit that the clumsy assassination attempts that followed were merely a cover-up for his Embrace. Few actually know the truth of the matter. Nonetheless, Shadow Lord Galliards (and Ragabashes) have been known to tell and retell the elaborate legends and conspiracy theories of the true story of Rasputin.

## Boris Thunderstrike

The Thunderstrike Sept in Russia has been a stronghold of Shadow Lord alliance for generations. Over 25 Lords gathered there in the late 19th century as part of their resistance against the encroaching troops of the Russian Empire. Originally descended from emissaries to Catherine II, the dynasty of Shadow Lords who ruled there were a continual threat to the Russian Silver Fangs nearby. This was the heritage of Boris Thunderstrike.

While his family heritage would have ensured him a high-ranking position within the moots of his sept, Boris demanded the right to test himself through adversity by returning to the homelands. His wandering eventually brought him to the Sept of the Night Sky in Wallachia, where the Silver Fangs had held a tenuous hold over the caern for almost a century.

The local sept leader, Heart-of-Fury, was well-known for his hospitality toward traveling Garou. To his great amusement, he was even more well-known among the Shadow Lords for gloating to his guests of how the Silver Fangs had brought stability to the region, just as the Soviets had brought their own "stability" to the region.

Since Heart-of-Fury was powerful, Boris Thunderstrike petitioned to act as his Beta. While this public display instantly earned Boris Thunderstrike shame within his tribe, Heart-of-Fury knew he would be a fool to refuse the offer. In private meetings with the local shadow moots, Boris argued that it was his duty to support a strong leader. By convincing these disparate conspiracies to support him, he built an elaborate shadow moot that stretched across four countries.

Heart-of-Fury was certain that it was only a matter of time before he unmasked the treachery of his Beta. Ego, nonetheless, continued to motivate him to show off his position of power to visiting Garou. His egomania grew even stronger, and more powerful and promising visitors to the sept were recruited into the shadow moot. Soon, under the very nose of the esteemed Silver Fang, the sept became the center of an elaborate shadow campaign. From this vantage point, the success of the campaign was assured.

Heart-of-Fury's forced abdication marked a turning point in Shadow Lord history. The rewards that this Lord of the Summit received after acting as a Beta to a Silver Fang were well worth the risk. The Sept of the Night Sky is now a focal point in Shadow Lord politics, and the shame served to the Silver Fangs is now celebrated as an elaborate act of revenge.

# SHADOW LORDS™

| | | |
|---|---|---|
| **Name:** | **Breed:** | **Pack Name:** |
| **Player:** | **Auspice:** | **Pack Totem:** |
| **Chronicle:** | **Camp:** | **Concept:** |

## Attributes

### Physical
Strength_____●oooo
Dexterity_____●oooo
Stamina_____●oooo

### Social
Charisma_____●oooo
Manipulation_____●oooo
Appearance_____●oooo

### Mental
Perception_____●oooo
Intelligence_____●oooo
Wits_____●oooo

## Abilities

### Talents
Alertness_____ooooo
Athletics_____ooooo
Brawl_____ooooo
Dodge_____ooooo
Empathy_____ooooo
Expression_____ooooo
Intimidation_____ooooo
Primal-Urge_____ooooo
Streetwise_____ooooo
Subterfuge_____ooooo

### Skills
Animal Ken_____ooooo
Drive_____ooooo
Etiquette_____ooooo
Firearms_____ooooo
Leadership_____ooooo
Melee_____ooooo
Performance_____ooooo
Repair_____ooooo
Stealth_____ooooo
Survival_____ooooo

### Knowledges
Computer_____ooooo
Enigmas_____ooooo
Investigation_____ooooo
Law_____ooooo
Linguistics_____ooooo
Medicine_____ooooo
Occult_____ooooo
Politics_____ooooo
Rituals_____ooooo
Science_____ooooo

## Advantages

### Backgrounds
_____ooooo
_____ooooo
_____ooooo
_____ooooo
_____ooooo

### Gifts
_____
_____
_____
_____
_____

### Gifts
_____
_____
_____
_____
_____

## Renown

**Glory**
o o o o o o o o o o
□ □ □ □ □ □ □ □ □ □

**Honor**
o o o o o o o o o o
□ □ □ □ □ □ □ □ □ □

**Wisdom**
o o o o o o o o o o
□ □ □ □ □ □ □ □ □ □

### Rank
□

## Rage
o o o o o o o o o o
□ □ □ □ □ □ □ □ □ □

## Gnosis
o o o o o o o o o o
□ □ □ □ □ □ □ □ □ □

## Willpower
o o o o o o o o o o
□ □ □ □ □ □ □ □ □ □

## Health
| | | |
|---|---|---|
| Bruised | | □ |
| Hurt | -1 | □ |
| Injured | -1 | □ |
| Wounded | -2 | □ |
| Mauled | -2 | □ |
| Crippled | -5 | □ |
| Incapacitated | | □ |

## Weakness
FAILURE'S DAGGER:
-1 RENOWN FOR
FAILURE

**Attributes:** 7/5/3 **Abilities:** 13/9/5 **Gifts:** 1 Level One from breed, auspice and tribe; **Backgrounds:** 5; **Freebie Points:** 15 (7/5/2/1)

# SHADOW LORDS

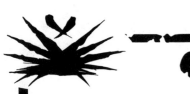

## Homid
No Change

Difficulty: 6

## Glabro
Strength (+2)_____
Stamina (+2)_____
Appearance (-1)_____
Manipulation (-1)__

Difficulty: 7

## Crinos
Strength (+4)_____
Dexterity (+1)_____
Stamina (+3)_____
Appearance 0
Manipulation (-3)__

Difficulty: 6

INCITE DELIRIUM
IN HUMANS

## Hispo
Strength (+3)_____
Dexterity (+2)_____
Stamina (+3)_____
Manipulation (-3)__

Difficulty: 7

## Lupus
Strength (+1)_____
Dexterity (+2)_____
Stamina (+2)_____
Manipulation (-3)__

Difficulty: 6

## Other Traits

_____ OOOOO
_____ OOOOO
_____ OOOOO
_____ OOOOO
_____ OOOOO
_____ OOOOO
_____ OOOOO
_____ OOOOO
_____ OOOOO
_____ OOOOO
_____ OOOOO
_____ OOOOO
_____ OOOOO
_____ OOOOO
_____ OOOOO
_____ OOOOO
_____ OOOOO
_____ OOOOO
_____ OOOOO
_____ OOOOO

## Fetishes

Item: _____ ☐Dedicated  Level ____ Gnosis ____
Power_____

Item: _____ ☐Dedicated  Level ____ Gnosis ____
Power_____

Item: _____ ☐Dedicated  Level ____ Gnosis ____
Power_____

Item: _____ ☐Dedicated  Level ____ Gnosis ____
Power_____

## Rites

_____
_____
_____
_____
_____
_____
_____
_____
_____
_____
_____

## Combat

| Maneuver/Weapon | Roll | Difficulty | Damage | Range | Rate | Clip |
|---|---|---|---|---|---|---|
|  |  |  |  |  |  |  |
|  |  |  |  |  |  |  |
|  |  |  |  |  |  |  |
|  |  |  |  |  |  |  |
|  |  |  |  |  |  |  |

### Brawling Chart

| Maneuver | Roll | Diff | Damage |
|---|---|---|---|
| Bite | Dex + Brawl | 5 | Strength + 1† |
| Body Slam | Dex + Brawl | 7 | Special |
| Claw | Dex + Brawl | 6 | Strength + 2† |
| Grapple | Dex + Brawl | 6 | Strength |
| Kick | Dex + Brawl | 7 | Strength + 1 |
| Punch | Dex + Brawl | 6 | Strength |

† These maneuvers do aggravated damage.

Armor: _____

# SHADOW LORDS

Nature: _____          Demeanor: _____

## Merits & Flaws

| Merit | Type | Cost | Flaw | Type | Bonus |
|-------|------|------|------|------|-------|
| _____ | ____ | ____ | ____ | ____ | _____ |
| _____ | ____ | ____ | ____ | ____ | _____ |
| _____ | ____ | ____ | ____ | ____ | _____ |
| _____ | ____ | ____ | ____ | ____ | _____ |
| _____ | ____ | ____ | ____ | ____ | _____ |
| _____ | ____ | ____ | ____ | ____ | _____ |

## Expanded Background

### Resources
_____
_____
_____
_____
_____

### Pure Breed
_____
_____
_____
_____
_____

### Contacts
_____
_____
_____
_____
_____

### Past Life
_____
_____
_____
_____
_____

### Kinfolk
_____
_____
_____
_____
_____

### Pack Totem
_____
_____
_____
_____
_____

## Possessions

Gear (Carried) _____
_____
Equipment (Owned) _____
_____

## Experience

TOTAL: [          ]

Gained From: _____
_____

TOTAL SPENT: _____
Spent On: _____
_____
_____

## Sept

Name _____
Caern Location _____
Level _____ Type _____
Totem _____
Leader _____

# History

## Prelude

_____
_____
_____
_____
_____
_____
_____
_____
_____
_____
_____
_____
_____
_____
_____
_____

# Description

Age_____

Hair _____

Eyes_____

Race_____

Nationality_____

Sex_____

|       | Height | Weight |
|-------|--------|--------|
| Homid |        |        |
| Glabro |       |        |
| Crinos |       |        |
| Hispo |        |        |
| Lupus |        |        |

_____
_____
_____
_____
_____
_____
_____

_Battle Scars_ _____
_____
_____

_Metis Deformity_ _____

# Visuals

_Pack Chart_                        _Character Sketch_

# TWILIGHT RUNNING

DAMN! GOOD AND CORNERED . . .
GOT TO BREAK FOR THE UMBRA!
*SHE'LL* BE WAITING, OF COURSE. IS IT WORTH IT?
MAYBE IF I . .
WHAT AM I THINKING? BETTER HER THAN THEM!
I'M *THROUGH!*

STORY BY ETHAN SKEMP                    ART BY STEVE PRESCOTT

SET'S TEETH, I WAS ALMOST THROUGH PITTSBURGH, TOO. I SUPPOSE THAT'S WHAT I GET FOR TRUSTING ONE OF THOUSAND-TALES' SHORTCUTS.
WELL, I HAVEN'T LOST TOO MUCH TIME. BETTER MOVE QUICKLY. AT LEAST I'M GOOD AT THAT.
PLEAZE... PLEAZE LIZZEN TO ME...
PLEEAZZE...

3

6

The Long and Haunted Road

By Ethan Skemp and Robert Hatch

# Credits

**Authors:** Ethan Skemp and Robert Hatch

**Additional Egyptian research and guidance:** Ellen Brundige

**Developer:** Ethan Skemp

**Editor:** Ken Cliffe

**Vice President in Charge of Production:** Richard Thomas

**Art Directors:** Aileen E. Miles and Lawrence Snelly

**Layout & Typesetting:** Aileen E. Miles

**Art:** Andrew Bates, James Daly, Anthony Hightower, Matt Milberger, Alex Sheikman & Jack Keefer

**Comic Book Art:** Steve Prescott

**Cover Art:** Joshua Gabriel Timbrook

**Cover Design:** Aileen E. Miles

## Special Thanks

**Ken** "Bad Neighbour" **Cliffe**, for indulging in the traditions of fun, frolic and liquid patriotism.

**Rob** "Slatzcha" **Hatch**, for preferring Sascha Vykos to Fatima al-Faqadi — eeeww.

**Phil** "Seven Days My Ass" **Brucato**, for having a little difficulty in recreating the universe.

**Ian** "Blind" **Lemke**, for unintentionally missing the massacre of Noisy, Barmy and Irresponsible.

**Rich** "Zorak" **Dansky**, for his dedicated work for Mantis Civil Rights.

**Ethan** "Slavering Urbanite" **Skemp**, for becoming nostalgic for cow manure and weedwhacking.

**Ronni** "No Spellcheck, No Service" **Radner**, for throwing up some much-needed barricades.

**Cynthia** "Strong Female Protagonist" **Summers**, for being the center of a fantasy game in entirely too many respects.

735 PARK NORTH BLVD.
SUITE 128
CLARKSTON, GA 30021
USA

WHITE WOLF
GAME STUDIO

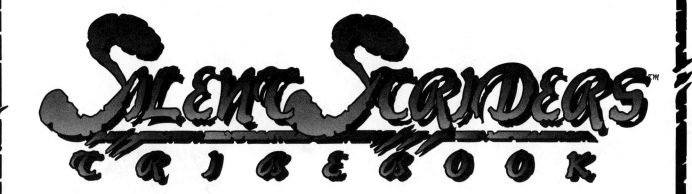

# Contents

# Introduction: First Steps

*Wealth I ask not, hope nor love,*
*Nore a friend to know me;*
*All I ask, the heaven above*
*And the road below me.*
— Robert Louis Stevenson, *Songs of Travel*

Well, so you finally caught up with me! Good. That's always a good sign in a young cub. Let me tell you, you aren't done walking yet.

So the elders told you what you are, eh? And then they told you there weren't any Silent Striders living at their caern? There's a surprise for you. Well, then I suppose your education's left up to me. I prefer to talk while I'm walking, though. I hope you had a drink of water before you started chasing after me.

Look around. You see the pines stretching over the road, the brown water in the ditches, the gravel holding the road dirt down, the rail fence over there? Take a good look. This is your inheritance. Not these lands, not that stand of trees over there — the sky and the roads, that's what your sire and dam left you. Open sky above and dirt road below. Take

a deep breath now, because not all roads are as pleasant as this one. But they're yours regardless, whether you want them or not.

Once night falls, it'll turn into a different sight entirely, too. Luna watches over you from above, but her light'll stretch the shadows out until you see fomori under every tree. They did teach you about fomori before they sent you after me, didn't they? Thank Gaia for small favors.

Once it becomes night, we'll do our walking on wolf paws. Human senses just can't cope with the road in darkness. We can also run faster that way, and believe you me, we very well might have to. Let your hackles down, cub, I never called you afraid. But somewhere along the road, you probably will be.

# Chapter One: Dust

*Teach him what has been said in the past; then he will set a good example to the children of the magistrates, and judgment and all exactitude shall enter into him. Speak to him, for there is none born wise.*
— Ptahhotpe, *The Maxims of Ptahhopte*

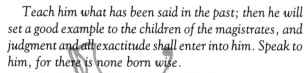

Thirsty already? I could use a drink myself. Come on, there's a stream about half a mile up ahead. We'll run.

Stop your complaining and pick up your paws! We'll rest when we're there!

## Beginnings

Ahh. It tastes good, doesn't it? Better than any water you'll draw out of a tap, because it's there to quench you after you've traveled. Pure water is the surest sign of Gaia's love that I know. Fouled water — well, that'll put you in a killing mood soon enough.

All right, now I'm in the mood to talk. Now hush up and listen, for the urge doesn't strike me often.

Sit and cool your feet in the stream, and I'll tell you the first Strider story.

## The First Descent

You see, back in the oldest times, the Garou hadn't split up into tribes yet. We were all one, even if we didn't always get along. Our differences weren't great enough to push us apart into tribes just yet, but it was getting there. If you could walk back to the First Times and spy on a moot of those Garou, you could probably tell a thing or two about who would sire what sort of cubs. The eloquent moot leader with a white coat? Probably a foremother of the Silver Fangs. Her rival, the intense Ahroun keeping to himself? Likely his six-times-great-grandchildren would be calling themselves Shadow Lords. The lupus radicals howling their arguments in favor of the Impergium? Red Talons-to-be, to be certain.

Now, the world wasn't always as we know it. Once matter and spirit were one — no Gauntlet, no Umbra, just one world where death was nonexistent and to name something was to define it. Then the Severing came. Some say when the Wyrm turned from balance to corruption, its pained thrashings tore the worlds of matter and spirit apart. Others say the Wyrm caused the Severing the instant it was born. According to our tales, however, the Severing came toward the end of the Impergium. We still aren't sure what caused it. But no matter what the explanation, everything was changed. It took the Garou a bit to adapt, but they did.

Well, back then death was still a fairly new thing to the world. Nobody really understood it all that well, but they knew it was a natural thing, and that was good enough for them. For most of them, anyway.

Before the Severing, you see, if something was destroyed it could simply rebuild itself. Desire and form were one and the same. But with the rise of the Gauntlet, a dead Garou was gone forever, after a fashion. You can probably imagine the mourning that came after the first battles with the Wyrm. Parents and children were gone, their bodies inert matter. The Theurges were only taking their first steps in the Umbra as we know it, and they had no idea where Garou spirits went after death. Why would the spirit of a mother abandon her cub?

One Garou asked all these questions, and refused to stop asking them. The elders didn't know the answers; the humans and wolves were even more ignorant. She made up her mind that the Severing had made the world very confusing, and that the spirits of the departed were just lost. With that, she made up her mind to go find them and lead them back.

She left her pack behind, and walked into the woods. She walked for a long time in the physical world, and then she walked for a long time in the Umbra. Finally, she sat and rested under a spreading tree, and an owl came and rested in the tree's branches.

"Where do you travel, daughter?" the owl asked. "There are many new roads in the world, and surely you do not seek to walk down them all."

"No, owl," she replied. "I am looking for the spirits of my parents, who have been lost since they went for a walk with that newcomer that the elders have named Death."

"Ah!" cried the owl. "Why, I have seen them. But they walked down the darkest road of all, and have not returned."

"Well," she said, standing up, "I must go and find them, then, and lead them back. Can you tell me the way, owl?"

The owl ruffled his feathers, and replied, "I can. But you are likely to become lost, for you cannot see in the dark as well as I do."

The young Garou shrugged. "Perhaps so," she said, "but neither can my parents. Please tell me which way they traveled, owl, for I miss them and want to see them again."

"You are a stubborn one," complained the owl. "If you still feel you must follow them, then I will go with you to show you the way." And with that, he took flight.

The young Garou thanked the owl, which is proper and polite, and set out after him. He was a swift flyer, however, and it was all she could do to keep up. She took the wolf form for speed, and still she had to run as quick as possible to keep the owl in view. It was a long, tiring run, and as they turned onto the darkest road, she had been stretched out long and lean.

Now, the road the owl had guided her to was unlike any road in the new-formed Umbra. It led down and down, and as she walked along it, the countryside she passed was leeched paler and paler, until there was no color in it at all. The only color she could see was the burning yellow of the owl's eyes. But she kept on down that road until they came to a great gate made from a dark, glassy stone. There the owl rested on a gate pillar, and she made to open the gate.

The gate was locked, however, and a great black spirit arose from the ground as she touched the handle. In a voice like a rockslide in a hollow well, it demanded to know her business.

"I have come to find the lost spirits of my people's families," she replied. "You must undo this gate, for it likely confuses them and prevents them from returning to us."

The great midnight spirit laughed, and asked, "Why must I do that? They have died unready, and have brought nothing to appease me. What will you offer to persuade me to open this gate?"

The young Garou quietly opened her chest and drew forth her heart. Amazed, the spirit dropped to its knees before her and took the heart in its hands. Its tongue carefully flicked over the still-beating heart, tasting its virtue. Finally, the great black spirit shook its head and placed her heart back in her chest, closing her skin back as if new.

"Your heart tastes of life, young one," it sighed. "It is a taste I rarely sample, and it is far too rich for me. I will open the gates for a short time, and those who wish to follow you home may do so. However, I must close the gates again, so they had best be quick."

With that, he opened the gate wide, shouting, "Run! Those of you who would see the sunlit world again, run!" The owl took wing as well, crying, "Run, young Garou! If you would lead your kin home, run!" And so she ran, and as she ran back up the darkest road, she felt the presence of spirits at her back.

But when she reached the physical world again, she was almost alone. Most of the human spirits had been afraid, and never passed through the gate. A few did run with her, but couldn't keep up. These were stranded between one world and the other, and became the first wraiths.

The Garou spirits that followed, however, kept up. Among them was her father, who said, "We cannot stay long, child. The rules are no longer the same, and Gaia will be angry if we defy Her will. But your courage has showed us the way back here. Now, should you call, we will return to advise you for a short time. And so shall you return to advise your descendants, and so on until the End Times."

And just as he had promised, the Garou spirits ran from the Umbra to the young seeker's caern, laughing and calling to their children. But the young Garou who had brought them back only walked quietly after them. Some of her people were startled to see her, for her travels on that road had stretched her lean and strong, and the Dark Umbra had stained her coat a deep black. From that day, she spoke little of what she had seen. And yet she would often return to that one tree in the Umbra, and Owl would come and rest in the branches, and they would talk.

# The Impergium

Ahhhh. This water feels damn fine, doesn't it? Tell you what, since I'm feeling so flat-out chatty, I might as well pass on a little more of our history.

Have they told you of the Impergium yet? Some tribes look on it as the glory days of the Garou, the time when all was right with Gaia. Never mind that the Wyrm had already uncoiled and sunk its fangs into our hearts. No, what mattered back then was that the humans knew their place. And if you listen to the Talons, the Impergium was a failure because we didn't take it far enough and exterminate our human kin!

Here. Just close your eyes and think about it. Let's say that there's a small camp of humans, with ragged skin tents and some meager, smoky fires. Their best spears are made of sharp flint strapped to the straightest wood they can find. Now let's say that one of the young women has just given birth to twins. Twins! Why, they celebrate that sort of thing these days, don't they? Imagine how proud your sept would be now if you walked back to the caern one evening with twins in your arms — Kinfolk, or maybe even Garou.

Oh, it wasn't cause for celebration during the Impergium. That was a sign that the humans were getting just a little too fertile. Sure enough, a Garou would have to see that one of the humans died. Maybe one of the newborns — that would be fair, wouldn't it? Maybe one of the clan elders — why not kill the firemaker? That should keep them in their place. As long as you're at it, why not kill the mother of the twins for the crime of making too many

humans? Or her mate, one of the clan's most promising hunters?

Now I won't lie to you and say that the Impergium was something unnatural or wrong to Gaia. Not on its own terms, it wasn't. Spending some time in the wild should teach you that well enough. Look at the way the lions and hyenas of Africa go to war. They kill one another's cubs out of spite easily enough. And yet both species have lasted for years on top of years. It's hateful, cruel business, but it's the way things are.

No, what was unforgivable about the Impergium was the sheer idiocy of such a practice. Not just idiocy, but hypocrisy! Did we cull the wolves to make sure they wouldn't run amok and someday tear Gaia apart? No. We lived among them, guided them, helped them. And all the while we battered and abused the other half of our kin, the humans. Actually, I shouldn't say "we" — even back then, our thousand-times-great-grandparents saw the foolishness in the killings. Why were the Garou so surprised when our abused cousins became abusive? We hardened their hearts, set them against their Mother and her animal children. We raised the Veil, unknowingly destroying our chances of ever being able to fully share a world. In their Rage, the Garou of so long ago made a terrible mistake. And now our Mother suffers from our error.

Come on, let's get walking again.

# The War of Rage

As long as I'm opening old wounds, I might as well tell you of our other great failing. When we appointed ourselves humanity's keepers, we set ourselves above all other sons and daughters of Gaia. Not all skin-changers wore the pelts of wolves, you see. We knew of the Children of Cat, Cobra and Crocodile — there were others, too. But pride told us that we were first in the eyes of Gaia, and in our pride we fell on our shapeshifting siblings.

Of course, we had the advantage of numbers. After all, Gaia had crafted us to be her warriors — it was only natural that we'd win a full-scale war against the others. Our Changing Breed cousins were all but exterminated, and only a few survived. These days, we know that at least three races have died out completely. Funny how it wasn't them who started the War, isn't it?

Anyway, once both the Impergium and the War of Rage had ended, the tribes split. Everybody was bitter as hell about the way things had worked out. So groups of like-minded Garou each selected a territory or human culture to watch over, and went their separate ways. As for us, we selected a just-beginning-to-blossom group of humans, a newborn civilization that lived along a great river.

# The Land of Khem

Egypt.

Now, be patient, listen to my ramblings, and you'll learn something.

It's a hard thing, remembering how it was thousands of years ago, but we remember anyway. Egypt

was ours. Even if we forget the details, the whys and whats, Ibis is always able to remind us.

Too many times, I've heard thoughtless humans or even Garou scoff at the land that was once ours. Desert, they think, and promptly dismiss Egypt as a homeland worth having. They don't know anything. Our homeland was a fertile strip of vibrant green between the great red deserts. Red and green — that's what we still say where others mean "black and white." The green was ours, but we also walked freely in the deserts. The sands were the place of spirits, Set's place. You recognize his name? God of darkness, they called him. It wasn't too far from the truth.

But I'm getting ahead of myself.

The Egyptians were a culture fascinated with death, true. Some of that was our influence. Once the Impergium had ended, we freely walked among the people of the Nile. We were careful not to rend the Veil, but our Kinfolk knew, and many others remembered the killing nights. Look at the paintings of Anpw and Heru, the beast-headed gods. You don't recognize the names? Hmph. In Greek they came to be known as Anubis and Horus. Ah, now you know who I'm talking about. You see, some spirits remember the old names of the gods, and many Seekers have delved into human libraries deep enough to unearth the old truths. It's hardly necessary to know the old names, but it's respectful.

Those were rich, full times. The Nile gave us the most fertile, giving land in all the deserts, and the people were full of love and vigor. Morbid? Not the people of the land of Khem! "Eat, drink and make merry, for tomorrow we shall die" — that was Egyptian philosophy, cub. They invented the phrase! You see, they figured that the Duat, the underworld, was a green place. So if you worked hard, played hard, and went to your judgement with *ma'at* in your heart, then you were sure to spend eternity as happy as you were in life.

Damn. If only.

Well, we've seen the Shadowlands of the dead. For most folk, it's a far cry from what the Egyptians called the Duat. But the underworld's a big place, and Anpw and Tehuti's court may still exist somewhere down there. That's why we have to keep to *ma'at*.

I can already hear your question: What's *ma'at*? All right, listen closely. *Ma'at* is all things true, just and balanced. It's the force that our Philodoxes strive for, the law tempered in justice. It's many things, just as the ankh is many things as well as life. *Ma'at* is part of your heart, the purity of soul that all Garou should pursue. You see, once the Wyrm itself was a force for *ma'at*. But with its turn to corruption, that job fell to us Garou. Do you see?

Here, think about this old legend. A man dies, and prepares to enter the Duat. Anpw takes him by the hand, and escorts him to the hall of Maati, where the dead man is judged. If his heart is light and pure as the feather of *ma'at*, he is worthy and may pass on. If not, he's cast to a soul-devouring beast.

A clever metaphor, isn't it? We Garou were appointed by Gaia to shepherd the humans, to teach them. If they don't learn the ways of *ma'at*, then the Wyrm devours them forever. Now, the problem is that our fellow tribes, even our tribesmates, are falling from the grace of *ma'at*. If they don't learn otherwise soon, they'll be lost. That's why we Striders travel among them, reminding them of what they're meant to do. We could be more successful, too, if we hadn't been split and scattered by the false gods, the ancient vampires of Egypt.

## Set and Osiris

Our undoing always comes back to these two. Ancient and terrible, they were, and if only we'd slain them when we'd first met! For these two, I prefer the Greek words — keeps things simple, and they don't deserve the respect of the true names. Osiris and Set. Damn them both to Atrocity, they were the ones who cast us out.

Set was the lord of the desert, the red king of Upper Egypt. Osiris was master of the delta, Lower Egypt. Now the two of them hated each other for any number of reasons. For one, both wanted control of the whole country. But most important was that Osiris was an ascetic, which was highly uncommon in those days. He hated the corrupt part of being a vampire, and all the temptations thereof. Naturally, Set represented everything he despised — red and green, like I said. So the two went to war, with all their cold-fleshed minions for soldiers.

We didn't much care for either side — would you want a Leech reigning over your land? But of the two, Set stank far worse of the Wyrm's fetid touch. So we slew the children of Set when we encountered them, and picked off the occasional follower of Osiris. After all, we reasoned, when one was destroyed and the other weakened, we would be able to drive the survivor from our lands. We also learned of the mummies during the war. No, not bandage-wrapped lurching corpses, but immortals created by ancient

ritual. One such was Horus (not Heru, mind), an ally of Osiris and his sorceress wife. When Osiris fell beneath Set's power, Horus took up the banner. Their midnight war lasted for thousands of years while we quietly went about our business.

Finally, Horus was driven out and Set was triumphant. Foolishly believing him weak and unprepared, we threw ourselves at him. But by this time, the Dark One had created his own bloodline of vampires, descendants that drew their power from rot and depravity. We fought hard, but it wasn't enough. Set had grown vile and strong in the long years, and he was able to beat off our attacks. While we slew his children by the hundreds, he learned the names of our greatest heroes. Names, you know, hold great power. And with that power, he doomed us all with the most powerful curse that has ever been spoken.

*"By the names I have spoken, O Lupines, I curse you. I place my mark upon you, that you shall be forever severed from thy dead fathers and mothers. I damn you with my touch, that never again shall you rest in the lands of thy people. May the names of your ancestors be forgotten, and may their ghosts fade from hunger in the Duat. As I was cast out, so then shall you be exiled, voiceless and lost forevermore."*

And that was it. Somehow Set marked us, the whole tribe, with his vast power of corruption. Not one of our ancestors has ever come to the aid of a descendant again. Some say they journeyed deep into the Umbra, and there found Ancestor-spirits of our tribe, but I don't know what to think of those tales. Personally, I don't know if I could face one of my many-times-great-grandparents. Better, I figure, that I don't feel the loss even worse than I do now.

## Scattering

Our exile marked the end of our tribe as a concentrated group. Ten thousand roads led in ten thousand directions, and so we went our separate ways.

Some of us went into Africa. There we ran with the jackals and dealt with the human tribes, but very carefully. After all, the other shapechangers still held sway in Africa, and the wounds we Garou had dealt them were still sore. The culture there was quite to our tastes, but our ancestors had to dodge a few werecats to trade knowledge with the humans.

A few tried tracking the Croatan, Uktena and Wendigo, to see where they'd traveled. We never heard from these ones again.

Many traveled to the East, where they traded riddles with Stargazers or walked the high mountains. It's here that we met the Romani, and began our long association with them.

And some trailed the Greek invaders back to Europe. That's when we struck our first friendly relations with the Black Furies, and that's where we watched the rise of a whole new empire.

## Rome and Christendom

Too much law stifles a place. The Roman Empire was so caught up with its own self, with its glory and power, that it was hardly a fit place for us. They say Romulus was suckled by a she-wolf — well, if that was true, he would have surely wept to see what his city became. Now, we didn't avoid Rome entirely. No, there's been a Strider or two nosing about almost any human society since Egypt. But we'd be damned before we'd walk the Empire in numbers.

Even when the Christians took over Europe, the continent wasn't to our tastes. So we wandered the back roads, dealt with the local tribes and generally watched quietly from the shadows. If we had any influence at all in Europe, it only came when we returned in greater numbers with the Gypsies.

## The Gypsies

Our association with the Gypsies has nothing to do with what you might think. Their name's just that — a name. Other folk called them the Ægyptians, or Gypsies for short, but the Romany had nothing to do with the land of the Nile. No, we adopted them and bred with them because we recognized kindred spirits among the humans. I'm sure you've heard the stories of how they were cursed to wander forever, or maybe how they were blessed by the God of the Cross for stealing a Roman nail. I don't know if some of these stories came to be after the Rom began dealing with us, or if these stories were what drew our ancestors to them in the first place. My personal feeling is that they reminded us of our Egyptian relatives. After all, both groups were thoroughly devoted to enjoying themselves in this world and whatever came after. A love for life and an interest in death — the two aren't exclusive, you know. Whatever the reasons, we'd found more Kin. Our association continues even today.

And so some of us traveled with the Rom caravans into India, and back to Europe again. I think one of every four Striders that I've met over the years was

born to Gypsy parents, but that's hardly a scientific count.

Anyway, we returned to Europe in numbers (such as they were) when the Gypsies traveled there. Of course, we scattered again just as soon as we got there. Some of us took note of the Renaissance, and followed the rise of learning with interest. Others prowled around the fringes of European society, dealing with rebels and outcasts. A few even went into the bustling cities, there marking the rise of the Weaver and the taint of the Wyrm. We reestablished our feud with the vampires around this time, and more than one city night saw outright bloodshed between Garou and Leech.

## Colonialism

When the Europeans learned of a New World, it naturally caught our interest. To many, it was the promise of a new home. Surely in that vast continent there would be room for a vagrant tribe.

Not hardly. The Garou that first made the journey found that our lost cousins, the Uktena, Wendigo and Croatan, had claimed rights to the continents. Well, he choked back his disappointment and parlayed with the locals. He even made peace of a sort with them, and agreed to act as a go-between for them and the European tribes.

But then the other tribes arrived on the American coast, hungry for new territory. Sure enough, it was war again. But it was a long, slow war of attrition, one that the Pure Ones were doomed to lose. When the Croatan vanished, we were one of the few tribes to weep.

I wish I could say that we never did the Pure Ones any wrong, but it just isn't true. Many of the Wayfarers took English money and Silver Fang fetishes in return for scouting out the local caerns. A few more Striders stepped places they shouldn't have and unsealed things that should've remained sealed. That's our shame, and the rest of us are still trying to make amends for it. I hate to sound like a Child of Gaia, but we need to have the Uktena and Wendigo fighting alongside the other tribes. But when you don't travel in numbers, it's hard to be taken seriously. And so the few of us that were there could only watch as things worsened.

Even worse, it happened all over again in Australia. And this time, one of the Garou tribes was completely exterminated. I can only imagine our ancestors helplessly watching, seeing the whole story unfold again, powerless to stop it.

# A Changing World

Giving you a history lesson of the last few centuries would be ridiculously long-winded. We were everywhere, so what's to say? We saw the Gnawer Kinfolk turn the British away at Bunker Hill and were chased by the ghosts swirling around Madame Guillotine. We slipped behind Napoleon's lines, and we watched the Boxer Rebellion fail. Even if a Strider wasn't present for some great war or cultural shift, there was another one along later to sift through the spirits and learn what had happened. The Fianna pride themselves on being Garou lorekeepers, but we make it our business to know as much as possible about everything. Our knowledge is the only possession that can't be taken from us.

Of course, there were a few times and places that were of particular interest to us. And in at least one case, we're one of the few tribes who dares to remember what happened.

## The Old West

We came to the Americas in ones and twos, and most of us showed up during the 1800s. Curiosity compelled us to meet our long-lost cousins in the Pure Lands, and so we tiptoed into their territory to see how they were doing. Not so well, it turned out.

You'll never hear most tribes talk about the Old West. Truth be told, most would just as soon forget about the events of those days. Nowhere else was the fighting between European and native Garou greater. Damn few would listen to reason; no, they kept brawling over caerns and ambushing one another. Only we would pass between the sides, trying to teach them and learn from them as well.

Whew! You'd never have believed the Umbra in that place and time, either. Wyldlings went tearing across the Umbrascape, ripping into whatever Weaver or Wyrm spirits they came across. It was a stormy, furious mess. It was only the coming of the Storm Eater that got the tribes to act together as they should have. Even today, no tribe that isn't a Pure One will talk about what happened. Most were too ashamed to tell their children that they helped unleash the Storm Eater, and the secret died with them.

Now, their story isn't mine to tell, but in 1890, the Storm Eater was gone. Unfortunately, the Wyld's hold on the West was broken during the struggle. There are still wild spaces out there, but malls and convenience stores clot the land, same as everywhere else. One Seeker I talked with once told me that in the quiet time that followed the Storm Eater's passing, Pentex itself was born. Some victory, eh?

## Into the 1900s

Let's go back to Egypt for a bit. The Victorian era and the turn of the century saw a lot of change along the Nile, not to mention the rest of North Africa. Some of us were there when the English began gutting the tombs of our ancestors, but they weren't able to stop the unearthing of the Boy Pharaoh.

The opening of Tutankhamen's tomb changed things for us. Suddenly, Egypt was popular among the Europeans and Americans. They began to flock to the Nile's banks, looking for souvenirs and photographs to carry home. Locals would dig up their ancestors, hawking the foreparents' bones to curious whites. One relic after another found its way to Britain, there to sit behind glass as sightseers wandered past. Look at the influence that Egyptian culture had on Western architecture and art of the time.

Things changed in the Dark Umbra, too. As all the interest in dead things swept the living world, the Deadlands were stirred by the new tides of sentiment. You see, the Restless are creatures of passion. It's emotion that holds them to existence, and emotion that fuels their powers. Not only that, but the Dark Umbra is just as much a reflection of the physical world as is the Middle Umbra. That's why there are places where you never want to step into the Dark Umbra. Think about the spiritual mirror-image of a battlefield or concentration camp, and what it might look like. Whatever you can imagine, the real thing is probably worse.

As you can probably guess, the First World War had a pretty strong effect on the Dark Umbra. It would be nice to say we were shocked by the level of slaughter, but a lot of Striders were just plain resigned. We'd seen our share of human wars, and this one was just as pointless as all the others. The only thing that was different was the scale.

As I was saying, there was a lot of European interest in Egypt, and it didn't slow down for some time. A lot of archaeologists, amateur and otherwise, took it upon themselves to do more digging than ever before. It was a race to see who could drag out the most ancient gold or the most unusual bones.

We took it upon ourselves to keep the bones of the dead buried. Nothing howls louder than a hungry wraith whose goods have been stolen, you see. Be-

sides, we did it out of respect for the dead. More than one ancient chief's burial curse came true, if not the way he'd expected, as his tombrobbers fell beneath Strider claws.

## The '30s

In the 1930s, when the Depression squatted in America, pretty much the whole world went bust. If you take a look at the pulps, you can tell that most considered this an adventurous time. Now, you already know enough about this world to realize that the "great white adventurers" weren't all they were put up to be. What do you expect? Nobody would have bought pulps based on ragtag cliques of minorities, Anglos and foreigners.

From what I understand, though, it was a strange time to be alive. Hitler's madness had already infected Germany, and the Nazis were stirring up likeminded evils from all over the globe. There was a secret revival movement among occult-minded humans, and little good was coming of it. And, of course, archaeologists kept rabidly tearing up whatever tombs they could find. The end result was that

there was a lot that needed doing, in all manner of distant places. And with our penchant for being where the action is, we had our work cut out for us.

## World War II

We had few enough kin at the time the Second Great War began, and fewer when it ended. Many of us heard the thunder before the storm, and stayed well clear of Europe for the war's duration. That was a mistake. Hitler's ethnic purges lashed out at the Gypsies like no other persecution of the Rom throughout history.

We had no choice: We had to go into Germany. Cub, if ever you want to know what the war was like, then step into the Umbra and wander over to Atrocity. While the Get of Fenris tore at each others' throats, we slipped into the back streets and shadows, doing what we could to get our Kinfolk out.

One or two of us made the mistake of entering the Umbra to sneak inside the concentration camps. In some places, you can still hear the echoes of the screams.

# The Apocalypse

Here's the worst part: No matter how hard our past has been, it's nothing compared to what's ahead.

Who do you think Phoenix brought the Prophecy to? Not the Fangs, no matter what they say. It wasn't the Furies, despite their claims that they're the keepers of every scrap of important mystic lore. No, it was one of the Garou that was a Strider before there were Striders. We're the keepers of the Prophecy, and have been ever since Phoenix first spoke those words a mountain's lifetime ago. We're the prophets, the oracles, the seers of the days to come.

And a long time ago, Phoenix showed one of our ancestors the Eighth Sign. The end of the final battle.

Easy there, youngling. That's not something you learn the whole of until you've walked a lot more miles than you have. I'll say this much, though: It's not pretty. In fact, it's pretty damn grim, but there's still room for a touch of hope yet. Once you've proven you can keep a secret, we'll teach you the words that we've handed down from parent to cub for centuries.

But you'd better be able to keep that secret. Can you imagine what would happen if the Get of Fenris discovered we knew the truth about Ragnarok? And if we told it to them, and they didn't like the answer? I'd bet my *d'siah* that they'd figure we were lying to them, just to lower their spirits. And you don't have to be Klaital Stargazer to figure out what would happen next.

That's why you have to be able to keep a secret. Remember, whatever truth you learn, or whatever rumor you find, you have to think carefully before you share it. *Ma'at* is a hard thing to carry, and not everybody is prepared shoulder the burden. Pick your friends carefully. Teach them to keep secrets. And keep in mind that they don't have to know everything you do.

# Further Lessons

Come on then; we still have a ways to travel, and you still have a lot to hear before we set you on your own road. Enjoy it while you can — we're at our most talkative when we're instructing cubs like you. So if you miss something the first time, you'll probably have to figure out some way to learn it on your own. I hate repeating myself, and so do most of our kin. Try to keep up.

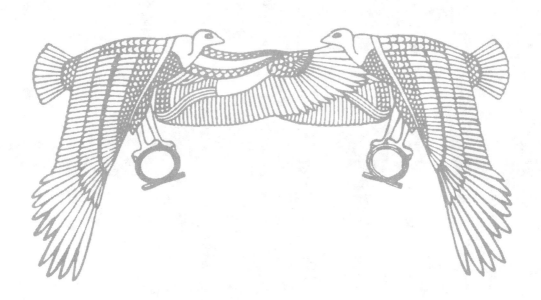

# Chapter Two: Shared Roads

Where'er we tread 'tis haunted, holy ground.
— Lord Byron, *Childe Harold's Pilgrimage*

You're not hallucinating, cub, that's music you hear up ahead. There's a camp of Gypsies just down the road; from what I can hear of the songs, they're Kinfolk. Sounds like they knew we were coming. I wouldn't be surprised if there are one or two other Striders just "dropping by" tonight, either. It'll be good to exchange some quiet words with tribemates.

I've rambled long enough. It's time somebody else did the talking.

## Moots

*For solitude sometimes is best society,*
*And short retirement urges sweet return.*
— John Milton, *Paradise Lost*

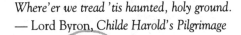

Welcome, young one. I am Aset Speaks-for-Many, Galliard to the Silent Striders. For the past ten turns of the seasons, it has been my satisfying duty to instruct young cubs in the ways of our tribe. This is, I presume, why your elder companion has brought you here.

Do the music and dancing distract you? Would you rather be among the young ones around the fire than listening to the words of a gray-haired Garou woman? If you would prefer, you may dance. Go and celebrate with the others, and I shall keep my dusty wisdom to myself.

No? And why not? No, don't tell me. I can already see why. You want to revel, but you feel set apart from the dancers. Although they'd let you join in, you wouldn't feel truly welcome. And not just that, either — were you to pass the evening enjoying yourself, you wouldn't get a chance to hear a few secrets.

You're a true Silent Strider, you are. This is what attending moots is often like for us, particularly moots held by a mix of tribes. While the others posture, brawl and howl to Luna, we wander from elder to elder, gathering lore and news. The Fianna would call it lonely business, but would they really welcome us to their drunken dances and wild hunts? No. We are the walkers on the outside, and the role suits us well.

Ah, but our tribal moots are an entirely different story. I have attended only three in all my years, and I am no more standoffish than the next Garou. We meet very infrequently. But when the Striders gather in numbers, it is the finest of things.

We have few caerns to call our own. Thus, most of our moots are held far from wide roads, often on a forgotten bald or remote stretch of plain. It takes a long time to gather all

the Striders in the area. Can you imagine? The only way to find most of us is by happening across one of our trails, or by chance meeting. The last moot I attended was called three years before it convened. Even then, some arrived late.

The other tribes would be astonished were they to see a Silent Strider moot. You may have noticed that we only speak freely among ourselves. Look at your guide over there, by the fire with that young man. Neither one would converse so casually with a Get of Fenris or a Wendigo. But among one another, we… well, we don't become verbose, but we do talk openly.

## Of Tales

Now if you want to listen to the finest stories of a moot, you'll have to learn something of our other languages. You see the dancer there, the one with the blue sash? Watch her carefully. She is telling a story, weaving a dance-tale. That is the *Pakiv Swatura*. The closer you watch her, the more of the story you will see. Look at her energy, her passion. She leaps as lightly as a hare, and twists as would a leaf in a dust devil. And yet every step, every gesture is a word. See? She tells of heroism and wonder, of open sky and swift running. Were the Fianna to see her, they would likely gnaw at their wrists with jealousy. You see, we are not always somber!

It looks exciting, does it not? Perhaps she will agree to teach you something of the art. Once you have the time, that is. Best learn to walk first, then to dance!

We have another custom of talesharing, but this one is much simpler. In fact, you will likely be expected to participate when you attend your first moot. If one of the Striders begins a ridiculous, comical tale, pay attention. This is the *Darane Swatura*, told simply to bring humor to a dark night. You will be expected to carry on the tale, adding to it and improving upon it. The tale only ends when all present are clutching at their sides, weeping with laughter.

It is the height of excellence to weave a true story into the *Darane Swatura*, distorting it until it is outrageously impossible and intolerably funny. Of course, it is equally admirable to tell as patently incredible a fiction as you can. And why not? With the *Darane Swatura*, we laugh at ourselves as hard as we can. We have little other time to do so.

Even a splash of color can tell volumes to another Strider. If you see a red berry stain smeared on a rock, that can mean that danger is nearby. Green is our color for safe haven and peace; blue means purity, innocence or *ma'at*. These associations are as old as our tribe, and come from our Egyptian roots. By simply wearing a scarf of a certain color, we can communicate wordlessly amongst ourselves, even at a Shadow Lord moot. Remember! Knowledge is priceless, and quiet communication is an art of the highest order.

# The Forgotten

The music's loud and fast tonight. Listen. When one fiddler tires, the next picks up the tune as quick as he can. Nobody wants to listen to the empty air between songs tonight.

No, cub, I grew accustomed to silence a long time ago. All of us have, and so will you. But sometimes it is painful to gather with others of the tribe on a still night. You see, our gatherings can remind us that we are all we have — the Striders still alive are the only ones we can reach. In losing the spirits of our forebears, we have lost almost all of our past.

Whenever we gather, not one of our ancestors is with us. The air may be filled with ghosts, but they aren't kin. Set's curse saw to that. Even after millennia, we still feel the loss as a tribe. It colors even our moots. Most times we simply carry on quietly, but not always. Tonight we sing, dance and play.

# Totems

As a tribe, we have run into the Umbra more times than any other. We have also made many allies there. As a Silent Strider, you may well walk under the blessings of many different totems in your day. While you are young and strong, you are a fine child of War, appearing from nowhere to cut at your enemies and then vanishing again. Once you have trod many lands, then perhaps your focus shall shift. With maturity comes Respect, and the example you set may guide those who watch you run. True Wisdom will come when you are honed by experience.

But who am I to name the direction in which your paws will take you? The spirit allies of our tribe know you as well as you know yourself. Look within, and your totem will meet your gaze.

# Owl

Great Owl is a most selective guardian, and admits only the wisest into his broods. Is it any wonder that we have access to secrets of which even the Stargazers and Uktena know nothing?

We are as one with Owl because that is the way things should be. Tell me, do you know of any bird that flies more silently, or sees more in the shadows? Owl knows the ways of death and the Dark Umbra; his wisdom has guided those of us who have walked the paths of the Underworld. His eyes reflect all things, and yet he keeps counsel with very few. He is master of the night and the things that run through it.

My first pack ran under Owl's protective wings. He lent us his eyes, and I saw countless things I would not have otherwise seen. He lent us his quiet, and I ran swift as lightning, the sounds of my passing as soft as a lazy snowfall.

And he lent us his wings, and in the Umbra, I flew. Now I serve a different totem, but I am still a Silent Strider. My heart will always be dedicated to Owl, and I shall always remember.

# Ibis

Ibis is a wise and perceptive bird, and he remembers much. We remember his old name of Tehuti, and he graces us with his stories of the past. Ibis holds the power of memory, which he shares with Crocodile, and holds the power of *ma'at*. Ibis grants us long memories and strong minds; his wings spread over our thoughts and lend them strength. Many Seekers pay homage to Ibis, and he will never let them forget their knowledge.

# Crocodile

Even we have our Totems of War. Our greatest is Crocodile, the lord of the rivers. Crocodile counsels us to wait and bide most quietly, but his anger is pure and terrible. He enjoys being called Sebek, as it is by this name that our ancestors and their Kin knew him. Crocodile has a long memory, and remembers any slights done to him or his children. Although other Garou may disdain you if you ally yourself with him, you may find you have other allies of a most… unusual cut.

# Scarab

There is power in knowledge, and therefore those who learn many ways are greater for their learning. Scarab teaches patience, a wise lesson for any of our kind. She is a builder, and at the same time her tunnels can bring down fortresses. Always the key is patience. If you choose to follow Khephra the Scarab, she will lend you such quiet diligence that no knot nor maze will hinder you.

# Sphinx

We Striders speak with Totems of Wisdom even more enigmatic than Owl or Ibis. One such is Sphinx.

Some years ago in Mexico, my pack was pursued by Black Spiral Dancers. We slipped into the Umbra and scattered, the better to avoid our enemies. I myself ran deep into the spirit world, pausing neither for food nor rest. I had no idea where I ran — to this day, I could not show you the paths I took. Finally, I came upon a scene from the land of Khem itself.

Faceless humans toiled in the fields. Chariot-soldiers brandished reeds at one another, while spears sprouted from the riverbanks. The sun shone with cold light, while the moon burned with fire. Then I saw a lion, with the face of a human neither man nor woman. Its gaze fell on me, and a question sounded in my mind. *"Are you lost, cub?"*

I awoke in the physical world, curled inside a forgotten caern of the Uktena. The rest of my pack lay around me, still asleep. I have been Sphinx's child ever since.

## Tsetse Fly

Each tribe has its lost and angry. And although most of us spend our Rage in the full and furious way that Gaia intended, a few bottle it up. These ones wither away to mere skins covering hate and maliciousness, almost as bad as the Wyrm-dancers we fight against.

The bitter ones sometimes call on Tsetse Fly. She's a wise old totem, but she's spiteful. She embraces the Striders that turn to her as if they were her grandchildren, as any totem should. But she makes for a horrible, vindictive crone of a grandmother. If anyone crosses one of her adopted kin, she demands that her young ones repay the offender in blood. Tsetse Fly may not be of the Wyrm, but she's not a clean one. Best to avoid her and her grandchildren, lest you wind up with a curse on your back simply for failing to say "good evening" in a properly fawning tone.

Well, I've spoken my piece. Excuse me — I believe I'll dance for a bit now.

# Solitude in Numbers

Hey, cub, you waiting for Aset to get back? Don't bother; she's pretty much done. Talking, at least.

Name's Lerli Moonless-Sky. Sit back, relax, I won't bite you. Your traveling companion asked me to stop by and have a few words with you. Always good to get more than one perspective, you know. Besides, any one of us can only talk for so long without getting antsy. Hope there's room in that head for some more learning tonight, because I'm not staying with you to answer more questions tomorrow morning.

Well, what do you know? You're an attentive one! Good. Now, pass me a beer from that ice chest, and I'll share some of what I've learned.

## Kinfolk

Well, as you can see from our celebration here, even we have Kinfolk. But our Kin are a lot fewer and farther between than those of the other tribes. We are related to so many bloodlines, so many ethnicities, you see — from Arab and African to Indian and the rare Anglo. No Strider could possibly keep track of all our blood relations, but we do our best to remember who's wandering where.

And I do mean wandering! Our Kin are circus performers, vagabonds, nomads, grifters… our wandering habits rub right off on them. At least we have something in common. In fact, the best thing about circus Kin is that they often keep wolves with them, as part of some act or another. Oh, there are a few sedentary Kinfolk families as well, but rumor has it they don't breed true quite as often.

They say it's part of our curse — I figure that's just pessimism talking.

## The Rom

But of all the ethnic groups we breed with, we're most often associated with the Gypsies. No wonder — we're kindred spirits. A cub like me that's born into a Romani family grows up learning history by remembering stories. It's a lot easier to carry a library in your head than on your back. Even if a *kumpania* is only Kin, it feels something like family.

But I'll tell you to be careful. For one, a Strider who's not of the Blood will likely be treated like any other *gaje* when she comes calling. Some Romany Kinfolk allow you to marry into the family, but only if you're a true Strider. Second, many of the Gypsy families have nothing to do with us. And why not? Many of us Striders are born of other folk.

Now, the trick here is that there are some vampires roaming the world that claim Rom blood. *Shilmulo*, we call them. And some Gypsy families — the Ravnos, for instance — don't so much mind allying with the dead. Watch out, cub, or you might find yourself sharing a campfire with a Leech who wants to sample Garou blood. Although you won't be coming to blows while you're with the *kumpania*, you'd better watch your back after you leave. No amount of family relation is going to dim the hate between Garou and vampire.

## Camps

The camps that have formed within our tribe aren't so much societies or factions as they are mindsets. We're not given to gathering frequently, so a camp is a philosophy you agree with and carry out. You can still find allies among members of your own camp, but you'll tend to only run into them randomly. Old news, hey?

## Harbingers

Well then. It would almost do them disrespect to toss out their name and open up their philosophies just as a coroner dissects a slab of cold meat. Anyway, you should learn a thing or three about them, because one might save your life someday.

Some say that the Harbingers were the first Garou to take the Prophecy of the Phoenix seriously. They gathered together, spoke words that none but the Harbingers remember, and split up to wander the far corners of the world. There they found Wyrmsign, and began to carry the news back. But the nearer they drew to the caerns of their brothers, the more Wyrm-taint they noticed. In their initial travels, they saw so much of the Wyrm's tracks that they still aren't done telling the Garou of all the dark places. I've also heard that they believe the Apocalypse can't be staved off — but that Gaia, like Phoenix, will rise

again from the flames. And so their role is to help others fight back the tendrils of the Wyrm. But most of all, they bring hope.

Of course, these are just stories. The dead-certain truth is that they're among the wisest of all Garou, and if one tells you to jump, your feet had damn well better leave the ground before she draws breath again.

## A Harbinger Cautions

*Your Caern Warder speaks falsely. The Wyrm is coiling at your doorstep, and has its fangs in the hearts of your own Kin. If you would cut it from their breasts, then go ye to the campground upon the river and find the minions of the Wyrm that rest there.*

## Seekers

We're all Seekers, in some form or another. Human society doesn't hold much for us; Garou society is just as bad. So the only option left is to pack your bags and find your own way.

An old friend once told me that the mind carries far more than a thousand broad backs. He was a Seeker, of course. He didn't need any journal or tape recorder to recall what he'd learned — no, his memory was good enough for him. He had most of the traits I've come to associate with the camp: clever, resourceful, inquisitive and stubborn as all hell. If you want to learn something specific, your best bet is to find a Seeker. If she doesn't know it herself, she can tell you where to look. The Harbingers may know what's to come, but the Seekers hold the lore of what's happened and what's happening now.

## A Seeker Reminisces

*Whew. How was Russia, you ask? Just as damned miserable as I thought it'd be. Toward the end of my visit, I slipped into a local chantry to do a little reading. The residents chased me all the way to the Kunlun Shan, which was another horror story in and of itself. I'd ask what the world's coming to, but I already know the answer, dammit.*

## The Dispossessed

I can't help but be concerned with the Dispossessed. Their members are trying nothing harder but to settle down. The problem is that there's nowhere for them to go. This is something we Gypsy-bloods are well used to, but even so we sympathize. In fact, some Striders of the Rom join the Dispossessed, figuring that they deserve a home both from their human blood and Garou heritage. It never works, though. Something — be it human settlers, territorial Garou or the Wym's touch — always forces them to move on.

This eternal rejection must affect them in some way. I spent time among a few, and they gave off the stale scent of Harano. You don't smell it at first — but once you've shared

company with one for a month or so, you pick it up. They're as morbid as they come. Maybe that's why they study all about the Apocalypse. Like carrion crows, they watch for the portents and croak out warnings to those who'll listen. They always seem to be right. But the Final Days are moving so quickly now, their advice always seems to be too little, too late.

## A Dispossessed Snarls

*We have wandered long enough! Even the man-children of Israel now have a home, and we faithful of Gaia must still meander from caern to caern? No, I tell you, no.*

*You were wise to ally yourself with us. Once the Apocalypse is at an end, then we shall have a land to call our own once more. Of course, the sooner it begins, the sooner our victory shall come. Here, listen to my plan....*

# Wayfarers

Now, these ones really raise my hackles. There's no place for their breed of selfishness among our tribe. The very idea of looking at our war as a profit opportunity — hrrr, the Wayfarers need to grow up fast. Of course, that won't happen any time soon. The other tribes want access to our talents, but don't enjoy dealing with most of us. They understand the Wayfarers, though. Greed isn't respectable, but it is comprehensible. Your average Shadow Lord probably looks on the Wayfarers as cousins!

I have to admit they're a talented group. Once a Wayfarer gives you a guarantee that she'll run your message for you, she'll do it. They avoid giving out guarantees, though, unless they're certain the job is well within their skills. Such assurances also cost extra.

There are actually a few in this camp who look on their task as a duty and not a career. These runners are an honorable lot, and are said to have long-standing ties with the magi. They'll even forego asking a fee, if they figure the job's a good one that needs doing. Unfortunately, most Wayfarers argue that they need to ask for payment, in accordance with the "way things are." These folks argue that just as you should offer chiminage to a spirit in exchange for favors, you should present payment to a Garou willing to do you a service. I figure this is going too far.

## A Wayfarer Bargains

*Whoa! Easy there, friend. No need to get huffy. I'm just following one of the oldest of Gaia's laws, y'know? It's pure and simple. I'll drop that chunk of jade into the Abyss for you, and you pass over that medicine pouch. I help you — you help me. What could be fairer?*

# Secret Societies

We're a solitary and taciturn lot. The other tribes never truly accept us, and we don't have enough of our own to satisfy some of our children. So a few Striders start turning inward, gathering with others and sharing their discontent. The two most famous of these groups are hardly tolerated by tribe elders. If anyone from these societies approaches you about joining them, stall for time. Then when you've got your opportunity, run. Better to walk alone than waltz arm-in-arm with a friend into the Wyrm's maw.

## Eaters of the Dead

One of the most gruesome reasons that we're associated with the dead is the Rite of Dormant Wisdom. Now, our ancestors figured out fairly early that the brain is the seat of knowledge. Thing is, they decided that by eating the brains of humans, they could gain a measure of the humans' knowledge. They were right.

Now, right after our exile, some of the more foresighted elders saw that this rite was a sure way to open ourselves to the Wyrm. They declared the rite taboo, citing the Litany to back up their ruling. So we stopped — all of us, that is, but the Eaters of the Dead. They kept on devouring human brains, in even more secrecy this time. They've grown learned over the centuries, but they've begun to smell strange. If we find one, we gift him with the Voice of the Jackal, and warn him to change his ways. Other tribes would do worse.

They've been getting worse of late, if you believe the rumors. They say that a cult of Eaters has been carefully preying on the Leeches, attempting to learn the secrets behind vampiric powers and influence. Of course, once you kill a vampire for good, the corpse returns to the state it should be in for its age. And naturally, the most knowledgable vampires are the really old ones. So these Leech-Eaters basically stake their prey, or immobilize them some other way, and pry out their brains while the Leeches are still conscious. Think about that for a while. You'll probably agree that some knowledge isn't worth the learning process.

### An Eater Reassures

*There, there, my friend. The worst of your hurting is behind you now, yes? Of course it is. Rest easy. I do apologize for what I'm about to do, but be assured that you are going to participate in one of the greatest of our sacraments. You might find it a bit gruesome, but I'm sure that you've encountered worse in your own studies. You see, I've wondered about your type of magic since the first time I heard of your ilk. I wish I could ask a few questions of your chantrymates, but the social morés of our*

*respective kinds rather forbid it, don't they? Not to worry — the Rite should do nicely.*

*Ah, here's my bone saw. Shall we?*

## The Bitter Hex

Then there's the Bitter Hex. They keep their names secret, but they don't hide their existence. The poison's gotten into them pretty fierce. You see, the Hexers are so ill-natured and spiteful at this point that they've taken it upon themselves to avenge all the slights the Striders have suffered over time. No, they aren't some violent terrorist cell like some of those Fianna you occasionally hear about. The Hexers' favorite weapon is the curse, the evil eye, the bad mojo, the *amria*. Cross one of them and you're likely to take a sending that'll twist your guts into knots and leave you puking and feeble as a cub for a week. They're a dangerous mob. They say they're acting on our behalf, but with cousins like them…

### A Hexer Snarls

*So, the mighty conqueror has bested the mongrel Strider, has he? Well, savor your victory this night, for you'll know no peace on any other. By my blood, spit and tears, I swear my Rage'll drive you mad by the next moon. Ptui!*

# Breeds

*Live with wolves, howl like a wolf.*
— Russian proverb

## Lupus

In the times of old Egypt, we had a strong lupus population. Some say that we bred with the black jackals or wolves of North Africa, the ones that you can only see today in hieroglyphs and ancient paintings. Without our protection, they vanished. I sought after their spirits in the Umbra, back when I was young. I never found them. Some Theurges I've met claim to have found the lost ones' spirits, but they're gone in the flesh. You can still see their features, though; our purest-bred tribemates often resemble their distant wolf ancestors.

Our lupus blood is much thinner now. We breed when the opportunity is there (with quality mates, mind), but the truth is we've few packs to call our own. Recently, though, some of the packs have birthed wolf cubs that resemble our lost kin, if only a little. Now most of us are willing to do whatever we must, even bargaining with the Shadow Lords and Get of Fenris, to gain hunting grounds for these wolves. No tribe can survive losing its wolf blood. We have to preserve our kin.

## Metis

Sigh. We breed where and when we can; few of us have the luxury of traveling with Kinfolk. I won't burden you with theories and excuses, but sometimes the partner you never see again is Garou. And believe it or not, occasionally we even fall in love with other werewolves. Anathema though it may be, I'm sure you know how difficult it is to deny your feelings.

What this is leading up to is that we have a healthy metis population, so to speak. It's nothing we're proud of, but Garou is Garou. Our metis pups have inherited fewer blessings and a harder road than the rest of us, but they don't deserve ill treatment for it.

## Homid

What can I say about those of us who are human-born? What haven't you guessed already?

Most homid cubs of our tribe don't grow up in what Middle America would consider an "ideal family environment." The majority only ever know one parent; many even believe themselves orphans until a Strider comes to collect them. We homids are the most numerous Garou, and at the same time those born farthest from Gaia's mysteries. Perhaps this is why we Striders choose outsiders, nomads and recluses as our human mates. The children born to such lifestyles begin life free of many of civilization's conventions. They don't grow up slaves to materialism and scientific rationality, and so their Garou nature comes easier to them.

Yes, loneliness also comes easier to them… us. But we're better prepared to deal with solitude. We do not offer the solace of numbers (and many of our tribe would reject such consolation), nor a true home, but we can give a child learning.

# The Litany

Even we have rules. The Litany is the oldest code of laws, older even than the pharoahs' reign or the firstborn laws of Sumer. Not all of the Litany's laws suit our tribe, but we must respect its authority. Learn the tenets and wear them in your heart.

That said, you should also realize that nothing is perfect. The Litany cannot foresee the infinite situations that we encounter just by being alive. The world is vastly different than it was in the days of the Impergium; human society has evolved to a point where it would be unrecognizable to our ancestors. I'm sure that the hoary Silver Fangs and the Fianna lorekeepers would tell you that the Litany is inviolate; if the subject ever comes up with them, smile, nod quietly and say absolutely nothing. They'll either assume you agree, or they'll be driven crazy by your silence. Neither is that bad an option.

news from sept to sept, you're going to end up crossing somebody's territory without permission. Many Garou shrug their shoulders and let us pass; they know we're not exactly looking to move in. The rest are considerably less understanding. My advice is to run quietly, cub; what they don't know can't hurt them, at least in this case.

## Accept an Honorable Surrender

Most Garou would rather be throated than yield to a Silent Strider, so "honorable" surrenders are few and far between. Still, it's a good rule, and one that should be upheld. We werewolves aren't getting any more common….

## Submission to Those of Higher Station

Respect your elders, cub. They've been places you can't imagine and have outrun things you wouldn't believe. Most importantly, they know things. And the only way they'll share their learning is if you treat them with respect! Now, I'm not saying you have to offer your throat to every senile Silver Fang who's feeling testy and imperious, but you should always watch your elders carefully. Pretty soon, you'll figure out who's full of hot wind and who's got the wisdom you'd damn well better attend to.

Why yes, cub, I'd love another beer. Thoughtful of you to ask.

## The First Share of the Kill to the Greatest in Station

This is sheer courtesy, and a right-thinking leader will keep the loyalty of his packmates in mind. Some among us tend to pocket certain goods taken from fallen enemies, not bothering to let their elders know. This goes double for valuable information: coded messages, maps and the like. I don't know about the other tribes, but if I found out one of my packmates was keeping secrets from me, I know I'd be downright enraged. Something to think about.

## Ye Shall Not Eat the Flesh of Humans

We're not one of the tribes that frequently gets carried away with bloodlust. Now, I said before that we used to ritually devour humans to gain their strength and knowledge. From what I know, it's true, but that doesn't make it acceptable. Humans and wolves are not prey animals for Garou, and that should be the end of that.

## Garou Shall Not Mate With Garou

I'll be honest with you: It gets lonely on the road. Sometimes you'll find yourself being — well, a little less careful than you could be. We Striders accept this, but other tribes often won't be as understanding. Still, for all the intolerance and condemnations, a lot of Strider metis have the blood of a second tribe in their veins.

## Combat the Wyrm Wherever It Dwells and Whenever It Breeds

Common sense forbids that we follow this rule to the letter. We're far more useful to Gaia if we find all the places where the Wyrm dwells and breeds, and then let the local Garou know what they're overlooking. Somebody's got to point out the soft underbelly to the Ahrouns, right? We're scouts, not shocktroopers — let those full of piss and hellfire do the bulk of the killing. Our task is just as vital.

## Respect the Territory of Another

Ahem. We can't exactly keep to our own lands, can we? If you go looking for truth under every stone and carrying

# Respect for Those Beneath Ye — All Are of Gaia

You are our future. If you live long enough to see your own cubs draw breath, you'll understand. We're bound to instruct you just as you're bound to obey us. Extend respect both above and below, and you'll be all the better for it.

# The Veil Shall Not Be Lifted

This is pure common sense. Life's difficult enough without the rank-and-file of humanity learning we exist. It doesn't matter how long you're going to be in a given place — do *not* let the locals find out about your true nature.

This even applies to the Gypsies, most of the time. Some families know of our existence and are Kinfolk like any other. If you're of the Blood, then they'll never speak of your nature to the *gaje*. But there's no harm in keeping a few secrets to yourself, hey?

# Do Not Suffer Thy People to Tend Thy Sickness

If I were too weak to run, I wouldn't want to live any longer. In this, the old ways are best. Perhaps in death we'll all find our homeland at last.

# The Leader May Be Challenged at Any Time During Peace

If the leader is being a fool, he forfeits his right to lead. No self-respecting Silent Strider follows an idiot. If you can't beat him in gamecraft, a facedown or battle (and remember that he'll choose which!), then maybe you should think about leaving.

## The Leader May Not Be Challenged at Any Time During War

I can see the point of this tenet, but it has its limits. The leader whose reason has slipped, as I said, is no leader at all. True, all must be ready to sacrifice themselves for Gaia. Just remember that as a Strider, you won't be able to return to aid your descendants. A pointless death is the worst fate we can suffer.

## Ye Shall Take No Action That Causes a Caern to Be Violated

There are some among us who resent the fact that other tribes have more caerns than we do. Therefore, if they don't have an equal share of a Garou holy place, they don't give a damn about guarding it. Listen! Not even the Shadow Lords let the Wyrm into our midst! Those Harano-taken fools say we've already lost everything. Well, violate this tenet of the Litany and you'll appreciate just what you have left — before we take it from you.

## Departure

Looks like Aset and I've talked your ear off for the better part of the night. Still, there's some light in your eyes yet. Think you'll remember what you've been told? Good. A strong memory's worth more than any human gold or Garou fetish. If you can remember well and true, then you take any road you walk down, any caern you visit, along with you on your travels. Lacking a land to ourselves, we do our best to own the world.

Easy there — don't fall over! Tired, are you? Well, lay your head on this blanket, and close your eyes for a while. May your rest be quiet and dreamless, for your waking hours are going to be full of speed and fury.

Give me a kiss for the road, and to sleep with you.

# Chapter Three: Ten Thousand Leagues

*I am half inclined to think we are all ghosts, Mr. Manders. It is not only what we have inherited from our fathers that exists again in us, but all sorts of old dead ideas and all kinds of old dead beliefs and things of that kind. They are not actually alive in us; but there they are dormant, all the same, and we can never be rid of them.... There must be ghosts all over the world. They must be as countless as grains of the sands, it seems to me. And we are so miserably afraid of the light, all of us.*

— Henrik Ibsen, *Ghosts*

So, did you enjoy yourself last night? That Lerli's a fine-looking Strider, she is. Clever, too, which counts for twice as much. Had I the time…

Never mind that. You're now due for the last part of your education: learning about the world and your neighbors. I say this is the best part of all. For one, it never ends. Every day you spend breathing Gaia's air, drinking Her water, is a day you spend collecting knowledge. Gather a new taste every night, and you're richer than Solomon by the end of the year.

Right. I'll bring you before one more Strider with something to say. He's tired of treading physical roads, though. I've seen it hit Striders before — you get tired of having no home of your own in this realm, so you go into the Umbra and never come out again. A Harano all our own, you might say. As if we needed another kind.

Oh, and be sure to watch where you walk when we get to his territory. The Twice-Born are always coming and going, bringing him news and listening to his tales. If you step on one of those skeletal Mouse-spirits, you're going to cause some offense.

Come on then; let's cross over to the Umbra. I'll go slowly for the first of it.

## Walking the World

Greetings, my friends. Come to visit an old Ragabash in his twilight years? Heh. Never thought I'd last long enough to see myself an authority figure, much less an honored counselor.

But you've come to ask about the wide world, and what I've seen, eh? Well, I must admit I've been more places than most people, shapeshifters and spirits in all of Gaia. So listen carefully, cub. Since you'll be traveling these roads, like it or not, you'll be wanting to know where they lead.

Remember, first and foremost, that you won't be heartily welcomed wherever you go. Many septs respect us and what we have to say; many more don't. Human society can be even worse, which is a shame because their libraries, computers and storytellers have a lot of information that you'll be wanting to carry away.

Travel. Watch quietly. Offer advice when it's invited; hurl the truth in their faces when it's not. Make friends and allies where you can. And always note the quickest way out.

# Africa

If any Garou has business in Africa, we do. Some Bone Gnawers eke out a living there, just as they do anywhere, and a few Glass Walkers occupy the cities, but only we can truly walk the wild places of Africa.

Even then, we have our boundaries. What few Children of Cat survive don't welcome Garou to their plains, jungles and savannahs, and the Children of Crocodile make river travel a risky thing. Worst of all, we're still barred from Egypt by the hand of Set. I hear that those who try to settle there have a creeping doom come on them in the night, one that leaves them withered and lifeless for the morning sun. Some Harbingers say that someday there will be a reckoning, but most of us feel such a thing could only happen if we survive to the last battles of the Apocalypse.

Still, you might do well to walk the ruins and plains of North Africa. There's much to learn there, and many memories that wait to be remembered again. We have scattered villages of Kinfolk there, and the blood runs pure in their veins. If you would choose a mate to bring a strong new Garou into the world, you could do far worse than to visit this land.

# The Americas

Ah, the New World. Spectacular country, quickly going to hell. Between the Uktena and Wendigo on one side and the Silver Fangs leading the Europeans on the other, there's little room to lie down for a nap. But there are still plenty of back roads crisscrossing the continents. That's where we spend most of our time.

Oh, there's plenty to be done in the Americas. For instance, some tribes say the Amazon is the decisive battlefield of the Apocalypse. Whoever wins there, wins forever. Not necessarily true, but it does point out how important the rainforests are. Then there are the "Pure Tribes." They have a thousand thousand restless ancestors wailing at their heels, and they're not quite sure what to do to placate their kin's ghosts. We might be able to advise them — if they let us. And don't forget that Industrial America's so filled with the Wyrm's toxins and bureaucrats, you could spend ten lifetimes fighting and make only a tiny mark.

The Americas are fairly young countries by most standards, and the newest to us. But they have their secrets, just like any place does.

# Europe

We have few good memories of Europe. We also have few if any caerns there. Gypsies are still unwelcome in Germany and Eastern Europe, so if we go there at all, we do so to protect our remaining Kin.

The struggle to control Europe would cost far more than it's worth, even if we were inclined to try. The Get and Silver Fangs vie for the North, the Furies rule the South and the Shadow Lords squat in the East. They're welcome to the continent; here's hoping that they manage to keep it in one piece.

# Asia

India's cities resemble nothing so much as cesspits, but there are countless secrets in the crevices and ruins. A few of us are of Indian blood, and they're often the best sources for Asian news. However, Asia is for the most part not Garou territory. The *hengeyokai* can be dangerous to cross, particularly since we've very little information on them. That doesn't mean we don't wander over into their territory, but you do have to to be careful. In Asia, they are as numerous as we are few. Watch yourself.

# Australia

You'd think the Oz would be the ideal place for us. Open, dusty roads, miles and miles between towns… Well, it's a lot more than it seems. There's no land more haunted than Australia, and the worst part of it is that we're responsible for the ghosts. We scouted the outback for our allies, and opened the way for the War of Tears. If you're the sensitive sort, they say, you can sometimes feel the blood on the red dirt under your paws.

Still, we've an obligation there. The ghosts of the Bunyip must be placated, and these days nobody walks the Dreamtime better than we do. Once you're fit and have a number of miles under your feet, go to Australia and find the Strider Circus. There are far worse ways to spend time and effort than trying to find any Bunyip who survive in the Dreamtime. A fool's quest? Only for those who cannot look ahead.

# The Umbra

Well, look around you. It's not the most hospitable of realms, but then, neither is the physical world.

I've been back and forth across the spirit world, just like the physical. Parts of it are utter hell — literally — others are the kind of paradise that could make you forget the wolf. At any given time, there's probably one of us in any particular Realm you'd care to mention.

Once you've gotten accustomed to your place in Garou society, I recommend you go on walkabout in the Umbra

for a time. It'll broaden your mind better than anything. It's also a fine place to meet new and interesting friends — and enemies.

# The Dark Umbra

We still remember the "darkest road," too. But I'll tell you, the Dark Umbra's a dangerous place to go. It's nothing like the Duat we remember. No, the spirits of those who die unfulfilled inherit an afterworld that's a far cry from a green and vibrant paradise. If the Duat lies somewhere in the Dark Umbra, I've never seen it.

Down there, the ghosts have their own society. It's some sort of colossal empire, forged out of the souls of the weak or criminal. And the empire's in chaos. This howling stuff called the Tempest wails around the lands of the dead, sucking the careless down into it. As far as I know, it's impossible to swim in that phantasmal whirlpool — Owl himself would have to get you out if you fell in. I hear that the bottom of the Tempest is just one more of the Wyrm's hungry mouths.

But if you can avoid the Bane-ghosts they call Spectres, and find your way through that gray pit, you can talk to people dead a *long* time. The temptation of such knowledge, of learning the secrets of the past from those who lived it… powerful stuff. But don't go looking for the ghosts of your family — there's nothing but grief in that.

A few of our Galliards visit the Dark Umbra to listen to the songs of the dead. I have to say that their howls are never again the same.

# Among the Garou

There just aren't enough of us to go around. That's why we join intertribal packs. Listen, cousin, you're going to rely on another tribe's hospitality more times than you can count. So you're best off knowing when to smile, when to give a little bow, and when to run.

They don't understand us. Most of them don't even try. But you should make the effort to understand them.

# Black Furies

They're a gruff bunch, they are, and there's no denying that they're never quite as chatty with our males as with our females. Still, we have a good professional relationship with the Furies. You see, they're always looking out for whatever "lost treasures" they can get their paws on. They're great hands at archaeology, but most of them don't get around much — they take their caern guardianship very seriously.

That's where we come in. Our tribes have been partners in the arcane and mysterious for quite some time. You have to put up with a lot of holier-than-thou "Goddess talk" when you deal with Furies, but when the Wyrm's on the march, they're as brave and ferocious as you could ask for.

## Bone Gnawers

Although they don't look it, the Gnawers are privy to many more secrets than some believe. They're close to the underbelly of human and Garou society alike, and more than one gets approached by recruiters for the Wyrm. Now, they aren't the most hygenic of companions — you have to set your more rarefied tastes to one side if you want to deal with them and keep smiling — but if you're ever in the mood for macabre humor, drop by one of their moots and ask about the truth behind those urban legends they're so fond of.

## Children of Gaia

It's hard to find quarrel with the Children. If you slap one of them in the face, half the time she'll smile back at you instead of going for your throat. That means that they're fine companions on a midsummer eve, but you do have to kick them a little when you need them riled up and ready to fight.

## Fianna

They tell some of the best stories around, even if you do have to sit through a deluge of rambling to hear the rarest tales. Don't drink too much of their brew (only the Fianna would bind a spirit into a jug of alcohol), and be careful about bringing up the subject of tribal unity. But if you can catch one while he's sober and curious, you can learn quite a bit with practically no prodding.

## Get of Fenris

Oh, they're a charming crew. They consider themselves superior to all other Garou — "at least we've kept our blood and homeland true," they argue. Naturally, they don't care for a raggletaggle Gypsy-blooded tribe, particularly one that seems to know more than they do. Fine! We don't have to live next to them, and if their Kin would just quit pestering ours, we could get along wonderfully.

In the times to come, they'll surely tear the Wyrm a new hole, but die to the last in the process. Berserkers that they are, they'll love every second of it.

## Glass Walkers

Very clever, very adaptable Garou. You have to respect their ability to keep pace with time. Human society has become an excellent resource for them, even if they have all but lost their wolf blood. I don't think I'd care to bind my freedom into the Pattern Web, but they're certainly entitled to their choice.

## Red Talons

We value the homids among us, and therefore we are unfit in the eyes of the Talons. Oh well. They're fierce and straightforward, which are good things. But they're so impossibly short-sighted that there's really no point in explaining yourself to them.

## Shadow Lords

They've had their unblinking hungry gaze on the Silver Throne so long, their eyes are watering fit to blind them. If they'd take one quarter the effort they waste on their politicking and spend it on the crisis at hand, they'd actually be pulling their own weight. As is, they're pretty damn troublesome. Half as clever as they think and twice as thick-headed as we'd like — that's the Shadow Lords for you.

## Silver Fangs

Every wolf pack has an alpha, but is there a King Pack who rules all other packs? Has human government ever clearly benefited from the control of a group whose members are elite only by blood? Have the Silver Fangs reigned justly and well? Were they right in the War of Rage, in the Impergium, in the War of Tears?

You see? Some questions you just can't answer.

## Stargazers

Wise fellows, even if they do spend too much time contemplating the insides of their eyelids. They've a fine touch for gamecraft and they're creative thinkers, but they don't concern themselves enough with the here-and-now. And this from the lips of a Strider, no less!

If they focused on what *is* or what *will* be instead of what *may* be, we'd call them siblings. However, they've had enough time to refine their philosophies. If they haven't yet settled on what they believe, they're not going to do anybody any good when the world catches fire.

## Uktena

I wish we'd grown alongside the Uktena. We can see much of ourselves in their curiosity and thirst for knowledge. However, we're definitely a tribe apart from our cousins. They're going down roads that they shouldn't be walking.

See, I wonder if our cousins (meaning the tribes that aren't native to the "Pure Lands") didn't encourage them to become the way they are. When the colonists went tearing through their lands, kicking open all their buried secrets, I figure it changed the Uktena. Now they scramble among the magics of human, vampire and Garou alike, looking for some hex that'll swing things back their way. Poor fellows, I hope they can find it without sacrificing themselves in the process.

## Wendigo

Now here's a fine tribe. Proud as the Fangs, angry as the Get, righteous as the Furies and pure as the… well, the Croatan. You have to admire them, because they'll compromise nothing when they know they're in the right — and they're in the right a lot more than you might think. Funny thing is, they're almost in the same boat as we are. 'Course, there's still a chance for them to take their homeland back. I sincerely wish them luck. I just hope they'll be able to set aside their territorial concerns and join in the battle when the Wyrm makes to swallow the sun.

# The Others

When you wander into as many shadowy corners as we do, you soon realize that you aren't alone. I think we're the tribe that's had the most dealings, bad or good, with what humans call "the supernatural." Our "relations" are another side effect of our meandering into other people's territories. It's just that every territory is usually claimed by multiple factions, some of which aren't Garou. Think about that before you next jump into a major city's culture centers.

# The Changing Breeds

You know that there are others who wear shifting skins. Many are still our enemies, but we are trying to make peace with a few. The Children of Crocodile, in particular, despise all Garou for the thoughtless rage of our cousins. Sometimes one will agree to speak with a lone werewolf, but I wouldn't bring your pack to its river.

There are many Tribes of Cat, of which only a fistful won't treat us as blood foes. In particular, the Bubasti sometimes offer to exchange lore and wisdom. Such trades usually fail, though; they're unwilling to offer their most prized secrets, as are we. Recently, there's been an odd scent to them and their dealings. If you ever converse with one of these Egyptian cat-shifters, be careful with your words.

# Wraiths

Our connection with the Restless Dead runs deep and true throughout our past. We were the openers of the ways since the first times, the guides of the dead. But when we were exiled, we were cut off from our duty. Necessity demanded that we look after ourselves first, and worry about the dead when we could.

Now you see, wraiths are those who die with something unresolved. It could be an unavenged murder, a need to look after an impoverished mother, or even a lasting hatred for all things human. In the old times, we helped people work things through both in life and death. There were fewer wraiths that way — at least where we lived. Now we're tied to an old duty, and we don't have time nor opportunity to do it proper justice these days. Not that the wraiths know that.

So watch out when you step sideways. If you get caught between worlds, the Restless may find you. When they do, they'll usually beseech you to act as their hands in the

physical world. Most of their requests are fairly harmless. But be careful what you agree to! Sometimes one'll want you to kill a blameless woman, just because he figures she wronged him. Sometimes their demands are even worse.

# Vampires

Hrrr. I'll avoid speaking of Set; by now you should know enough about him and his children. His bastard lineage of Leeches that build temples to him and flock to the foulest parts of man's cities — I hold them responsible for polluting the name of Iart the cobra to human ears. Never trust a Follower of Set — they're as ancient and dire an enemy as ever we'll have. But there are more breeds of undead than Set's whelps. Be careful, now, because you can find them wherever you find crowds of humans. Makes sense, doesn't it?

Many vampires enjoy putting on false faces and shows of emotion, trying to win your pity with tales of how wretched their unliving lot is. I've known a cub or two who believed their piteous mewlings. Others, typically Glass Walkers, believe they can outwit the vampires at their own game, and attempt to get the better of them by bargaining and exchanging favors. Such naive Garou always end up on the wrong side of a silver-loaded shotgun, or worse. Always remember, cub: Vampires lie. They lie, and they hate us.

Perhaps soon you'll hear a howl for Buries-the-Dead, one of the greatest Silent Strider Ahrouns alive today. When you travel to the Sept of the South Wind, ask the Moon Dancers there to tell you of Buries and her war on the undead of Africa. On my last visit, they sang of how she destroyed a Garou turned vampire, a creature who was once of our tribe. The very thought of such an abomination freezes my blood. May the wind never carry the scent of Buries-the-Dead, and may her klaive never dull!

# Mages

Sometimes when you're running in the Umbra, you come across somebody who doesn't seem to belong. As often as not, it's a human that has mastered some form of magick. I tend to avoid the magi, since you never can tell how they'll react. Some of them gleefully embrace the Weaver and its choking technology; others seem born of the Wyld itself. Still others are loyal to the Wyrm. They choose their own paths; granting them any measure of mercy would be pointless and foolish.

Oh, and even be careful of the ones who seem to be on your side. Their Naming powers rely on nothing less than changing parts of Gaia's being, and that tends to make Her shift in Her sleep. The fallout gets nasty.

# Mummies

Be careful who you repeat this to, but there are a number of humans who have gained the secret of eternal life. We should know; it happened in our lands. These folk are called mummies, although they look nothing like the film versions. Some are our friends, others our enemies.

They say the only way to kill one for certain is to slay its physical body, then pursue its two-part soul in the Dark Umbra and kill the spirit there. This strikes me as optimism.

Know, too, that Set has created his own bestial versions of these creatures. We gave them the name Bane Mummies when we first saw them, and no better name has arisen since. They're corrupted without and within, like twisted, immortal fomori. We harry them when we find them and destroy their bodies when we can. We have yet to slay one in both the material world and the Dark Umbra, but we'll keep on trying.

# The Fae

Although there's truth in the Fianna tales of the fae, you shouldn't concern yourself much with currying the Old Folk's favor. They can smell the touch of death on us, and they avoid us for it. From what I've heard, all they own is built of the dreamstuff born from celebrating life. We would make sorry companions for them.

# The Forked Path

Well, looks like here's where you finally set out on your own. We've told you the barest of secrets; the rest is left to you. Just try to stay alive. You've the weight of our history on your shoulders, but it's not unbearable. Remember, and be strong and fleet.

Run swift and light over your roads, friend, and may we meet and share tales again before the final battle.

# Appendix One: Souvenirs

## Tribal Weaknesses (Optional)

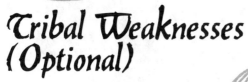

An optional rule was introduced in the first **Werewolf** tribebook: tribal weaknesses. These are quirks each member of a particular tribe possesses, usually due to the social or even genetic nature of the tribe. Weaknesses should not always be enforced. There are some rare situations in which a Bone Gnawer may not suffer a higher difficulty on Social rolls. Exceptions to the weakness are rare, but depend on the situation. For instance, a Get of Fenris may despise all Weaver-stuff, but may fall in love with a Glass Walker and feel affection toward the "Urrah."

It is up to the Storyteller to enforce these rules when an appropriate situation occurs in the game. After all, a player may be unwilling to remind the Storyteller that her Uktena's curiosity may get her into trouble.

### Silent Strider Weakness

**Haunted**

Because of the ancient curse laid upon them by Set, Striders are doomed to be haunted by the spirits of the dead, in mockery of the role they played in Pharaonic Egypt. Accordingly, whenever a Strider botches a roll to enter or exit the Umbra, she gains a ghostly haunter while caught between the worlds. This wraith is not always malevolent (though it often is), but usually demands a service of the Strider before it leaves her in peace.

Clever Striders can actually bargain with these departed souls; this is one way in which Striders become privy to information not available to other Garou. Moreover, the spirit is unable to follow the Strider beyond a certain distance (usually the area of a state, county or similar political unit).

## Merits and Flaws

### Long-Distance Runner (3 pt. Aptitudes Merit)

You must have a minimum Stamina of 4 to purchase this Merit. When running, you may double your normal speed for one hour per point of Stamina. Gifts improving movement are calculated from the new speed. Thus, possession of this Merit and movement-improving Gifts allows you to travel at amazing velocity.

### Noted Messenger (3 pt. Garou Ties Merit)

Your reputation as a reliable and uncorruptible messenger precedes you. You can enter most septs unchallenged, as long as you have a message for someone residing there. In addition, few Garou will attempt to hinder you in your duties, and most will let you cross their territories unmolested. However, the mere word of your presence will sometimes stir up rumor and intrigue, as the locals wonder what message it is that you carry.

### Freak Magnet (4 pt. Supernatural Flaw)

You attract the very worst sorts of ghosts. Thus, when your "Haunted" weakness comes into play, the ghost attracted to you is always a Spectre (see **Wraith: The Oblivion**). For those of you without **Wraith: The Oblivion**, a Spectre is the absolute nastiest kind of ghost — for all practical purposes a powerful Bane — that will either seek to do you physical or psychological harm or corrupt you into ruin.

## Strider Communication

The Silent Striders have developed several alternate methods of communication through the years. The wisest and best-traveled among the tribe are familiar with many forms of trail markings, the Strider language of colors (derived from Ancient Egypt's symbolism, not that of Western culture) and the dance-tales of the *Pakiv Swatura*.

Silent Strider characters who devote one dot of Linguistics to "Strider Communication" should be considered fluent in all these means of speech without speech. Characters of other tribes should be allowed to learn these methods only with the Storyteller's explicit permission; secret speech becomes worthless if it is explained to every friend or ally a Strider may pick up.

Even those who haven't learned these "languages" can occasionally glean some meaning from them. Any who watch a practiced dancer perform the *Pakiv Swatura* can roughly understand the story by successfully rolling Perception + Expression (difficulty 7). Similarly, a Garou can sometimes interpret Strider trail markings, although they will almost always miss the subtleties. (Roll Perception + Enigmas, difficulty 9, to read a trail marking.)

## Gifts

• **Tread Sebek's Back (Level Two)** — A Silent Strider may call on the river to support her steps. By activating this Gift, a Strider may walk or run across water or other liquids. However, her feet are not protected — running across a pit of Wyrm-toxin is still a hazardous enterprise. Some Striders are rumored to have crossed seas by use of this Gift. It is taught by a Crocodile- or Basilisk-spirit.

**System:** The Strider spends a Gnosis point and rolls Dexterity + Survival (difficulty 7). Each success allows her to travel across water as if it were open ground for an hour.

• **Eyes of *Ma'at* (Level Three)** — When a Strider invokes the power of *ma'at* itself, she may discern levels of truth invisible to even the canniest investigators. With this Gift, she may perceive innocence and truth, should they reside in the breasts of those she encounters. This Gift is taught by an Ibis- or Baboon-spirit.

**System:** This Gift acts much as the Philodox Gift: Truth of Gaia. However, the Garou may make a Perception + Empathy roll to determine the nature of any truths or lies the target may speak. ("Please, no, I never set foot inside her house!" "That is true, but you forced the door open so that your companions could enter. The guilt is plain and written on your heart.")

• **Dam the Heartflood (Level Four)** — No tribe loathes the blight of vampires more than the Silent Striders. By using this Gift, a Strider may block the flow of blood in a vampire's veins, preventing him from using any supernatural powers tied to the blood. This Gift is taught by Cobra-spirits, who resent being viewed as a symbol of Set.

**System:** This Gift can only be used on a supernatural creature with a Blood Pool who gains power from that blood (vampires, ghouls, etc. — even Ananasi). The Garou spends a Gnosis point and rolls Manipulation + Medicine (difficulty of the target's Willpower). Each success prevents the target from spending any Blood Points, for whatever purpose, for a full turn. A Garou may only use this Gift once per scene against a given target, but multiple Garou may use this Gift on a target once each. Strider Packs armed with this Gift are among the fiercest Leech-slayers known to the Garou.

• **Invocation of the Pharaoh (Level Five)** — This awe-inspiring Gift is only available to the greatest Strider heroes. The Strider must be in Homid form, must spend a Gnosis and a Willpower point, and must enact a 10-minute chant to the greatest of ancient Egyptian spirits. Once this is done, the Garou expands and grows, becoming a giant similar to the depictions of pharaohs on mastabas and sarcophagi. This Gift is taught by Sphinx.

**System:** The Garou grows to a height of nearly eight feet, but otherwise remains in Homid form. The Garou gains the Physical Attributes of a Crinos, but loses no Social Attributes; indeed, the Garou's Charisma and Manipulation are treated as 6 when making Leadership or Intimidation rolls. A Garou in Pharaoh form does not inflict aggravated damage, but adds one to all Brawl and Melee damage inflicted against Wyrm-foes (or adds two when facing Followers of Set). The Garou regenerates as a Crinos, but is invulnerable to silver and cannot frenzy. Essentially, the Pharaoh form combines the best of both Homid and Crinos forms. This form lasts for one scene.

## Eaters of the Dead Gift

• **Touch of Death (Level Four)** — The Garou can touch a target; the target will then receive a premonition of his own death, as if someone "walked on his grave." The Garou must touch the target (normal combat action), spend two Gnosis points, and roll Manipulation + Occult (difficulty 8). The number of successes is the number of dice removed from the target's physical Trait Dice Pool (allocated by the Storyteller); these lost dice are "healed" as if they were aggravated wounds. The Garou will not know what the target sees, and the target will not remember afterward, but the target's fur/hair will be streaked with white thereafter. This may be used only once on a given target — ever. This Gift is taught by a Death-spirit.

## Harbinger Gift

• **Troubleseeker (Level Two)** — The Harbingers are noted for their intuitive ability to find trouble or Wyrm-corruption, no matter how well hidden. They sometimes appear from nowhere, just "happening across" some problem or threat. This Gift allows a Harbinger to discover trouble without really searching for it — he just starts down a road and sees where it takes him. Almost invariably, his path crosses some threat that needs seeing to.

**System:** The Harbinger rolls Perception + Enigmas (difficulty 8). Success indicates that his travels will indirectly but quickly take him to a "trouble spot" of some gravity. Multiple successes on the roll allow the Harbinger to discover more dangerous or subtly hidden threats, at the Storyteller's discretion.

# Rites

## Descent into the Dark Umbra (Mystic)

Level Three

Most Umbra-traveling Garou journey through the spirit world: the area mages refer to as the Middle Umbra. This sinister rite enables Silent Striders to cross into the world of the Dead: the Dark Umbra.

The Strider must sacrifice a living creature (usually an animal, though there are rumors…) and make an Intelligence + Rituals roll (difficulty 7). She must then make a normal roll to enter the Umbra. If both rolls succeed, the Garou enters the Underworld (see **Wraith: The Oblivion** for details of this frightening place). If she botches the rite, she becomes stuck sideways between the physical world and the Dark Umbra.

## Rite of Dormant Wisdom (Mystic)

Level Four

This forbidden rite is known only to the Eaters of the Dead. The practitioner and his aides may gain the knowl-edge and memories of a dead person by ritually devouring the deceased's brain. The corpse can be long dead, as long as the brain hasn't fully decomposed. Those participating in the rite must roll Intelligence + Occult (difficulty 9). The number of successes determines how complete the memory transference is: one indicates that the Eater gains the dead one's most recent memories, while five confers total life memories. No special abilities (Disciplines, Gifts, or the like) can be learned from this rite, but the Eater may learn any number of passwords or occult knowledge.

However, the Wyrm's touch is on this rite. If the rite is practiced more times than the character has Gnosis, then the character will become wholly of the Wyrm, servant of Fœbok, Urge Wyrm of Fear. A botch will also destroy the character's mind, making him an insane slave to the Wyrm.

If the ritemaster and his aides each spend a permanent Gnosis point, they may perform this rite on a Garou or mummy. The rite also works on immobilized or torporous vampires, although cutting into a Leech's cranium will certainly awaken it.

# Fetishes

## D'siah

Level 3, Gnosis 4

Certain Silent Strider Theurges carry *d'siah*, the "blades of the moon." These ritual flint blades are carved into the shape of the crescent moon, and are used against Banes and other evil spirits. They inflict Strength + 1 damage (difficulty 5 to hit); against Wyrm-tainted creatures, the wounds are aggravated. Each successful strike also drains one Gnosis point from the foe. The *d'siah* are particularly effective against serpentlike enemies or even the vampiric Followers of Set; when striking these foes, the *d'siah* inflicts Strength + 4 damage, all aggravated.

 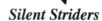

## Sarcophagus of Anpw

Level 3, Gnosis 4

This item is used by Striders who know they will be facing vampires, particularly Followers of Set. The user sleeps in the sarcophagus for eight hours and spends a Gnosis point. Upon rising, the Strider is effectively "dead" for the following 24 hours. She is unaffected by supernatural powers designed specifically to affect mortals (Eyes of the Serpent becomes much less useful when used against dead things). The Garou is unaffected by illnesses, heart seizures and the like (including Thaumaturgical spells designed to simulate such things). Because her pain receptors are dulled, wound penalties are reduced by one. Also, since she is partially dead, all difficulties to enter the Dark Umbra are reduced by one. Finally, the Strider's blood tastes clotted and foul, like the blood of the Risen; vampires seeking to drain the Strider must succeed in a Willpower roll (difficulty 9) or immediately gag up any blood imbibed.

Note that this "life-in-death" state is extremely unnatural; Garou only use this item in emergencies. Garou who make excessive use of the Sarcophagus may well cross permanently into the realms of the dead.

## Cheops' Brick

Level 4, Gnosis 5

This brick did not actually come from the pyramid of Cheops, but the name has stuck. In any event, Cheops' Brick, when placed in the center of a campsite which is then warded against evil by a competent Theurge (Rank 2+, Rituals Knowledge 3+, one hour's time to draw the warding glyphs), will manifest a mystical field warding against creatures of the Wyrm (including Followers of Set). Such creatures must make a Willpower roll (difficulty 8) to penetrate the ward and must subtract two from all Dice Pools if they do penetrate it.

## Mask of the Assanbonam

Level 4, Gnosis 5

This interesting fetish was brought back by Strider travelers to sub-Saharan Africa. It is an oblong ebony mask carved in the shape of a leering demonic visage. Its power may only be invoked on a moonless night. The mask allows the wearer to become an insubstantial, wraithlike creature seemingly made of smoke — except for the mask, which not only remains substantial, but becomes animated.

The wearer may fly at double ground speed. He may not manipulate objects, but may hold them in the mask's mouth. The wearer may use the mask to bite in combat, inflicting damage as a Hispo. Finally, because the wearer is mostly insubstantial, any dodge successes scored by the wearer count double (i.e., three dodge successes effectively act as six). These effects last until he removes the mask, or until daybreak.

## Mummy Amulets

Level 5, Gnosis 8

Striders have long fostered alliances with mummies, and a few have been bequeathed mystic amulets by their mummy companions. A mummy amulet raises a particular Attribute to 6 (in Homid form; other forms adjust accordingly) while it is worn. Each amulet is dedicated to one Attribute, and one only. Wearing one of these amulets for more than a scene at a time affects a Garou adversely, often driving him into Harano for weeks at a time. Some also whisper that when a Garou dons an amulet, he makes his presence known to the Bane Mummies.

These are among the most prized of fetishes, especially since no Garou knows how to manufacture them. Those who let a mummy amulet fall into the hands of a vampire or mage of any sort immediately lose two points of permanent Wisdom Renown and one point of permanent Honor.

# Totems
## of the Eternal Wanderers
### Totem of Respect
#### Scarab

**Background Cost: 4**

The quiet burrower, Scarab builds and destroys with relentless patience. Symbol of the ancient pharaohs, Scarab is equally honored by Striders for her tenacity and timelessness.

**Traits:** Scarab grants her followers Enigmas 2 and decreases by one their difficulties to breach the Gauntlet. Additionally, Scarab can impart Pharaoh's Majesty: Once per story, a Strider may invoke Scarab and be treated as though he has Pure Breed 5. Finally, Scarab teaches victory through patience: Followers of Scarab who spend Willpower while making extended rolls may add two successes rather than one, but only if they spend the Willpower on the second or later turn of the roll in question.

**Ban:** Followers of Scarab must help defend a threatened caern, no matter what the odds. They must also seek to improve the reputation of the Silent Striders, usually by example.

## Totems of War
### Crocodile

**Background Cost: 5**

The patient lurker in the muck, Crocodile is placid in peace, yet terrible in war. Striders honor Crocodile for his balance and his perfect control over his frenzies.

**Traits:** Crocodile's brood gain Stealth 2 and an extra soak die versus all attacks not involving fire or cold. His children also gain the ability to communicate in the Mokolé tongue (this is automatic and does not involve the expenditure of a Linguistics dot). Finally, Crocodile's brood add an extra damage die to all bite attacks.

**Ban:** Followers of Crocodile may not attack or seek to bring harm to Mokolé. Garou who assist the werealligators are more likely to earn Crocodile's favor, although other Garou may well regard them as traitors.

### Tsetse Fly

**Background Cost: 5**

Cruel and sinister, Tsetse Fly is the implacable mistress of vengeance. Once angered, she will not rest until her foe is slain. Her bite is virtually impossible to defend against, and she prefers to strike when a foe least suspects. Striders following Tsetse Fly are relentless foes, nurturing thousands of years of frustration and anger into a simmering stew of Rage, then lashing out from the shadows.

**Traits:** Striders following Tsetse Fly gain Medicine at 2 and can put the "mojo" on their enemies. They must truly hate the enemy (i.e., must spend at least five Rage points against him), must have a piece of his body or a personal effect, and must make a Manipulation + Intimidation roll (difficulty of the opponent's Willpower). Success inflicts the mojo curse on the foe; all the foe's Dice Pools are halved for a duration of one night per success scored. A botch turns the mojo against the caster for a night. A mojo may only be cast on a given foe once per year (Tsetse Fly expects her followers to take advantage of a weakened enemy!).

**Ban:** Followers of Tsetse Fly must always gain revenge against their enemies. Additionally, because Tsetse Fly is seen as an unclean totem, followers of Tsetse Fly subtract one point from any temporary Honor rewards they gain.

## Totems of Wisdom
### Ibis

**Background Cost: 5**

The ancient bird of Thoth, Ibis imparts wisdom and aids recollection. Striders revere Ibis, for only through him may they regain even a fraction of their sundered memories.

**Traits:** Followers of Ibis gain the power of Eidetic Memory — they may make an Intelligence roll (difficulty variable) to remember anything seen, heard or smelled, however briefly. Also, the difficulties of all magic used against them (including magick, hedge magic and vampire Thaumaturgy, but not wraith, werewolf or changeling powers) are increased by one.

**Ban:** Followers of Ibis may never harm a bird (this applies to Corax as well). They must also seek out lost and forgotten lore.

### Sphinx

**Background Cost: 6**

The eternally vigilant Sphinx is the guardian of the ages, and eternity is bound in its ancient riddle. For Striders, Sphinx serves as a reminder of all that they have lost and all they hope to regain one day. Strider Theurges often petition Sphinx, seeking portents of the impending Apocalypse, but many who delve too far into the unknowable sink into Harano and worse.

**Traits:** Followers of Sphinx gain an extra dot of Wits. Additionally, they may spend a Willpower point once per story and thereby gain any Knowledge at 6; this Knowledge lasts for a scene.

**Ban:** If a follower of Sphinx loses or refuses a riddle contest, she sinks into a deep Harano curable only by a successful Umbral quest for forgotten lore.

# Appendix Two: Vagabonds

*If a man does not keep pace with his companions, perhaps it is because he hears a different drummer. Let him step to the music which he hears, however measured or far away.*
— Henry David Thoreau, *Walden*

Other Garou often have difficulty understanding the reclusive and taciturn Silent Striders. This is only compounded by the individuality of the Striders, who vary greatly in temperament and beliefs. One Strider might be an embittered warrior seeking to avenge a fallen pack, while his current companion might be a gentle talesinger who shares her knowledge with those who simply ask. Since they both likely keep their feelings hidden, onlookers tend to become all the more confused.

Of course, all Striders share a common bond. They are all outcasts, and they are constantly haunted by the spirits of the human dead. This combination usually sets them apart, driving them to the solitude so familiar to the tribe. Those who reach out to a Strider often find that the haunted Garou doesn't extend friendship easily. However, when a Strider befriends someone, she does so for life, and often turns up at the most unexpected times to lend aid to her companion.

# Tricks-the-Dead

**Quote:** *One of us will dance in Hell tonight. Are you game?*

**Prelude:** You were born amid the Louisiana bayous. Mama died in childbirth, and Papa could be right mean when he had a mind to. Sometimes, if he wasn't too drunk or he hadn't lost too much money gambling, you found you could distract him. Hell, you could beat him at five-card stud with your eyes closed. But he was a mean drunk. You had to leave after your First Change — even the sheriffs in this parish weren't gonna take lightly the sight of Papa all strewn every which way and yonder, belt and guts all mixed up till you didn't rightly know which was which.

You were hitchhiking down the lonely roads one night when you heard the muffled pad of footsteps behind you, and felt a fetid breath on the nape of your neck. Without looking behind you, you greeted your visitant in as cheerfully nonchalant a voice as you could muster. It followed at your heels, forever trying to get you to look at it. Whenever it whistled, low and mad like a whippoorwill, you whistled back, mimicking its call and adding your own flourishes. It started mimicking your mimicry then, a grotesque parody of "Dueling Banjos," and the game was on. You matched it note for eerie note, whistling, walking, until the first cockcrow greeted the Mississippi sunrise and you heard it vanish with a mournful wail.

You now know that even Things from Outside like to gamble. And just like Papa, they can be made to lose. Now you travel from Wyrm-caern to Wyrm-caern, challenging the inhabitants to riddle games, fiddling contests and, above all else, a good game of five-card stud. The ante's your soul, sure, but you've always got a royal flush up your sleeve.

**Concept:** You prey on the Wyrm's own malevolent arrogance, tricking it at the very games it plays with others. You have become expert at riddles, conundrums and all manner of games of wits.

**Roleplaying Hints:** Self-assurance is your poker face, for without it you'll be damned for eternity in short order. You exude a light, breezy caprice, but deep down lurks an inner terror at all the monsters you've confronted. Still, you know your place in the scheme of things, and you wouldn't give up your avocation for Realm and Umbra alike.

**Equipment:** Knapsack, denim clothing, bus schedule, gris-gris bag.

# SILENT STRIDERS

**Name:** _____  **Breed:** Homid  **Pack Name:** _____
**Player:** _____  **Auspice:** Ragabash  **Pack Totem:** _____
**Chronicle:** _____  **Camp:** _____  **Concept:** Tricks-the-Dead

## Attributes

### Physical
Strength _____ ●●○○○
Dexterity _____ ●●○○○
Stamina _____ ●●○○○

### Social
Charisma _____ ●●○○○
Manipulation _____ ●●●●○
Appearance _____ ●●○○○

### Mental
Perception _____ ●●●○○
Intelligence _____ ●●○○○
Wits _____ ●●●●●

## Abilities

### Talents
Alertness _____ ●●●○○
Athletics _____ ○○○○○
Brawl _____ ●○○○○
Dodge _____ ●●○○○
Empathy _____ ●○○○○
Expression _____ ●●○○○
Intimidation _____ ○○○○○
Primal-Urge _____ ●○○○○
Streetwise _____ ○○○○○
Subterfuge _____ ●●●○○

### Skills
Animal Ken _____ ○○○○○
Drive _____ ○○○○○
Etiquette _____ ○○○○○
Firearms _____ ○○○○○
Leadership _____ ○○○○○
Melee _____ ○○○○○
Performance _____ ●●●○○
Repair _____ ○○○○○
Stealth _____ ●●○○○
Survival _____ ○○○○○

### Knowledges
Computer _____ ○○○○○
Enigmas _____ ●●●●○
Investigation _____ ○○○○○
Law _____ ○○○○○
Linguistics _____ ●○○○○
Medicine _____ ○○○○○
Occult _____ ●●●○○
Politics _____ ○○○○○
Rituals _____ ●●○○○
Science _____ ○○○○○

## Advantages

### Backgrounds
Contacts _____ ●●○○○
Rites _____ ●●●●○
_____ ○○○○○
_____ ○○○○○
_____ ○○○○○

### Gifts
Blur of the Milky Eye
Persuasion
Sense Wyrm
Speed of Thought

### Gifts
_____
_____
_____
_____
_____

## Renown

### Glory
○○○○○○○○○○
□□□□□□□□□□

### Honor
●○○○○○○○○○
□□□□□□□□□□

### Wisdom
●●○○○○○○○○
□□□□□□□□□□

### Rank

## Rage
●○○○○○○○○○
□□□□□□□□□□

## Gnosis
●●●○○○○○○○
□□□□□□□□□□

## Willpower
●●●●●○○○○○
□□□□□□□□□□

## Health
| | | |
|---|---|---|
| Bruised | | □ |
| Hurt | -1 | □ |
| Injured | -1 | □ |
| Wounded | -2 | □ |
| Mauled | -2 | □ |
| Crippled | -5 | □ |
| Incapacitated | | □ |

## Weakness
HAUNTED:
STEPPING SIDEWAYS
BOTCHES ATTRACT
GHOSTS

# Haunted Soul

**Quote:** (Cackle) *Are you MAD, man? Can you not SEE? It comes — it's just over your left shoulder…!*

**Prelude:** You were comparatively lucky for a Silent Strider, for you always knew the security of home and the comforts of family. Oh, granted, your home was referred to as "the hainted Hecubus House in the old swamp," and your family reviled as "those devil-tainted Hecubuses," but at least you had something to belong to. Yes — while the other werewolves roamed eternally under the bloated moon, forlorn and alone, you had family: your dark-browed father, who never spoke for years on end except to mutter Those Names; your mother, who sat and rocked eternally in the attic; your brother, who had to be chained in the cellar following that incident with the scissors; your sister, who climbed down the well in the back one night and never came back up. When a certain moonless night leered down and you were finally left alone in the rotting old mansion, nothing really even changed.

Now you sit, and stare, and guard the caern out back of Hecubus House, and you listen…always listen. Sometimes, high and far off when the earth rumbles or the lightning blazes, you can hear them singing, like sirens in a vast tempest. Every year they seem to get a little closer, and now you can decipher their mad, shrill songs of blood and devotion and love…and, above all, family. Soon enough, you know, the last scion of the Hecubus line will go to his beloved, and Hecubus House will collapse into the slime that gave it birth.

**Concept:** The Striders tolerate you as the caern warder of Hecubus House, but even they come rarely, for they find the Gnosis received from it…distasteful. You are never lonely, however, for your family and their…friends…often come to pay their…respects.

**Roleplaying Hints:** Try desperately (and fail miserably) to come across as gracious and in control. Invite werewolves to sit and engage in civilized conversation that inevitably disintegrates into hysterical gibbering.

**Equipment:** Library with many a quaint and curious volume of forbidden lore, study with leering ancestral portraits, antique furniture (bloodstained), refrigerator containing…traces…that the VICAP would be very interested in obtaining, closet complete with skeletons.

# SILENT STRIDERS

**Name:** _____  **Breed:** Homid  **Pack Name:** _____
**Player:** _____  **Auspice:** Theurge  **Pack Totem:** _____
**Chronicle:** _____  **Camp:** _____  **Concept:** Haunted Soul

## Attributes

### Physical
Strength _____ ●●○○○
Dexterity _____ ●●○○○
Stamina _____ ●●●●○

### Social
Charisma _____ ●○○○○
Manipulation _____ ●●●●○
Appearance _____ ●●○○○

### Mental
Perception _____ ●●●●○
Intelligence _____ ●●●●○
Wits _____ ●●○○○

## Abilities

### Talents
Alertness _____ ●●○○○
Athletics _____ ○○○○○
Brawl _____ ●○○○○
Dodge _____ ●●○○○
Empathy _____ ●○○○○
Expression _____ ○○○○○
Intimidation _____ ●○○○○
Primal-Urge _____ ●○○○○
Streetwise _____ ○○○○○
Subterfuge _____ ●○○○○

### Skills
Animal Ken _____ ○○○○○
Drive _____ ○○○○○
Etiquette _____ ●●○○○
Firearms _____ ●○○○○
Leadership _____ ○○○○○
Melee _____ ○○○○○
Performance _____ ●○○○○
Repair _____ ○○○○○
Stealth _____ ●○○○○
Survival _____ ○○○○○

### Knowledges
Computer _____ ○○○○○
Enigmas _____ ●●●○○
Investigation _____ ●●○○○
Law _____ ○○○○○
Linguistics _____ ●●○○○
Medicine _____ ●○○○○
Occult _____ ●●●●●
Politics _____ ○○○○○
Rituals _____ ●●○○○
Science _____ ○○○○○

## Advantages

### Backgrounds
Allies _____ ●●○○○
Fetish _____ ●●●●○
Rites _____ ●○○○○
_____ ○○○○○
_____ ○○○○○

### Gifts
Smell of Man _____
Spirit Speech _____
Sense Wyrm _____
_____
_____
_____

### Gifts
_____
_____
_____
_____
_____
_____

## Renown

**Glory**
○○○○○○○○○○
□□□□□□□□□□

**Honor**
○○○○○○○○○○
□□□□□□□□□□

**Wisdom**
●●●●○○○○○○
□□□□□□□□□□

**Rank**
[ ]

## Rage
●●○○○○○○○○
□□□□□□□□□□

## Gnosis
●●●●●●○○○○
□□□□□□□□□□

## Willpower
●●●●●○○○○○
□□□□□□□□□□

## Health
| | | |
|---|---|---|
| Bruised | | □ |
| Hurt | -1 | □ |
| Injured | -1 | □ |
| Wounded | -2 | □ |
| Mauled | -2 | □ |
| Crippled | -5 | □ |
| Incapacitated | | □ |

## Weakness
HAUNTED:
STEPPING SIDEWAYS
BOTCHES ATTRACT
GHOSTS

# Spirit of Vengeance

**Quote:** *Woe unto thee, transgressor! I have seen your face flickering in the mere-fires; I have heard your name borne on owls' wings. Tonight a great doom comes for you. There is no escape!*

**Prelude:** Sin. It surrounded you from the moment of your unhallowed spawning — slimy as the afterbirth of your Litany-breaking mother, indelible as the deed of the shiftless wretch with whom she whelped you.

You left the caern early, with little fanfare and even less goodwill. You slunk into the city late one night, hoping to erase your existence in the faceless throngs. But, far from being the Lethe you sought, the city took your sin and magnified it a thousandfold. Sin leered all around you: from tenements, from skyscrapers, from department-store windows and trashcan fires. This was the Blight, even more blighted than you — and nowhere near as remorseful. And yet your cousins spat on you, even as they allowed this abomination to exist!

Then you knew what your penance was to be. Years of eluding your septmates' mockery had made you very good at hiding, and your cursed ruin of a body was more than capable of eradicating the sins that so mirrored your own. A high-powered executive was the first to die; his ingratiating charm had won him a vice-presidency, but you saw the Defiler's grin leering from his All-American face. Garnering evidence of various sorts, you began leaving messages on his private voice mail. On the fifth night, when you could smell the terror leaking from him, you came for him. The satisfaction you felt at erasing his blandly beautiful features nearly erased your shame at your own wreckage of a face.

**Concept:** You are a metis through and through; even Nosferatu would blanch to look at you. You are obsessed with punishing the wicked, particularly those Wyrm-tainted individuals in positions of power and thus immune to the law's long arm. You have grown increasingly melodramatic in your dispensing of "justice" — though, of course, you are saving your most cinematic embellishments for your noblest deed — your own suicide.

**Roleplaying Hints:** Speak in doleful and lugubrious tones of the vengeance to come. Revel in the terror of your victims, rattling out litanies of their unpunished crimes and promising full-scale restitution. You often like to forewarn a target in Homid form by day, then come for him in Crinos by night. You sometimes fixate on purity, such as that found in small children and beautiful, unattainable maidens. You will lurk outside your "charges'" windows by night, guarding their sleep and gazing in on them with wistful longing.

**Metis Deformity:** Hideous

**Equipment:** Opera cloak, mask, broadbrimmed hat, dark suit, bandages, instruments of vengeance, sunglasses.

# SILENT STRIDERS

**Name:**           **Breed:** Metis        **Pack Name:**
**Player:**          **Auspice:** Philodox     **Pack Totem:**
**Chronicle:**       **Camp:**               **Concept:** Spirit of Vengeance

## Attributes

### Physical
- Strength ●●●●○
- Dexterity ●●●○○
- Stamina ●●●○○

### Social
- Charisma ●●○○○
- Manipulation ●●●○○
- Appearance ●○○○○

### Mental
- Perception ●●●○○
- Intelligence ●●●○○
- Wits ●●●○○

## Abilities

### Talents
- Alertness ●●○○○
- Athletics ●●○○○
- Brawl ●●○○○
- Dodge ●○○○○
- Empathy ○○○○○
- Expression ○○○○○
- Intimidation ●●●●○
- Primal-Urge ●○○○○
- Streetwise ●●○○○
- Subterfuge ○○○○○

### Skills
- Animal Ken ○○○○○
- Drive ●●○○○
- Etiquette ○○○○○
- Firearms ●●●●○
- Leadership ○○○○○
- Melee ●●○○○
- Performance ○○○○○
- Repair ○○○○○
- Stealth ●●●●○
- Survival ○○○○○

### Knowledges
- Computer ○○○○○
- Enigmas ○○○○○
- Investigation ●●●○○
- Law ●○○○○
- Linguistics ○○○○○
- Medicine ●○○○○
- Occult ○○○○○
- Politics ○○○○○
- Rituals ○○○○○
- Science ○○○○○

## Advantages

### Backgrounds
- Contacts ●○○○○
- Fetish ●●●●○
- _____ ○○○○○
- _____ ○○○○○
- _____ ○○○○○

### Gifts
- Sense Wyrm
- Speed of Thought
- Truth of Gaia

### Gifts
- 
- 
- 

## Renown

### Glory
○○○○○○○○○○
□□□□□□□□□□

### Honor
●●●○○○○○○○
□□□□□□□□□□

### Wisdom
○○○○○○○○○○
□□□□□□□□□□

### Rank
[ ]

## Rage
●●●●●●○○○○
□□□□□□□□□□

## Gnosis
●●●○○○○○○○
□□□□□□□□□□

## Willpower
●●●●●●●○○○
□□□□□□□□□□

## Health
- Bruised □
- Hurt −1 □
- Injured −1 □
- Wounded −2 □
- Mauled −2 □
- Crippled −5 □
- Incapacitated □

## Weakness
HAUNTED:
STEPPING SIDEWAYS
BOTCHES ATTRACT
GHOSTS

# Gypsy Chanteuse

**Quote:** *This one goes out to Meredith — wherever she may be.*

**Prelude:** The road was always your home. Your mother bounced you from trailer park to ramshackle apartment, city to city, boyfriend to boyfriend (hers, not yours — though several of the scumbags tried to get a two-for-one deal). You visited every state in the Union before your 16th birthday; you knew the sunscorched promise of Route 66, the cacophony of the Jersey Turnpike and the pine-shrouded endlessness of I-75. When you ran away at 14, it seemed only natural.

You hitchhiked and hoboed from city to city, singing for food (but refusing to do anything else, no matter who tried to force you). You grew distant and guarded, wearing the same mask for officers and would-be pimps, social workers and shelter volunteers and drug dealers alike. A young girl like you had to — society had grown mobile and fluid, like a human ocean; but, like the ocean, there were sharks aplenty to surprise the unwary. You became adept at defending yourself, both emotionally and physically — bus stations and bars were no place for someone your age.

The Change happened at 16; in a way, you had known it was coming. You ran with the spirits and the Lunes under the gibbous moon, and for the first time in your life you felt as though you had a home. All the half-formed street-poet verse you'd scrawled coalesced into something greater and immaculately beautiful, and your first recitation of Shu Horus' *Legacy* moved even the eldest Ahroun to tears.

You quickly moved on after your Rite of Passage. When you performed at a nameless hole-in-the-wall Philly bar, you floored the locals, attracting a band in the process. Now you and your band travel from city to city, eternal vagabonds, singing songs of the endless, lonely road.

**Concept:** You sing of Gaia, but a different Gaia from that of your Fianna cousins. You sing of Her ancient mystery, of subtle longing and secrets never shared. Your songs are moody, wistful, driving your listeners nearly to Harano, but in the process purifying them and reassuring them that others understand what they feel.

**Roleplaying Hints:** You are guarded and inscrutable with those you don't know; this translates into an aura of enchanting mystery when you perform. Offstage, you are demure and impeccably polite, though you always refuse interviews.

**Equipment:** Jewelry, quasi-Egyptian clothing.

B.

# Silent Striders

**Name:**                  **Breed:** Homid         **Pack Name:**
**Player:**                **Auspice:** Galliard      **Pack Totem:**
**Chronicle:**            **Camp:**                 **Concept:** Gypsy Chanteuse

## Attributes

### Physical
Strength ●●○○○
Dexterity ●●●○○
Stamina ●●○○○

### Social
Charisma ●●●●○
Manipulation ●●●○○
Appearance ●●●○○

### Mental
Perception ●●●○○
Intelligence ●●○○○
Wits ●●●○○

## Abilities

### Talents
Alertness ●●○○○
Athletics ○○○○○
Brawl ●●○○○
Dodge ●●●○○
Empathy ●●●○○
Expression ●●○○○
Intimidation ○○○○○
Primal-Urge ●●○○○
Streetwise ●●●○○
Subterfuge ●○○○○

### Skills
Animal Ken ●○○○○
Drive ○○○○○
Etiquette ○○○○○
Firearms ●○○○○
Leadership ●○○○○
Melee ○○○○○
Performance ●●●○○
Repair ●○○○○
Stealth ●●○○○
Survival ○○○○○

### Knowledges
Computer ●○○○○
Enigmas ●●○○○
Investigation ○○○○○
Law ●○○○○
Linguistics ○○○○○
Medicine ○○○○○
Occult ○○○○○
Politics ○○○○○
Rituals ●○○○○
Science ○○○○○

## Advantages

### Backgrounds
Allies ●●○○○
Contacts ●●●○○
○○○○○
○○○○○
○○○○○

### Gifts
Mindspeak
Persuasion
Speed of Thought

### Gifts

## Renown

**Glory**
●●○○○○○○○○
□□□□□□□□□□

**Honor**
○○○○○○○○○○
□□□□□□□□□□

**Wisdom**
●○○○○○○○○○
□□□□□□□□□□

### Rank

## Rage
●●●●○○○○○○
□□□□□□□□□□

## Gnosis
●●●○○○○○○○
□□□□□□□□□□

## Willpower
●●●●●○○○○○
□□□□□□□□□□

## Health
| | | |
|---|---|---|
| Bruised | | □ |
| Hurt | -1 | □ |
| Injured | -1 | □ |
| Wounded | -2 | □ |
| Mauled | -2 | □ |
| Crippled | -5 | □ |
| Incapacitated | | □ |

### Weakness
HAUNTED:
STEPPING SIDEWAYS
BOTCHES ATTRACT
GHOSTS

# Black Dog

**Quote:** (mournful, eerie howl reverberating over the moor like the scream of the damned)

**Prelude:** You remember little of your pre-Change life: scratches behind the ears, saucers of milk, children's laughter on the dales, the rustic comfort of a Midlands cottage. You remember the events leading up to the Change quite well: the slashes on the walls as the Wyrm-things forced their way in, the saucers of milk turned to rivers of blood, the children screaming on and on and on, the cottage and its inhabitants torn asunder and left in mangled ruin.

The smell of your owners' blood inflamed you, and you swelled to a size rivaling the now-disemboweled ponies twitching in their intestines in the yard outside. You pounced into the Wyrm-things, and your world faded to a bitter red haze flavored only by the sour foulness of the things' flesh shredding under your jaws.

The intruders lay dead, but so did your owners. Your instinctive Howls of the Departed combined a sentient being's grief with a loyal dog's sense of failure. The mournful noise attracted the attention of a passing Silent Strider, who took you to a caern. But you didn't want another home or another family. Bidding the Garou farewell, you set off down the lonely roads. There were other monsters out there — you could smell them. You would die before you failed again.

**Concept:** You embody the ancient legends of the Black Shuck: the grim supernatural hound on the mere. You are a guardian through and through — a predator of predators. You are adept at solitary survival on the streets and in the wild alike; you have slain monstrous foes in silence, not 30 yards from where a party of Boy Scouts lay laughing and telling stories around the campfire.

**Roleplaying Hints:** You are even lonelier than most Striders, and even less hopeful. (If only the humans knew what lurked just out of sight — why aren't they more careful?) Still, the dog within you is strong, and it is your function to be the humans' eyes, ears and — when necessary — teeth and talons. You have grown distant and detached from humans and Garou alike, but occasionally approach someone small and innocent, like a young lost child, play with him and gently shepherd him back to his anxious family. Your gentle demeanor sheds like your fur when facing Wyrm-things; for them you have neither patience nor mercy.

**Equipment:** Spiked collar, tag bearing the inscription "CORKY."

# SILENT STRIDERS

Name:      Breed: Lupus      Pack Name:
Player:      Auspice: Ahroun      Pack Totem:
Chronicle:      Camp:      Concept: Black Dog

## Attributes

### Physical
Strength ●●●●○
Dexterity ●●●○○
Stamina ●●●●○

### Social
Charisma ●●○○○
Manipulation ●●○○○
Appearance ●●○○○

### Mental
Perception ●●●●○
Intelligence ●●○○○
Wits ●●○○○

## Abilities

### Talents
Alertness ●●●○○
Athletics ●●○○○
Brawl ●●●●○
Dodge ●○○○○
Empathy ●○○○○
Expression ○○○○○
Intimidation ●●○○○
Primal-Urge ●●●○○
Streetwise ○○○○○
Subterfuge ○○○○○

### Skills
Animal Ken ●●●○○
Drive ○○○○○
Etiquette ○○○○○
Firearms ○○○○○
Leadership ○○○○○
Melee ○○○○○
Performance ○○○○○
Repair ○○○○○
Stealth ●●●●●
Survival ●●●○○

### Knowledges
Computer ○○○○○
Enigmas ●○○○○
Investigation ●●●○○
Law ○○○○○
Linguistics ○○○○○
Medicine ○○○○○
Occult ●○○○○
Politics ○○○○○
Rituals ●○○○○
Science ○○○○○

## Advantages

### Backgrounds
Allies ●○○○○
Pure Breed ●●●○○
Rites ●○○○○
_____ ○○○○○
_____ ○○○○○

### Gifts
Heightened Senses
Razor Claws
Sense Wyrm
_____
_____
_____

### Gifts
_____
_____
_____
_____
_____
_____

## Renown

### Glory
●●○○○○○○○○
□□□□□□□□□□

### Honor
●○○○○○○○○○
□□□□□□□□□□

### Wisdom
○○○○○○○○○○
□□□□□□□□□□

### Rank
[ ]

## Rage
●●●●●○○○○○
□□□□□□□□□□

## Gnosis
●●●●○○○○○○
□□□□□□□□□□

## Willpower
●●●●○○○○○○
□□□□□□□□□□

## Health
| Bruised | | □ |
|---|---|---|
| Hurt | -1 | □ |
| Injured | -1 | □ |
| Wounded | -2 | □ |
| Mauled | -2 | □ |
| Crippled | -5 | □ |
| Incapacitated | | □ |

## Weakness
HAUNTED:
STEPPING SIDEWAYS
BOTCHES ATTRACT
GHOSTS

# Appendix Three: Trailblazers

Although the Silent Striders rarely travel or congregate in numbers, they acknowledge their heroic and infamous just as the other tribes do theirs. A renowned Strider hero might have to wait a while to sing of her deeds at the next moot, true. However, word has always traveled quickly among the tribe. Many a Galliard has entered a moot (or even a concolation!) to sing of the deeds of his pack, only to find that the Striders present will nod expectantly and helpfully remind him of any details he has neglected to mention.

In fact, were the Silent Striders not so taciturn and soft-spoken, their heroes would become as famous as the champions of the Silver Fangs. Because they travel freely from sept to sept, they certainly have opportunity to casually mention their tribemates' exploits to any number of Garou. But the Striders know that were they to play themselves up so, the other tribes' pride would begin to rankle — and soon every Garou would carefully watch the Striders, just to see if they were as truly impressive as the tales say.

As is, the Striders mention their noblest and wisest only when it is proper to do so. But word still travels, and although Strider heroes (and villains) seem no more numerous than those of any other tribe, their fame does seem to stretch a little farther. Therefore, it's not unusual that Canadian Wendigo have heard the name of Buries-the-Dead, an African Strider who has killed numerous vampires and two Abominations (one of which was a member of the infamous Black Hand). Similarly, the Australian Garou have heard tales of Montu Blackpaws, who successfully crossed Russia from end to end, and of Mephi Faster-than-Death, who has brought back strange Gifts from the Dark Umbra.

Gaia recognizes her own, and her children follow suit. The following Striders have earned their place in legendry, whether for good or ill. No matter what else, they will be remembered long after they have vanished beyond the Paths of the Dead. Until Set's curse is lifted, it is as much as they could ask for.

## Shu Heru — Shu Horus

Striders all across the globe revere the ancient Egyptian Shu Heru, who led the tribe into its exile. Although his name is all-too-often remembered in the tongues of the conquerors, he is hailed as the mightiest Strider in peace and in war. He counseled his tribe to treat with the mummies when they were first born, and he was one of the few Garou leaders to establish a temporary truce with Bastet and Mokolé alike. He also was a proven slayer of the hot-blooded vampires of ancient times, and destroyed almost countless childer of Set. Shu Horus even eventually did battle against the Antediluvian himself, Set the Ruler, Set the Usurper.

Alas, he and the tribe were cursed for their pains, and Set could hardly have put a greater doom on the defiant Striders. Yet Shu Heru's strength was so great that even in his tribe's darkest hour, he was able to lead them to their new lives. Although most tales of Shu Horus end with his tribe's exile, Strider Galliards know that his deeds of valor did not end when he forever left the land of Khem.

It is unrecorded where and when this legend among Garou died. And even today, his descendants and tribesfolk curse Set's name, for the ancient vampire's malison caused no greater ill than severing the Silent Striders from the guiding spirit of their greatest hero.

## Vic Stryker

If adventure had a name in the *fin de siecle* '30s, it was Vic Stryker. With his companions — the Son of Ether genius Professor Emil Zoltan and the merrily enigmatic eshu changeling Vesadda — Stryker wandered the globe in the service of Gaia, Garou and country. Whether smashing Setite skullduggery in Cairo, fighting ferocious fomori in Hong Kong, mangling the Machiavellian machinations of the Nazi Get of Fenris Blut-krieg in Amsterdam, or indulging in a simultaneous Parisian dalliance with the Lasombra *antitribu* Lucita and Marlene Dietrich, Vic Stryker was the red-blooded werewolf for the job. The apex of Stryker's career came during the notorious Malachite Scarab Incident, when he met True Love in the form of Samantha Westcott, a feisty Fianna Kinfolk with eyes you could fall into and a left hook that could rock a Crinos-shifted pug back into Homid (as Stryker found out when he called her "dame").

Then, in the '40s, the real world caught up. An impersonal barrage of Nazi shrapnel brought an explosive end to Stryker's uncanny luck, ruining both his mobility and his self-confidence. Professor Zoltan, returning to the Ukraine to assist in the Rodina's defense, made the mistake of being taken alive during a Sabbat attack; he spent his last nights as an agonized "experiment" in the torture-dungeons of the Fiend Sascha Vykos. Vesadda, now cynical and embittered, returned to India to protest British colonialism. He ended up with a heart so full of hate he was Undone — his faerie seeming vanished forevermore. As for Stryker's beloved Samantha, well, she took sick of polio and died in the postwar years — Gaia calling back one of Her own, but it was a hard thing nonetheless.

Worst of all, when the partially recovered Stryker returned to heroism in the early '50s, a McCarthy-dominated Congress declared him a "loose cannon" affiliated with "questionable elements" (particularly the Russian Zoltan) and called him to Washington for a hearing. Unable to reveal (or explain) his supernatural origin, Stryker was instead denounced as a Communist, arrested on trumped-up conspiracy charges and sentenced to a year in prison. Upon release, the embittered Stryker emigrated to Tangiers, there to lose himself in Harano and heroin. During one particularly bad smack binge, Stryker saw a ghostly Anubis jackal leave his body, and he knew that he had lost the wolf.

Unable to face his former Garou companions, Vic eventually returned to the streets of New York as a derelict. It was there, late one Friday night, that his bleary eyes lit on a mugger, eyes glazed with PCP and bloodlust, holding a pistol to a terrified nun. Wolf or no, Vic Stryker couldn't just stand by. With no Gifts or Delirium to aid him, and all too vulnerable to the mugger's Saturday Night Special, he hurled himself at the salacious villain. The satisfaction he felt at laying out the crook with one punch exceeded any of his pride at rediscovering artifacts, rescuing princesses, trekking through Horizon Realms or fearlessly slaying vampires. And, though his ears weren't so good anymore (and he refused to use a damn Weaver-spawned hearing aid), he could have sworn he heard an approving howl in the distance.

And so Stryker spent part of his golden twilight as a private investigator, setting up a small office near the Central Park Caern. Oh, he never met another Samantha (though he tried). But even without Methuselahs to be put down, Wyrm-spawn to slay or Nephandi dictators to overthrow, Vic could still hold his own against the garden-variety human scum which, when it came down to it, really caused most of the world's problems.

Stryker, a feisty nonagenarian, now patrols the quaint rural Maine township of Pleasant Port as vigilantly as he ever did a Strider bawn. Despite everything, he has the constitution of a man half his age (as no few of Pleasant Port's dames — er, ladies — will attest). Should evil rear its head, should Wyrm-spawned terror threaten the innocent, Vic Stryker'll show those minions of darkness that a good right cross is a match for Bane fetishes and Black Spiral talons any day.

## Bennu

Though barely 18, the young Philodox Bennu bears a weighty responsibility, for she embodies the hopes of Striders everywhere. Indeed, the word "Bennu" is Ancient Egyptian for "hope," and the mere mention of her name is often enough to lift the worst Harano from the old, tired wolves loitering around the caern fires.

Few of the cynical Strider elders suspected that the fragile, wide-eyed girl brought before them would survive her Rite of Passage, much less come to occupy a place of honor at their moots. However, during the climax of her rite — a pitched battle with a Setite coterie — Bennu shocked her packmates by crying out in Ancient Egyptian, intoning a chant that sent the eldest Setite priestess howling back into the darkness of her temple. Continuing to chant, Bennu led the pack into the ranks of the now-demoralized Setites, slaying them all.

Bennu, it turned out, had channeled the spirit of the great Shu Horus himself — a miracle among the Striders, whose lack of ability to contact their ancestors had plagued them since the onset of their diaspora. Amazed Strider Theurges determined that Bennu alone among the tribe had the power to invoke Strider Past Lives. Why she, of all Striders, had escaped Great Set's curse was unknown, nor did the tribe leaders care — here was a living link to their past and a possibility to claim their future.

Now Bennu possesses a station far outweighing her tender years and unworldliness. She has made her share of enemies in the process — jealous pack rivals would relish her fall almost as much as the tribe's enemies would. In particular, Sarrasine and Ghede, two powerful Setites, have vowed her destruction. Still, she is guarded night and day by a cadre of vigilant Ahroun, who would willingly give their lives and souls for what Bennu represents — the possibility, for the first time in millennia, that the Silent Striders can reclaim their sundered heritage and finally find a place to rest.

## Abnatha the Laughing One

Silent Striders grow silent indeed when the name of Abnatha the Laughing One is voiced in their presence. Indeed, Abnatha's name is among the closest thing the normally placid Striders have to "fightin' words." Once a respected Theurge, the disgraced Abnatha walks so close to the Wyrm as to be almost indistinguishable from it.

Formerly, Abnatha was viewed by the tribal elders as an up-and-coming hero; he displayed a sagacity well beyond his years and became renowned for his insight into matters of the spirit world. Abnatha carried a dark and terrible secret, though. A devout follower of the Eaters of the Dead camp, Abnatha supplemented his prodigious wisdom with necrophagous knowledge gleaned from the devoured brains of the dead. In his hubris he grew addicted to the secret knowledge buried deep amid juicy gray matter. He began to steal into Garou gravesites late at night, eating the brains of dead heroes for no reason save to benefit from their accumulated lore. He dug up human gravesites as well, voyeuristically sifting through the lives of complete strangers. And, worst of all, he began to eat the increasingly tasty cerebra of slain Wyrm-foes, reveling in the charnel knowledge taken so intimately into himself.

Such behavior left Abnatha open to psychic assault, and one enterprising Bane-minion of the Defiler invaded Abnatha's body in the form of a disease. This Bane-spawned illness manifested as a virulent strain of *kuru* — the exceedingly rare ailment previously manifested only in the Foré tribe of New Guinea. Contracted by the ingestion of parasites found exclusively in rotting human brain tissue, *kuru* normally induces a painful and lethal neurological deterioration. The symptoms of *kuru* are some of the most grotesque known — the victim begins to laugh neurotically and uncontrollably, in a fashion similar to Tourette's Syndrome. This laughter intensifies during *kuru*'s middle stages, when the victim's mind and reason deteriorate, and continues until the disease has run its inevitably fatal course.

Abnatha, however, was Garou, not human. The *kuru* infection coursed through his nervous system like an acid, but failed to kill him outright. Indeed, Abnatha managed to retain some shreds of health and sentience. Moreover, while the Bane-*kuru* certainly drove him into fits of lunacy worthy of a Black Spiral Dancer, Abnatha's intelligence *per se* was not affected — he remained as cunning as he had ever been. The disease's preliminary symptoms did afflict him, however — he began to laugh, convulsively and uncontrollably, shaking epileptically as spasm after spasm of hysterical mirth wrenched itself from his throat. He has not stopped laughing since — not even in his occasional bouts of nightmare-plagued sleep. Worse, the Bane-spirit riding him has dampened his judgment regarding just how "dormant" a brain "donor" has to be. Indeed, Abnatha has come to prefer the bouquet of brains extracted from living craniums.

Such practices could not be concealed forever, and the cannibal was declared outcast in short order. Now Abnatha wanders Realm and Umbra alike, often accompanied by a pack of rabid hyenas. His tittering, ululating call precedes him, while in his wake he often leaves entire villages of massacred humans, skulls cracked open, marrow sucked out and brain pans licked clean. He is technically Ronin and worse, and many sept wardens have placed him under sentence of death. But the fact that most of his carnage is directed toward Pentex employees, the performance of several acts of gruesome heroism in defense of Strider caerns, the fact that even Black Spiral Dancers hold him in dread, and pressure from hard-line Red Talons and Get of Fenris have kept Garou leaders from enforcing the death-hunt.

# SILENT STRIDERS

| | | |
|---|---|---|
| Name: | Breed: | Pack Name: |
| Player: | Auspice: | Pack Totem: |
| Chronicle: | Camp: | Concept: |

## Attributes

### Physical
Strength_____●OOOO
Dexterity_____●OOOO
Stamina_____●OOOO

### Social
Charisma_____●OOOO
Manipulation_____●OOOO
Appearance_____●OOOO

### Mental
Perception_____●OOOO
Intelligence_____●OOOO
Wits_____●OOOO

## Abilities

### Talents
Alertness_____OOOOO
Athletics_____OOOOO
Brawl_____OOOOO
Dodge_____OOOOO
Empathy_____OOOOO
Expression_____OOOOO
Intimidation_____OOOOO
Primal-Urge_____OOOOO
Streetwise_____OOOOO
Subterfuge_____OOOOO

### Skills
Animal Ken_____OOOOO
Drive_____OOOOO
Etiquette_____OOOOO
Firearms_____OOOOO
Leadership_____OOOOO
Melee_____OOOOO
Performance_____OOOOO
Repair_____OOOOO
Stealth_____OOOOO
Survival_____OOOOO

### Knowledges
Computer_____OOOOO
Enigmas_____OOOOO
Investigation_____OOOOO
Law_____OOOOO
Linguistics_____OOOOO
Medicine_____OOOOO
Occult_____OOOOO
Politics_____OOOOO
Rituals_____OOOOO
Science_____OOOOO

## Advantages

### Backgrounds
_____OOOOO
_____OOOOO
_____OOOOO
_____OOOOO
_____OOOOO

### Gifts
_____
_____
_____
_____
_____

### Gifts
_____
_____
_____
_____
_____

## Renown

### Glory
O O O O O O O O O O
□ □ □ □ □ □ □ □ □ □

### Honor
O O O O O O O O O O
□ □ □ □ □ □ □ □ □ □

### Wisdom
O O O O O O O O O O
□ □ □ □ □ □ □ □ □ □

### Rank
[ ]

## Rage
O O O O O O O O O O
□ □ □ □ □ □ □ □ □ □

## Gnosis
O O O O O O O O O O
□ □ □ □ □ □ □ □ □ □

## Willpower
O O O O O O O O O O
□ □ □ □ □ □ □ □ □ □

## Health

| | | |
|---|---|---|
| Bruised | | □ |
| Hurt | -1 | □ |
| Injured | -1 | □ |
| Wounded | -2 | □ |
| Mauled | -2 | □ |
| Crippled | -5 | □ |
| Incapacitated | | □ |

## Weakness
HAUNTED:
STEPPING SIDEWAYS
BOTCHES ATTRACT
GHOSTS

# SILENT STRIDERS

## Homid
No Change

Difficulty: 6

## Glabro
Strength (+2)_____
Stamina (+2)_____
Appearance (-1)_____
Manipulation (-1)___

Difficulty: 7

## Crinos
Strength (+4)_____
Dexterity (+1)_____
Stamina (+3)_____
Appearance 0
Manipulation (-3)___

Difficulty: 6

INCITE DELIRIUM
IN HUMANS

## Hispo
Strength (+3)_____
Dexterity (+2)_____
Stamina (+3)_____
Manipulation (-3)__

Difficulty: 7

## Lupus
Strength (+1)_____
Dexterity (+2)_____
Stamina (+2)_____
Manipulation (-3)__

Difficulty: 6

## Other Traits

| | |
|---|---|
| _____ | OOOOO |
| _____ | OOOOO |
| _____ | OOOOO |
| _____ | OOOOO |
| _____ | OOOOO |
| _____ | OOOOO |
| _____ | OOOOO |
| _____ | OOOOO |
| _____ | OOOOO |
| _____ | OOOOO |
| _____ | OOOOO |
| _____ | OOOOO |
| _____ | OOOOO |
| _____ | OOOOO |
| _____ | OOOOO |
| _____ | OOOOO |
| _____ | OOOOO |
| _____ | OOOOO |
| _____ | OOOOO |

## Fetishes

Item: _____ ☐ Dedicated  Level ____ Gnosis ____
Power_____

Item: _____ ☐ Dedicated  Level ____ Gnosis ____
Power_____

Item: _____ ☐ Dedicated  Level ____ Gnosis ____
Power_____

Item: _____ ☐ Dedicated  Level ____ Gnosis ____
Power_____

## Rites

_____
_____
_____
_____
_____
_____
_____
_____
_____
_____
_____
_____

## Combat

| Maneuver/Weapon | Roll | Difficulty | Damage | Range | Rate | Clip |
|---|---|---|---|---|---|---|
| | | | | | | |
| | | | | | | |
| | | | | | | |
| | | | | | | |
| | | | | | | |

### Brawling Chart

| Maneuver | Roll | Diff | Damage |
|---|---|---|---|
| Bite | Dex + Brawl | 5 | Strength + 1† |
| Body Slam | Dex + Brawl | 7 | Special |
| Claw | Dex + Brawl | 6 | Strength + 2† |
| Grapple | Dex + Brawl | 6 | Strength |
| Kick | Dex + Brawl | 7 | Strength + 1 |
| Punch | Dex + Brawl | 6 | Strength |

† These maneuvers do aggravated damage.

Armor: _____

# Silent Striders

Nature: _____    Demeanor: _____

## Merits & Flaws

| Merit | Type | Cost | Flaw | Type | Bonus |
|-------|------|------|------|------|-------|
| _____ | ____ | ____ | _____ | ____ | _____ |
| _____ | ____ | ____ | _____ | ____ | _____ |
| _____ | ____ | ____ | _____ | ____ | _____ |
| _____ | ____ | ____ | _____ | ____ | _____ |
| _____ | ____ | ____ | _____ | ____ | _____ |

## Expanded Background

### Allies

_____
_____
_____
_____
_____

### Contacts

_____
_____
_____
_____
_____

### Kinfolk

_____
_____
_____
_____
_____

### Mentor

_____
_____
_____
_____
_____

### Pack Totem

_____
_____
_____
_____
_____

### Pure Breed

_____
_____
_____
_____
_____

## Possessions

Gear (Carried) _____
_____
Equipment (Owned) _____
_____

## Sept

Name _____
Caern Location _____
Level _____ Type _____
Totem _____
Leader _____

## Experience

TOTAL: [          ]

Gained From: _____
_____
_____

TOTAL SPENT: _____
Spent On: _____
_____

# Silent Striders

## History
### Prelude

_____
_____
_____
_____
_____
_____
_____
_____
_____
_____
_____
_____

## Description

Age_____
Hair_____
Eyes_____
Race_____
Nationality_____
Sex_____

| | Height | Weight |
|---|---|---|
| Homid | | |
| Glabro | | |
| Crinos | | |
| Hispo | | |
| Lupus | | |

_____
_____
_____
_____
_____
_____

Battle Scars_____
_____
_____

Metis Deformity_____

## Visuals

Pack Chart

Character Sketch